STATEMENT CONCERNING PUBLICATIONS OF RUSSELL SAGE FOUNDATION

Russell Sage Foundation was established in 1907 by Mrs. Russell Sage "for the improvement of social and living conditions in the United States of America." While the general responsibility for management of the Foundation is vested in the Board of Trustees, the responsibility for facts, conclusions, and interpretations in its publications rests with the authors and not upon the Foundation, its Trustees, or its staff. Publication under the imprint of the Foundation does not imply agreement by the organization with all opinions or interpretations expressed. It does imply that care has been taken that the work on which a manuscript is based has been thoroughly done.

Stanley H. King, Ph.D.
Associate Director of Research
University Health Services
Harvard University

PERCEPTIONS of ILLNESS and MEDICAL PRACTICE

RUSSELL SAGE FOUNDATION
New York — 1962

Printed in the United States
of America

Printed December, 1962
Reprinted October, 1963
Reprinted September, 1968

Library of Congress
Catalog Card Number 62–19779

Contents

Tables

Preface

THE CHARTER of the World Health Organization states that health has its physical, psychological, and social aspects. The scientific study of the physical aspects of disease occupied the central place in medical education during the past century. The phenomenal growth of psychiatry since World War II is evidence of the increasing weight being placed by the physician on normal and abnormal psychology. It is only in the past decade that the study of social factors in health and disease by behavioral scientists began to have a meaningful impact on the care of patients.

This introduction of social science into medicine is not new; the family doctor of a hundred years ago used intuitively in his treatment of the sick his knowledge of such social factors as the family and community setting. What is new is the introduction of social science on a scientific basis into medicine.

During the first half of the present century, the rapid increase in the scientific knowledge of the physical aspects of man vastly complicated the practice of medicine from a number of standpoints. In carrying out the diagnosis and treatment of patients, the physician became more dependent on the large hospital and clinic, on the laboratory, and on many kinds of auxiliary workers in the health professions. Then, too, the modern physician so increased his horizons that he is no longer satisfied simply by discharging a patient from the hospital. He has come to realize that the total rehabilitation of the patient within the community is necessary. Preventive medicine occupies more and more of the thoughts of today's physician. These important developments, which stem from recent social changes in our society outside the field of medicine, are markedly influencing the practice of medicine.

Faced with the increasing complexities of psychological and social factors in giving the best kind of medical care to the patient, the modern physician can no longer deal with these factors on an intuitive basis any more than he can deal on an intuitive basis with physical factors. Fortunately, this need in medicine for understanding social and cultural factors has coincided with the coming of age as scientific disciplines of psychology, sociology, and cultural anthropology. Nevertheless, too few physicians are yet aware of the contributions that the behavioral sciences are making today, and will be making even more significantly tomorrow, to the optimal care of patients. This lag arises from the fact that most of today's physicians pursued their formal professional educations before the coming of age of these disciplines and their introduction into medicine on a scientific basis.

Perceptions of Illness and Medical Practice was written with the objective of providing a textbook for physicians and students in the health professions. In his volume Dr. King has described very well some of the many ways in which the findings of the behavioral scientist are applicable in the practice of medicine. Examples are given of the use of these sciences in the actual care of the patient. Among these examples are the effect of the social organization of the hospital on the recovery of patients, the importance of understanding cultural and social class differences among physicians and patients, and the ways in which the treatment of patients and disease is affected by the fact that physicians, nurses, and others in the health professions share—often without awareness—special sets of attitudes, beliefs, and rules of behavior.

At the 150th Anniversary Convocation of the Massachusetts General Hospital, a distinguished group considered "Medicine of the Future." In their panel symposium, the participants discussed the areas in which the greatest medical advances might be expected in the next fifty years. There was consensus that these areas would include the infusion of the concepts of mathematics and physics into the basic medical sciences and of psychosocial concepts into medical education and practice. The present book deals primarily with the latter development. In nontechnical language it sets forth the issues in a way that today's physicians and students can quickly gain a deeper understanding of the progress being made in the social sciences and how this understanding is relevant to medicine. In admirable fashion Dr. King points toward the many exciting vistas that the behavioral sciences can open up in the near future for the physician.

GEORGE PACKER BERRY, M.D.
Dean of the Faculty of Medicine in
Harvard University and President
of the Harvard Medical Center

Acknowledgments

IN 1954 RUSSELL SAGE FOUNDATION sponsored a project which was undertaken at the Graduate School of Public Health, University of Pittsburgh for the purpose of studying the relationships of the behavioral sciences to public health in teaching and research. I joined the faculty of the School to direct the project, and it was during that period that the framework of this book was developed. Dr. Thomas Parran, then dean of the School, and Dr. James Crabtree, who was chairman of the Department of Public Health Practice, were especially helpful in making provisions for the work and encouraging me in my efforts. I also benefited a great deal from discussions with my colleagues on the faculty, especially Drs. Sidney Cobb, Victor Freeman, and Ellen Donnelly, and Dr. Otto von Mering from the School of Medicine. Miss Eleanor Cockerill, of the Graduate School of Social Work at the University of Pittsburgh, requested my help in conducting some workshops for students in her school and in the process helped me clarify many ideas and develop many illustrations. Her intellectual stimulation and friendship is much appreciated. Also, I must express my thanks to Mrs. Janet Lubic who aided me well in the review of the literature.

As the book began to take shape, Professor Lyle Saunders was a constant and invaluable critic, willing to read drafts of the manuscript, point to errors of both commission and omission, and offer encouragement. My thanks to him here can only partially repay his help. Also, from the beginning, other people have contributed much in terms of constructive criticism and moral support. Dr. Esther Lucile Brown stimulated and challenged my thinking at all times, and was particularly helpful in suggestions about writing style and illustrations. Mrs. Frances Cooke Macgregor, in addition to her aid as a critic of the manuscript, shared with me her rich experience in teaching nurses in school and hospital and held up high standards of theoretical criticism. Dr. Andie Knutson was also helpful in criticizing early versions of some of the chapters. Miss Harriett Bartlett did much to assist me in clarifying my ideas for the chapter on the medical social worker, sharing her knowledge and giving me of her valuable time. Professor Robert White was most helpful in reading the chapters in Part I, as well as lending support in other ways.

In the final stages a number of people gave their thought to a critical reading of the manuscript and offered suggestions for revision. In particular, I would thank Dr. George Reader, Dr. Mary Goss, Dr. Eleanor Bernert Sheldon, Dr. Leonard S. Cottrell, Jr., and Dr. Donald Young. Dr. Daniel Funkenstein aided in the writing of some final parts of the book. Dr. H. Jack Geiger patiently read the final draft with me and offered numerous suggestions for illustrations or other changes that would make the book more meaningful to the medical reader. A special note of thanks is due to Miss Margaret R. Dunne for her careful editorial work.

The production of a book can be helped a great deal by competent secretarial work, something in which I have been most fortunate. My thanks go to Mrs. Mary Jacks, Mrs. Ethel Hassen, Mr. Ned Hopkins, and in particular to Miss Elizabeth Keul, who played a major role in preparing the manuscript for submission to the publisher.

To all these people, who have given freely of their time and thought, I am most grateful. Although I must take ultimate responsibility for the material in the following pages, I feel the support of many hands and hearts in coming to this point.

STANLEY H. KING

PART ONE
TRENDS AND CONCEPTS

Chapter 1

Introduction

THERE ARE MANY WHO ASSERT that medicine as a practicing profession began primarily as a social art and continued so until the advent of the great bacteriologists of the past century. The practice of medicine then became one rooted in the biological sciences. Today there is good reason to believe that a fusion is taking place between these two phases in the history of medicine, so that it may be spoken of more properly as a practice that is biosocial in foundation. The necessity for a firm footing in both the natural and social sciences has been succinctly stated for one medical specialty, public health, by Mountin:

> Public Health is an applied technology resting on the joint pillars of natural science and social science. For the past century, the natural science foundation has been magnificently strengthened—strengthened to the point where we now have the technical knowledge to eradicate or reduce greatly much of the misery to which man has been heir. Yet vast amounts of preventable or controllable disease and disability remain because the social science foundation is relatively weak. Until both the pillars of natural and social science are strong, the arch of public health will not be firm.[1]

The few short years that have elapsed since Mountin made this statement have seen an increasing consideration for the problems of the health professions on the part of the social and behavioral sciences,[2] and a corresponding desire by nurses, physicians, public health specialists, and medical social workers to utilize in their practice the insights of anthropology, psychology, and sociology. Behind the favorable climate of mutual interest lie a number of historical trends that have now coalesced to the point where there may be a further strengthening of the behavioral science pillar of the health professions. As an introduction each of these trends will be discussed briefly, then consideration made of some of the potential contributions of the behavioral sciences to the health professions.

Shift in the Emphasis on Specific Etiology of Disease

Beginning with the precise experimentation of Pasteur and Koch and their followers, the concept of the specific causation of infectious disease became a dominant force in medicine. The results of its application were dramatic; in a relatively short time many of the scourges of man's recent history, of which smallpox was a striking example, were conquered. Not only did the germ theory of disease provide a framework for therapy and prevention, it also directly influenced the acquisition of new knowledge in the medical field. Koch's postulates, exemplifying the experimental approach, became a model demonstrating what could be done by careful, controlled research in the laboratory. Thus did experimental science triumph over clinical experience. The doctrine of specificity later was extended to include biochemical lesions as well as microbial agents, leading to great advances in understanding the degenerative and metabolic diseases. The importance of the concept of specific etiology is best summarized in the words of René Dubos in his Dyer Lecture of 1953:

> There is no doubt that the doctrine of specific etiology has constituted an instrument of unmatched power for the experimental study of pathological processes and has been responsible for most of the great advances, theoretical and practical, realized in medicine during the past century.[3]

Valuable as the concept of specific cause of disease has been for medicine, it has proved inadequate to explain many kinds of illness. Indeed, laboratory research has shown numerous incidents where a specific microbial or viral agent operated to produce disease only under certain sets of conditions. Dubos cites herpes simplex, or fever blisters, as an example. A virus, which is the specific cause of the herpetic blisters, is acquired early in life by man and remains in the infected individual. Although present in the body, it produces disease only when certain other conditions have upset bodily homeostasis in certain ways, as the result of overexposure to ultraviolet light, emotional stress, or infection with the common cold.

Epidemiologists have described this situation in terms of *necessary* and *sufficient* cause. Some factor, called the necessary cause, must be present for disease to occur but its presence alone is not sufficient to produce disease. Other factors, one or more, must coincide with the necessary cause and provide the sufficient conditions for disease. These other factors are called sufficient causes. In the case of herpes simplex, the herpes virus would be the necessary cause; without its presence the blisters could not occur. However, other factors such as ultraviolet light or menstruation would provide sufficient conditions under which disease would occur, given the presence of the virus.

The concept of multiple etiology of disease has been gaining emphasis in medicine over the concept of specific etiology for some time. It seems to provide a valid framework for understanding many of the serious chronic diseases, especially those that include a psychosomatic component, as well as certain of the infectious diseases like tuberculosis.

Widening search for sufficient causes that are associated with disease has led to consideration of the emotional state of the patient. Psychology thus takes a place alongside microbiology and other traditional medical disciplines as an important basic science in the etiology of disease. With greater understanding of the relation of emotions to social and cultural factors, sociology and anthropology are drawn in as well. The utilization of the concept of multiple etiology, therefore, has made it necessary to have the behavioral sciences represented in ongoing research concerning the cause of disease.

Emotion and Bodily Changes

Closely allied with the shift in the concept of disease etiology has been a broadened understanding of the interrelationship between emotions and body physiology. This has not been a startling discovery, or a new one; yet, it is only recently that we have been able to document experimentally what common sense has long told us. Moreover, experimental research has indicated that the bodily changes associated with emotion may be of sufficient intensity and long enough sustained for importance in clinical disease.

The pioneer in studying experimentally the association between emotions and bodily changes was Cannon, who saw the variety of physiological responses in a framework of emergency reaction. Faced with various threats from the environment, the animal responded with anger or fear and with physiological responses preparatory to fight or flight. By and large these bodily changes were mediated through the effects of epinephrine or adrenalin, though Cannon himself recognized that the action of epinephrine could not account for all the phenomena that he observed.

The thirty years subsequent to the publication of Cannon's main work[4] have seen a proliferation of research on the relation of emotional states to specific bodily changes. It would be impossible here to summarize the multitude of studies that have been conducted, but a few brief illustrations and a theoretical summation may make the point clear.

Funkenstein, King, and Drolette[5] studied healthy college students under a specified stress situation and ascertained their emotional and cardiovascular responses. It was found that subjects who reported anger against the experimenters also produced ballistocardiograph tracings that were similar to those produced by infusion of norepinephrine. On the other hand, subjects who expressed anger at themselves or reported that they were frightened produced tracings similar to those produced by infusion of epinephrine. Individuals had differing emotional reactions to the same stress situation, but in each case a specific kind of emotion was associated with a specific kind of cardiovascular response. Looking further into the previous history of each subject, it was found that subjects who reacted with an epinephrine-like pattern also had characteristic perceptions of the roles of their parents in discipline.[6] Father was seen as nondominant in discipline, and mild. In addition, the parents of these subjects were reported to be infrequent church attenders, and the subjects had relatively lower scores on a scale of religious conventionalism.[7] For the subjects who reacted with a norepinephrine-like pattern, father was perceived as dominant in discipline and stern, and the parents were reported to be frequent church attenders.

This research thus demonstrated an association between type of emotional reaction and type of cardiovascular reaction during stress, and also an association between important events in the background of the subject and his physiological changes during stress.

Friedman, Rosenman, and Carroll[8] studied a group of corporation accountants and a group of tax accountants over a six-month period, drawing samples of blood at regular intervals to ascertain the serum cholesterol level and blood-clotting time. At specified times during the study period the subjects were faced with severe occupational stress in terms of deadlines which they must meet, one of these being that significant tax date for most Americans, April 15. Each subject's highest cholesterol levels consistently occurred during periods of severe occupational or other stress, and his lowest at periods of minimal stress. Also, at the time of maximum stress there was a marked acceleration of blood-clotting time as compared with the clotting time during normal periods. Careful study was made of exercise and diet during the course of the project; yet there was no change in the diet or exercise pattern that could account for the variations in either serum cholesterol level or blood-clotting time.

The emotional reaction in the case of the corporation and tax accountants was a feeling of pressure for meeting a deadline, of having a tremendous amount to do within a very short time, and knowing that the work could not be finished late. The research is of further interest in that it indicated the manner in which the structure of society imposes stress on the individual. In a highly competitive society there are places in the social structure that are stressful indeed.

One of the classic studies is that by Wolf and Wolff[9] of Tom, the man with a gastric fistula. Tom had drunk some scalding clam chowder when nine years old, completely occluding his esophagus and necessitating an artificial fistula in his stomach and abdominal wall through which he was fed. For a resourceful investigator here was a perfect window into the world of gastric activity. When Tom was fearful or sad, infrequent emotions for him, there was a pallor of the gastric mucosa and an inhibition of acid secretions and muscular contractions. In a state of emotional conflict involving anxiety, hostility, and resentment, Tom showed an accelerated acid secretion, hypermotility, hyperemia, and engorgement of the gastric mucosa. A prolonged emotional conflict was associated with prolonged engorgement, hypermotility, and hypersecretion in the stomach, leading easily to hemorrhages, lesions, and eventually to chronic ulceration.

In the three studies just cited, the subjects in all cases perceived the environment as threatening in some way. They responded to the threat emotionally and with changes in their physiological adjustment. Two of these studies, and many others not mentioned here, have indicated that continuing perception of threat from the environment, emotional conflict, and altered physiology can lead to irreversible tissue changes and chronic disease. The important clue is the manner in which an individual perceives the environment, perception being compounded out of assessable pressure from the environment, and what the subject brings with him to the situation. This can best be stated by a quotation from Wolff in his excellent discussion of man's response to threat:

> The stress accruing from a threatening situation is based in large part on the way the affected subject perceives it: perception depends upon a multiplicity of factors including the individual's genetic equipment, basic needs and longings, earlier conditioning influences, and a host of life experiences and cultural pressures. No one of these can be singled out for exclusive emphasis. The common denominator of stress disorders is reaction to circumstances of threatening significance to the organism.[10]

The broad range of factors involved in Wolff's statement indicates the need for concepts and techniques from the behavioral sciences to be utilized in collaboration with those from physiology, biochemistry, and other natural sciences in the study of emotions and bodily changes and of man's response to his environment. Collaboration of such kind has been taking place for some years and there is every reason to believe that it will increase in scope.

Increase in Life Expectancy

A dramatic increase in life expectancy has occurred during the past four or five decades for people living in the highly developed and industrialized countries of the world. In the United States a white male at birth in 1900 could look forward to a span of 49 years but by 1953 this had increased to 67 years. For the white female the expectation in 1900 was just over 50 years as compared with 73 years in 1953. A further example of the fact that larger proportions of the population are now surviving to advanced age comes from the following data: in 1900, 59 per cent of the white population could expect to reach 50 years at least, but by 1953 this had increased to almost 88 per cent. Since 1953 the gain has been slower, but by 1959 the average life expectancy was 22 years higher than in 1900. Although life expectancy for Negroes is still somewhat less than that for whites, the difference between the two groups has decreased rapidly in recent years to the extent that it may soon be eliminated.[11]

The change in life expectancy has come about primarily through the control of communicable diseases by immunization and isolation and by public health sanitation, especially diseases so prevalent at one time among children. The use of antibiotics has further aided the situation, both among children and adults.

One effect of the increase in life expectancy has been a corresponding increase in the incidence of chronic diseases, the cardiovascular disorders, arthritic and metabolic diseases, cancer, and like maladies. This can be seen most strikingly in comparing the leading causes of death over the years, where influenza and pneumonia have dropped from first to seventh place, and tuberculosis from second to eleventh, to be replaced by diseases of the heart and cancer in the number one and two positions. Chronic, noncommunicable diseases, including mental disorders, have become the main health problem of the present age.

By and large, the chronic diseases present situations of complicated or unknown etiology. Present research indicates that in diseases such as rheumatoid arthritis or coronary artery disease a multiplicity of factors may operate, some more prominent in one individual, different factors of importance in others. Stresses deriving from psychological and social factors seem to be as important as assaults of a chemical or biological nature. In short, the problem of chronic disease etiology is a fusion of the first two points that have been mentioned in this chapter, multiple etiology and the reaction to threat from the environment as the individual perceives it. By the very nature of the problem, then, utilization of the behavioral sciences has become necessary in understanding etiology of chronic diseases. The aid of the behavioral sciences may also be utilized more and more in treatment, for the strengthening of social supports may have as much beneficial effect in long-term recovery as the use of drugs.

These first three factors have formed an interrelated cluster of pressures, each dependent on the other. We turn now to different trends, more difficult to evaluate in importance.

Preventive Health Planning

The factors behind increase in life expectancy and change in the leading causes of death are contributing to an important shift in attitude or psychological set in matters of health and disease. In the past the "set" toward these matters was one of emergency, of finding ways of dealing with the catastrophic diseases, the epidemics that killed sizable proportions of the population. Almost all of society's energies in health problems had to be expended on dealing with emergencies and individual members of society were conditioned to this end. *Avoidance* of injury, disease, and death was the primary goal, and closely allied was the emphasis on *treatment* of injury or disease.

Avoidance and treatment are still matters of great concern to the health professions but the energy needed for these matters is much less today, allowing an investment in other aspects of health and disease. In particular, the interest of leaders in medicine and public health has become engaged with *preventive health planning*.

Physicians and scientists have broadened the concept of prevention beyond immunization and sanitary control procedures and now are thinking of ways in which signs of chronic disease can be identified long before the full onset of disease; alteration can be made of factors in the physical and social environment that may be associated with stress diseases; and social planning can keep pace with rapid changes in economic organization and social structure. As examples of the first of these trends, we find increasing emphasis on yearly physical examinations for persons over a certain age, even to the point of including this service under payments from health insurance plans. Also, there are a growing number of longitudinal studies in which data of a physiological, psychological, and social nature can be studied in relation to later onset of chronic disease. Examples of the second trend can be found in greater emphasis being paid to diet, not only in terms of prevention of excess weight but also relative to the elimination of foods that may be associated with certain diseases such as atherosclerosis. We also find that physicians recommend strongly that patients who are subjected to heavy psychological pressures in their jobs take an annual vacation of some length. Finally, the statistics on cigarette smoking and lung cancer have led doctors to suggest changes in smoking habits. As an example of the third trend in preventive health thinking and action, there is the growing concern about problems of retirement. With technical advances in industry and with increase in life expectancy, greater numbers of our population are living to retirement age but there has not been corresponding social planning to prepare these people for retirement. Specialists in public health and preventive medicine see this as one of their legitimate concerns and now devote considerable time and energy in that direction.

Although preventive health planning has become well established in the health professions, a corresponding acceptance has not occurred among the consumers of health services. One of the major problems of preventive medicine is therefore that of motivating the public to plan for better health, to utilize current knowledge about preventive procedures, especially those procedures that affect the chronic diseases. In this endeavor the behavioral sciences have specific contributions to make; for example, estimating the climate of public opinion on given issues, selecting values to be emphasized in educational campaigns, studying the hierarchy of needs in different types of individuals as these relate to health and disease, and assessing the impact of particular kinds of health appeals. As the shift from avoidance and treatment to preventive planning becomes greater, the skills of psychology, anthropology, and sociology will find ever-increasing use.

Growth of the Idea of Social Medicine

The concept of social medicine is closely allied with that of preventive health planning, yet is broader in its definition and implications. Unfortunately, agreement as to the parameters of the concept is variable and often writers have defined it in terms of what it is not rather than what it is. Galdston, who has written about the problem with much insight, has this to say:

> Few among those occupied with social medicine agree entirely as to what it is. They do, however, agree that there is some such science in the making, and that whatever it may be, and how much it may parallel or overlap public health and preventive medicine, social medicine is different from both. Social medicine, they all agree, is not a new name for an old discipline. . . . Those who are laboring to achieve social medicine are convinced that in some significant respects medicine, including public health and preventive medicine, has failed, and the failure is in the nature of quality rather than of quantity, in intelligence rather than in skills.[12]

Galdston himself does not give a precise definition but he provides us with some important aspects of the concept. First, and perhaps most important, social medicine is a philosophy rather than a set of techniques or methodologies. As a philosophy its basic assumption is that the health professions can be effective only if they encompass the total picture of man and environment, not man as distinct from environment, but environment with man in it. By not considering the total man-environment situation, clinical medicine has sometimes been wrong in assuming that a disease was "cured," perhaps relieving a set of symptoms but missing the underlying pathology. The philosophy of social medicine would seek to alter perspectives, to expand the boundaries of the disease situation to include all of the forces, physical, biological, and social, with which man interacts, and to treat the whole man or whole society rather than the complaint.

A second aspect of the concept, as Galdston defines it, is that emphasis in the health professions should shift from death and disease to health and its fulfillment. He argues that medical education from the beginning concentrates on pathology, thus narrowing the vision of the physician in dealing with people. In contrast, Galdston proposes an emphasis on what he calls "eubiotic" medicine, where the individual is helped to achieve the best that he is capable of in his experience of living.

Social medicine is not the same as socialized medicine, terms frequently confused in the United States. Socialized medicine is a mode in the application of medicine, as is group or private practice. Social medicine is a philosophical approach to the problems of diagnosis and treatment that can be manifest in any of a number of different modes of the application of medicine. Thus, current medical thought and practice could perfectly well continue under socialized medicine, whereas social medicine envisages radical reform in thought and practice.

There are two ideas in the health professions that are now being taken seriously, each of which bears some relationship to the philosophy of social medicine but neither of which has used that label. The first is *comprehensive medicine*, which seeks to understand the pathologic process in relation to the patient's personality and all of the hereditary as well as environmental forces that mold his personality.[13] Comprehensive health care would marshal the resources of society, as well as those of the physician and other health workers, toward treating and preventing illness. Thus, comprehensive medicine has the aim of treating the whole patient and studying man in the environment, fulfilling in part one of the aspects of social medicine as envisaged by Galdston. The limitation rests on the fact that comprehensive medicine starts with the patient and his ills, while social medicine in addition would be interested in society and its ills and the way these affect the health of the individual.

The second idea is that of *positive health.* The use of the word "positive" as a modifier of health may at first appear redundant except that health has traditionally been defined as the absence of disease, whereas the new idea regards it more as the releasing of potential. The constitution for the World Health Organization makes this clear: "Health is a state of complete physical, mental, and social well-being and not merely the absence of disease or infirmity."[14] A similar definition comes from a national conference of professors of preventive medicine in medical schools:

> The goal of health now at mid-century calls for not only the cure or alleviation of disease. It calls for even more than the prevention of disease. Rather, it looks beyond, to strive for maximum physical, mental and social efficiency for the individual, for his family, and for the community.[15]

As the concept of positive health has developed there has been a focus on levels of health or wellness, culminating in what Dunn calls "high-level wellness," where functioning of the individual is oriented toward maximizing his potential, or achieving the greatest potential of which he is capable within his environment.[16] Here there is close convergence with Galdston and one aspect of his definition of social medicine.

The impact of these forces within medicine has been slow but has produced changes. Some medical schools have departments of social medicine that carry both teaching and research activities. Also, programs of teaching comprehensive medicine are found in increasing numbers throughout the United States as well as in other parts of the world. Positive health, however, still remains a tantalizing idea, difficult to demonstrate but a stimulus to thinking.

Medical education is in transition[17] and increasing emphasis has been and will be placed on the relationship between the patient and his environment. As this transition continues the behavioral sciences will become more important parts of the curriculum, and greater emphasis will be placed on premedical preparation in these fields. Social organization, the formation of beliefs and attitudes, social psychological stresses and conflicts, personality theory, and many other aspects of sociology, anthropology, and psychology are crucial to an understanding of man-environment relationships and broadened perspectives in treatment.

The Age of Psychological Man

One of the more interesting developments in the first half of this century has been the growing acceptance of man as a psychological being. For much of the past few hundred years emphasis was on spiritual man, then with the invention of the steam engine a shift was made to economic man. As Sanford has so well stated,

> I think we can make a reasonable case that we are indeed entering the century of the psychological man—or the psychological-sociological-anthropological man. Perhaps two hundred years from now, the first half of the twentieth century will be noted as the period in which society moved away from its preoccupation with man as an economic creature and began a period of progressive and enlightened confusion about man as a creature of predictable and potentially controllable emotion, ideation, motive, habit, attitude, aspiration, and creative impulse.[18]

There is evidence from many sides of the growing interest in man as a psychological being. It would be interesting, for example, to make a count of the number and scope of articles appearing in popular magazines and in newspapers that explain how people react emotionally, to suggest ways that one can handle emotional conflict and release untapped or blocked sources of emotional energy, or to point out how to get along with other people or to rear children.

Closely allied is the acceptance of the concept of psychosomatic medicine. Within the space of relatively few years, the use of the term has become common in many households. Again, good evidence on this point is found in the alacrity with which the news bureaus and wire services pick up articles in the professional literature that have psychosomatic implications. They know that their readers are as curious about such matters as they are about the latest "wonder drug" or surgical technique.

The source of the interest in psychological man can probably be traced to Freud more than to any one other individual, and history may judge his greatest contribution not in terms of a therapeutic technique but a molding influence on the thinking of men. Freud's most important emphasis concerned the action of unconscious forces on conscious activity, a point which has been generally accepted by the public today. Many people realize what happens when they are frustrated or blocked in the expression of emotions, how the feeling comes out in other ways, in what they do or how their bodies act.

Not only can the age of psychological man be characterized by an interest in the psychological forces that motivate action, but there are widening connotations of social and cultural effects. In spite of cultural pressures to regard the United States as a one-class society, there is growing acceptance of the fact that different social classes exist, and that there are differences between the classes in terms of fundamental values and practices. We are coming to see that man's actions are shaped not only by his psychological needs, but also by the pressures of the society in which he lives.

Sanford makes the point that in addition to the willingness to think differently about man's behavior, there is also a willingness to think differently about man's *welfare*. There seems to be a belief that by direct application of what we are learning through the scientific method about human behavior we can increase man's psychological and social well-being. Among other things an increase in well-being is due to the advances that medicine has made in conquering the devastating scourges of mankind, and the advances that physics and chemistry have made and are about to make in controlling the physical environment to man's advantage. Man now has the time and the freedom from worry about disease and poverty to concentrate on developing better personalities and creating better communities.

The Maturing of the Behavioral Sciences

Even though the climate be auspicious for the utilization of anthropology, psychology, and sociology in the health professions, these behavioral sciences would not stand a chance of acceptance if they could not take their place with some assurance beside the natural sciences. To be sure, the behavioral sciences cannot yet demonstrate finesse of technique, ability to quantify the results of experiments, certainty about stating laws and relationships to the extent that the natural sciences are capable of demonstrating. However, progress toward these ends has been of sufficient magnitude within the past two decades to grant the behavioral sciences full partnership in scientific research.

The maturing has taken place in a number of ways: through the development of better techniques for measuring the data of human behavior and interaction; through the utilization of stricter experimental controls; and through a growing sophistication of theory.

It would not be feasible here to describe in detail all the major research techniques that can be utilized by the behavioral sciences. In brief, however, we have learned much about the interview situation, the effect of the characteristics of the interviewer, and can apply our knowledge to train people in obtaining useful data. Questionnaire techniques have been perfected, the effect of order and wording of questions studied. Considerable advance has come in the theory and construction of attitude and value scales, ways of spreading opinions or feelings over a measurable continuum. Projective tests for gleaning information about unconscious or suppressed motivations have proved valid in the clinical situation, and many have been adapted for use in field surveys and group situations. Observation techniques have been refined and quantified, making possible an objective handling of data from ongoing small group situations. Laboratory techniques, such as the tachistoscope and stereoscope, and experimental communications networks have made it possible to study variables in social interaction under controlled and varying conditions.

Obtaining unbiased data through the use of random selection of subjects and adequate control groups has become standard practice in most research in the behavioral sciences. This is not always easy in studying social groups, but collaboration with statisticians has provided adequate devices for sampling from large populations and has emphasized control of major variables in the sampling. Analysis of data has been heavily influenced by statistics as well. Tests of significance, rather than armchair intuition, have become the basis for conclusions. Many behavioral scientists will say that control of collection of data and statistical analysis of the results are often the ideal rather than the practice, but it is said with less conviction each year.

Good research is the basis for workable theory in science. With the accumulation of pertinent data about human behavior, whether in individuals or groups, definite principles have emerged. Some of these will be presented in Chapters 2 and 3. In general, there is sufficient sophistication of theory in the behavioral sciences for its direct application to some of the problems faced by people in the health professions. The greatest application is in research problems but some of the practical problems of patient management may also benefit. Until recently there were few physicians, nurses, or others who had corresponding training in the behavioral sciences, and few psychologists, sociologists, or anthropologists who saw the health professions as an area for applying behavioral science knowledge. Application of existing theoretical knowledge, therefore, has lagged, both in research and in teaching students in the health professions, but the expanding group of behavioral scientists in the health field points to increased integration.

Purpose and Plan of the Book

In retrospect, we have examined a number of trends in society, generally, and the health professions, in particular, that affect the acceptance and utilization of the behavioral sciences in the health field. Although difficult to evaluate singly, taken together, they constitute signs of a ready acceptance of the behavioral sciences in medicine, nursing, public health, and medical social work. In fact, growing demand exists for help from anthropologists, psychologists, and sociologists, especially in teaching and research.

The aim of the book is to point to behavioral science knowledge that can be used by students in medicine, public health, nursing, and social work.[19] Professionals in these fields may also find a new approach to the familiar aspects of their daily work even though some of the material presented is on a somewhat elementary level. Contributions may take a number of forms: delineation of *concepts* that will be useful for understanding behavior, presentation of a *framework* within which these concepts can be integrated and pieces of behavior can be interpreted, drawing together the *results of research* that can be applied to everyday problems faced by those in the health professions, and fostering a *sensitivity to areas where research is needed* and to the use of multidisciplinary procedures in research. A conscious attempt will be made to fulfill the first three of these contributions with the hope that the reader will be stimulated to ponder the last one.

Chapters 2 and 3 will present a conceptual scheme in which an attempt is made to integrate systematically some of the major concepts from psychology, sociology, and anthropology in a way that will be useful to members of the health professions. With that scheme in mind, succeeding chapters will present relevant data, both theoretical and empirical, from the behavioral sciences that apply to disease and its interpretation, the people who treat disease, and the place where disease is treated. Here the book will deal with many aspects of the everyday working world of health specialists, showing how psychosocial variables influence the behavior of the consumer of health services and how they affect the interaction between the health specialist and the patient.

The aim is a simple one, to provide ideas backed by empirical findings, that will enable those in the health professions to see their tasks in wider perspective, to introduce a new dimension that may help to bring better medical care to more people.

NOTES TO CHAPTER 1

1. Mountin, Joseph W., "Foreword" in Roemer, Milton I., and Ethel A. Wilson, *Organized Health Services in a County of the United States*. Public Health Service, Federal Security Agency, Publication 197, Washington, 1951.

2. The terms "social science" and "behavioral science" may need some clarification for the reader who is a member of one of the health professions. Social science is an older term and traditionally has embraced sociology and social anthropology, economics, political science, and sometimes history, although the last named field more often is thought of as one of the humanities. Behavioral science has come into use only in recent years and includes those disciplines that deal directly with human behavior, psychology, sociology, and anthropology. Some writers limit the inclusion of psychology to social psychology, while others include all of psychology and psychiatry. It seems to me that the wider coverage of the term is appropriate and in that sense it is used in this book. The reader will note that "behavioral science" appears in preference to "social science," the reason being that the former term includes psychology, a field essential to the conceptual scheme which is the basis of this book.

3. Dubos, René J., "The Gold Headed Cane in the Laboratory" in National Institutes of Health, *Annual Lectures*. Department of Health, Education, and Welfare, Washington, 1953, p. 92.

4. Cannon, Walter B., *Bodily Changes in Pain, Hunger, Fear, and Rage*. 2d ed. D. Appleton and Co., New York, 1929.

5. Funkenstein, Daniel H., Stanley H. King, and Margaret Drolette, *Mastery of Stress*. Harvard University Press, Cambridge, Mass., 1957.

6. King, Stanley H., and Andrew F. Henry, "Aggression and Cardiovascular Reactions Related to Parental Control Over Behavior," *Journal of Abnormal and Social Psychology*, vol. 50, March, 1955, pp. 206–210.

7. King, Stanley H., and Daniel H. Funkenstein, "Religious Practice and Cardiovascular Reactions During Stress," *Journal of Abnormal and Social Psychology*, vol. 55, July, 1957, pp. 135–137.

8. Friedman, Meyer, Ray H. Rosenman, and Vernice Carroll, "Changes in the Serum Cholesterol and Blood Clotting Time in Men Subjected to Cyclic Variation of Occupational Stress," *Circulation*, vol. 17, May, 1958, pp. 852–861.

9. Wolf, Stewart, and Harold G. Wolff, *Human Gastric Function:* An Experimental Study of a Man and His Stomach. 2d ed., rev. and enl. Oxford University Press, New York, 1947.

10. Wolff, Harold G., "Changes in the Vulnerability of Tissue: An Aspect of Man's Response to Threat" in National Institutes of Health, *Annual Lectures*. Department of Health, Education, and Welfare, Washington, 1953, pp. 39–40.

11. These data have been drawn from *Progress in Health Services*, Health Information Foundation, New York, vol. 5, May, 1956, and vol. 9, December, 1960.

12. Galdston, Iago, *The Meaning of Social Medicine*. Harvard University Press, Cambridge, Mass., 1954, p. 30. The reader is also referred to Galdston, Iago, editor, *Social Medicine*: Its Derivations and Objectives, Commonwealth Fund, New York, 1949.

13. Matarazzo, Joseph, "Comprehensive Medicine: A New Era in Medical Education," *Human Organization*, vol. 14, Spring, 1955, pp. 4–9.

14. "Constitution of the World Health Organization," *Chronicle* of the World Health Organization, vol. 1, 1947. Issued by the Interim Commission, Geneva, Switzerland.

15. Clark, Katharine G., "Preventive Medicine in Medical Schools: Report of Colorado Springs Conference, November, 1952," *Journal of Medical Education*, vol. 28, October, 1953, part 2, pp. 3–4.

16. Dr. Halbert L. Dunn, who is Chief of the National Office of Vital Statistics, Public Health Service, has written a great deal about high-level wellness. Reprints are available from Dr. Dunn. The reader is also referred to his "High-Level Wellness for Man and Society," *American Journal of Public Health*, vol. 49, June, 1959, pp. 786–792.

17. Berry, George Packer, "Medical Education in Transition," *Journal of Medical Education*, vol. 28, March, 1953, pp. 17–42.

18. Sanford, Fillmore H., "Social Science in Public Health in the Years Ahead." Paper read at the Graduate School of Public Health, University of Pittsburgh, May 10, 1957. See also his "Creative Health and the Principle of *Habeas Mentem*," which appeared in the *American Psychologist*, vol. 10, December, 1955, pp. 829–835, and in the *American Journal of Public Health*, vol. 46, February, 1956, pp. 139–148.

19. Among the teaching materials already available are the following, all published by Russell Sage Foundation, New York:

Brown, Esther Lucile, *Newer Dimensions of Patient Care*, Part I, The Use of the Physical and Social Environment of the General Hospital for Therapeutic Purposes, 1961, and Part II, Improving Staff Motivation and Competence in the General Hospital, 1962; Freidson, Eliot, *Patients' Views of Medical Practice:* A Study of the Subscribers to a Prepaid Medical Plan in the Bronx, New York, 1961; Greenblatt, Milton, Richard H. York, and Esther Lucile Brown, *From Custodial to Therapeutic Patient Care in Mental Hospitals*, 1955, delineation and case examples of social treatment in mental illness; Macgregor, Frances Cooke, *Social Science in Nursing*, 1960, the distillation of a course for undergraduate nurses in social science; Paul, Benjamin D., editor, *Health, Culture, and Community*, 1955, a casebook that describes the handling of public health problems in many societies and under many conditions; Saunders, Lyle, *Cultural Difference and Medical Care*, 1954, an account of the culture of the Spanish-Americans in the Southwest as it affects their health needs; Simmons, Leo W., and Harold G. Wolff, *Social Science in Medicine*, 1954, a presentation of the importance of social factors in disease; Spicer, Edward H., editor, *Human Problems in Technological Change*, 1952, another excellent casebook, although not focused specifically on health problems.

Also available are the following:

Cumming, Elaine, and John Cumming, *Closed Ranks:* An Experiment in Mental Health Education. Harvard University Press, Cambridge, Mass., 1957. Jaco, E. Gartly, editor, *Patients, Physicians and Illness*, The Free Press, Glencoe, Ill., 1958, an extensive series of articles by behavioral scientists and physicians, well organized in a sourcebook; Mead, Margaret, editor, *Cultural Patterns and Technical Change*, UNESCO, Paris, 1953, an account of five different cultures and the many facets of change; Somers, Herman Miles, and Anne Ramsay Somers, *Doctors, Patients, and Health Insurance*, The Brookings Institution, Washington, 1961, on the organization and financing of medical care.

Chapter 2

A Conceptual Framework–I

MAN'S BASIS FOR ACTION in health and disease is a composite of many things, but one crucial variable is the way that he "sees" or perceives the situation of disease and all of the social ramifications that accompany it. Man is in constant transaction with his environment, and from the manifold stimuli that impinge on him he must select those he will attend to and must interpret them in some meaningful way as the basis for his subsequent behavior. As the infant matures into the child, he learns constantly from his parents, and from his own trial and error experience, about his environment, how to perceive it, how to define what is going on. The whole process of socialization is essentially one of helping the child become selective in his perceptions of the world, to give the proper meanings to those stimuli which he perceives.

Perception is one of the key concepts in human behavior, a major *intervening variable* between stimuli and behavior. Through the act of perception are brought to bear a multitude of physiological, psychological, and sociocultural variables; hence, perception is a factor around which much of the conceptual scheme of this book is built. It has special relevance for the health professions inasmuch as situations of disease or actions of various people can be perceived in many different ways and lead to a whole range of behaviors by both patients and health professionals. In order to deal effectively with the patient or with other members of the health team the physician, nurse, medical social worker, or other health specialist must take into account the variations and distortions in perception that are possible. Only by understanding the factors that lead to these variations can constructive action be taken.

At the outset, certain features of perception must be emphasized. First, the term is not used here in the narrow sense of the reaction of sense organs to the impingement of stimuli, but rather in the broad sense of cognitive processes concerning the stimuli. The emphasis is not only on the strength of the stimuli, the way they are grouped or patterned, or their sharpness, but also on their significance to the individual organism, *sign significance* as the psychologists are wont to call it.[1] Sign significance grows out of previous interactions which the person has had with his environment, these interactions giving meaning to the configuration of stimuli. To put it another way, an individual brings a complex of assumptions, or a psychological set to each situation that confronts him.

For example, consider two seatmates on an airplane, one of whom is dressed in black and wearing a clerical collar. His traveling companion sees the clerical collar and black clothes, but he also "sees" a lot more. Through previous experience he has learned that those who wear such clothes are clergymen, that his companion is probably a Roman Catholic priest, or possibly an Episcopalian, certainly not a Baptist or a Jew. This will lead him to be careful about the way he talks, avoiding any profanity, or refraining from telling a certain type of story.

This is not to deny that perception is a compounding of *objective* and *subjective* factors. The way that stimuli are arranged in the perceptual field has an effect on the way they will be seen by the perceiver. A woman with a red hat will be difficult to see if she is in the midst of a group of women, all of whom are wearing red. If she is with women who are wearing blue the contrast will make her stand out clearly. In the same way, a Negro in a group of his own race will not be noticed as easily as he would among a group of whites. To Caucasians all Orientals look alike in the beginning, and Orientals report the same things about Caucasians. Objective factors, or those that are part of the nature of the environment, do play a part in the way we view the world.

Subjective factors involve the assumptions we bring to a situation, the prior learnings, the meanings we attach to configurations of stimuli, the things discussed above. By and large, when we are dealing with physical events and objects, the objective factors assume greater consequence, there is less need to interpret them, they are less ambiguous. In the realm of social interaction, the subjective factors become of prime importance. Here, ambiguity of the stimuli is usually high, and we have to fall back on a whole series of conditionings or previous experience about the environment.

A scheme for understanding behavior that takes place in social settings most of the time, therefore, will have to rely heavily on knowledge about the subjective factors in perception. That will be the aim of later sections of this discussion.

A second feature of perception rests on the fact that there is variation among individuals in the way each perceives the same situation, especially one that involves social interaction, where ambiguity of the stimuli is high. It is incorrect to assume that someone else ought to see a given configuration of social and physical stimuli in the same way that we do. We think that what we perceive is the truth, is reality, but each person has his own idea of reality, each person sees things differently out of his own "private world."

A device often used to illustrate individual variation in perception is to have individuals in a group write a short story about one of the cards in the Thematic Apperception Test (TAT).[2] Card 18GF is a good one, for it shows two people, apparently women, at the bottom of some stairs. Ambiguously drawn, the picture shows one woman with her hands at the neck of the other. In any group of people, some will write stories in which violence is being done, a woman being choked, while others will say that someone is ill, or has fallen down the stairs and is being helped by the other woman. Different people perceive the same situation differently.

Granting the importance of subjective as well as objective factors in perceiving, and the variability in perception of the same situation by different people, we move then to a consideration of the *determinants* of perception. Classified broadly, there are three kinds of determinants: *physiologic*, *psychologic*, and *sociocul-*

tural. They do not operate independently of each other, but interact dynamically in any given situation. One gets a distorted picture, therefore, if only the psychologic factors are discussed, or only the sociocultural. All must be considered, and the manner in which they interact studied. In the following pages we shall take up each set of determinants in turn, then consider in Chapter 3 the matter of their interaction.

Before so doing, however, there are some limitations that must be noted in the use of the concept of perception relative to some of the material to be presented in this book. Perception as an important variable in human behavior relates primarily to individuals. Thus, it is relevant to an understanding of the actions of patients and their families, or to physicians, nurses, hospital administrators, and other health specialists. When social organizations are considered, perception may not be a relevant variable except to the extent that pressures of social structure affect the perceptual process. However, the social organization of a hospital or the informal arrangements in medical practice are important phenomena that need to be dealt with in their own right. In this book individual behavior will be the main center of interest and perception will be the organizing concept. When the focus shifts to social structural factors or to certain kinds of cultural factors, perception will not be the organizing variable.

PHYSIOLOGIC DETERMINANTS OF PERCEPTION

Chemical Imbalances

Hunger, thirst, fatigue, and sexual arousal are states that can have an effect on the process of perception. Food deprivation, for one, has been well studied. Levine, Chein, and Murphy[3] compared groups of college students who were hungry with those who had just finished eating. To each group they presented ambiguous pictures covered by a ground glass screen, and asked the students to describe what they saw. The hungry subjects more frequently reported seeing ham sandwiches, salads, and other foods than did those who were satiated, even though the same pictures had been presented to both groups.

In a different experiment, McClelland and Atkinson[4] tested 108 subjects by having them watch a blank screen. They were told that very faint pictures would be projected on the screen and were to report what they saw. Actually, no image was presented. Subjects were divided into those who had been without food for one hour, four hours, and sixteen hours. Longer periods of food deprivation did not produce a greater number of specific food responses, but there were more food-related responses. Subjects were asked at one point in the experiment to count the number of objects on the screen, such as forks, pencils, and other objects. Again, there were no actual pictures on the screen. When objects having something to do with food, for example, forks, were named, those subjects who had been without food for sixteen hours reported seeing large numbers of them but this was not the case with objects not related to food. Also when subjects were asked to judge the size of objects they were told were being projected, those who were very hungry judged food objects to be larger than nonfood objects.

There seems no question, from the laboratory, that perceptual processes and the resultant behavior are altered when people go without food. We can go beyond the laboratory to everyday experience and find the same thing. For example, one of the first lessons that a growing girl must learn is never to ask her father for a new prom gown just before his dinner. After a good meal he may see such matters in a more favorable light.

Thirst, fatigue, and sexual arousal have corresponding effects. Under conditions of sexual arousal, a couple may find it difficult to perceive the dangers of pregnancy, yet a half-hour after their love-making they may become aware, all too vividly, of the possible consequences. As to fatigue, when a person is exhausted by long hours of work, the taunts of a friend may drive him into a rage, while under normal circumstances he would be inclined to laugh and treat the remarks as a joke.

Other kinds of physiologic or chemical imbalances can be noted.[5] Dietary deficiency, as in pellagra, is associated in some patients with disorientation, confusion, and confabulation, while in other patients the effect may be excitement, mania, or depression. Sometimes paranoid delusions occur, especially in the form of fear or anger toward relatives. Studies of other dietary deficiencies indicate the frequency of quarrelsome behavior, moodiness, hypochondriasis, and tendencies toward hysteria. Individuals in this condition obviously do not perceive the world in quite the same way as when their body chemistry is more nearly in balance.

Change in the concentration of oxygen and other gases in the blood produces rather noticeable effects on the mental state. In the early stages of anoxia there are often exaggerated feelings of exhilaration and well-being, but continued deprivation results in an impairment of the capacity for self-criticism. High concentration of nitrogen in the blood under pressure results in nitrogen narcosis, a condition which the great French skin diver, Jacques Costeau, has called *l'ivresse des grandes profondeurs*, or rapture of the great depths. His description of the condition is so vivid that it seems worth quoting here in full.

> At two hundred feet I tasted the metallic flavor of compressed nitrogen and was instantaneously and severely struck with rapture. I closed my hand on the rope and stopped. My mind was jammed with conceited thoughts and antic joy. I struggled to fix my brain on reality, to attempt to name the color of the sea about me. A contest took place between navy blue, aquamarine and Prussian blue. The debate would not resolve. The sole fact I could grasp was that there was no roof and no floor in the blue room. The distant purr of the Diesel invaded my mind—it swelled to a giant beat, the rhythm of the world's heart.
>
> I took the pencil and wrote on a board, "Nitrogen has a dirty taste." I had little impression of holding the pencil, childhood nightmares overruled my mind. I was ill in bed, terrorized with the realization that everything in the world was thick. My fingers were sausages. My tongue was a tennis ball. My lips swelled grotesquely on the mouth grip. The air was syrup. The water jelled around me as though I was smothered in aspic.
>
> I hung witless on the rope. Standing aside was a smiling jaunty man, my second self, perfectly self-contained, grinning sardonically at the wretched diver. As the seconds passed the jaunty man installed himself in my command and ordered that I unloose the rope and go on down.
>
> I sank slowly through a period of intense visions.

> Around the two hundred and sixty-four foot board the water was suffused with an unearthly glow. I was passing from night to an intimation of dawn. What I saw as sunrise was light reflected from the floor, which had passed unimpeded through the dark transparent strata above. I saw below me the weight at the end of the shotline, hanging twenty feet from the floor. I stopped at the penultimate board and looked down at the last board, five meters away, and marshalled all my resources to evaluate the situation without deluding myself. Then I went to the last board, two hundred and ninety-seven feet down.
>
> The floor was gloomy and barren, save for morbid shells and sea urchins. I was sufficiently in control to remember that in this pressure, ten times that of the surface, any untoward physical effort was extremely dangerous. I filled my lungs slowly and signed the board. I could not write what it felt like fifty fathoms down.
>
> I was the deepest independent diver. In my bisected brain the satisfaction was balanced by satirical self-contempt.
>
> I dropped the scrap iron and bounded like a coiled spring, clearing two boards in the first flight. There, at two hundred and sixty-four feet, the rapture vanished suddenly, inexplicably and entirely. I was light and sharp, one man again, enjoying the lighter air expanding in my lungs.[6]

The effect of drugs on body chemistry should also not be forgotten. The ability of ethyl alcohol, commonly found in whiskey, gin, and like beverages, to produce disorders in perception and behavior is well known and it is probably the most widely used drug today. Under mild intoxication, there is an exaggeration of emotional expression and euphoria. Moderate amounts of alcohol in the blood produce quantifiable measures of behavioral changes with an increase in reaction time and an impairment of motor coordination. As Jellinek and McFarland[7] have indicated in their review, discrimination is more impaired than acuity. The intoxicated individual decreases in his ability to relate things to each other and to grasp overall content of a situation.

Other drugs have played an important part in man's history, one of them leading to a common word in our language, "berserk." The word goes back to the name of a legendary warrior in Norse mythology and was applied to a predatory group of brawlers among the Viking community during the early Christian centuries. In a fascinating review, Fabing[8] has shown that "going berserk," a term for describing disruptive behavior of this group, was probably due to the eating of a toxic mushroom, *Amanita muscaria*. A number of different tribes, in addition to the Viking group, have used various kinds of mushrooms as the agent to induce trance states and temporary psychotic conditions, not always of a violent nature. The effect on perception has been described by the Wassons, a husband-wife research team, using a variety of mushrooms eaten by the ancient Aztecs and other Mexican Indian tribes: "visual hallucinations in brilliant colors, an ecstatic state of heightened perception, loss of time and space perception and a serene feeling of inward peace while being drawn into an 'other-worldly detachment' during dissociation periods of at least six hours' duration."[9]

Chemical investigation has shown the agent to be bufotenine, or n-n-dimethyl serotonin, a substance currently under observation for its possible role in the etiology of schizophrenia.

Certain of the results of chemical imbalances during illness need also to be mentioned, as in fever, pain, or severe nausea. Usually the range of perception is drastically curtailed. People can walk into the room and hardly be seen, ordinary sounds will be missed, sensitivity to room temperatures may decline, important decisions can be regarded as irrelevant and avoided. More severe distortion can occur as well, especially with fever, when sights and sounds can be magnified out of proportion, or hallucinations occur. It is so easy to forget, when we are hale and hearty, how different the world looks when we are in pain or ill.

Constitutional Variations

A different kind of physiologic factor in perception is based on differences in height, weight, muscular strength and coordination, intelligence; and ranges in eyesight, hearing, and the other sensory modalities. Everyday experience provides a multitude of examples to illustrate the point. To a child the world looks like a different place from the way it appears to an adult, from size factors alone. When the four-year-old goes to the department store with his mother and they ride in the crowded elevator, the child will be surrounded by a forest of legs, will not be able to see any faces, and may perceive elevator riding as a rather frightening experience. When he goes home and plays out in the backyard with the neighbor's collie, he finds a row of teeth right at eye level. He also finds an animal that is big enough to ride, as the cowboys do on television. Hospital equipment, not to mention needles, can also be "oversize" and consequently frightening, beds near the top of his head, big lights, and many such things.

An obese person is limited in dealing with the environment by his very size. Strenuous physical activity, like tennis, bowling, even golf, is not easy. The muscular coordination involved is rendered difficult by the excess fat; hence, the obese person is more awkward in sports, and the necessary effort to move his weight around cuts down endurance rapidly. The spectator role is the only one open, as far as sports are concerned, yet much of our social life, especially in the early and middle years of life, is built around active sports activity. Other complications arise also, as in the ability to maneuver in small places. Theater seats are built to standard specifications of width that do not extend to the range of the obese, sportscars are the same, occasional chairs at tea parties are likely to break under excess weight, and subway turnstiles are a hazard indeed. Perception of situations by the obese person cannot help being influenced by his size.

Social attitudes toward obesity also enter the picture. The ideal American type is slender. Unlike some other cultures, fat is not highly regarded; it is even thought to be repulsive if excessive. The women who model the latest fashions in clothes are very slender, and the Hollywood ideal is not dissimilar. We see this reflected in the popularity of diet columns in the newspapers, the advertised caloric content of foods and beverages, and the increased use of reducing salons. For men, social pressure toward slenderness is not so great, but still not to be discounted. The obese person is quite aware of social attitudes toward overweight and will be influenced accordingly in perceiving his place in interpersonal relations.

Still another example is variation in the sensitivity of sensory organs, nearsightedness, hearing loss, disturbance of smell and taste. Individuals with such limitations have a reduced sensory input; they are less acutely tuned to changes in the environment. The person with reduced hearing finds that his ability to follow conversation decreases if there is considerable background noise; hence he will perceive crowded gatherings, especially cocktail parties, as quite unpleasant. Nearsightedness may mean difficulty in recognizing faces of people across a room, will reduce the pleasure of drives through the country, and may, in this age of speed, heighten the chances of accident.

The effect of constitutional variations on perception will in some cases be very slight, in others quite marked, depending on the departure from normal of the variation and the demands of the situation faced by the individual.

Altered Constitutional State

The final factor to be noted under physiologic determinants of perception is that of *altered constitutional state*, brought about through loss of organ or limb, or some other kind of deformity.

Facial disfigurement poses real problems to the individual thus afflicted, for the face plays a most important part in social communication. We read all kinds of messages from another's face and express the basic emotions of love, fear, and rage through facial action, often without a word being spoken. In meeting a stranger one looks first at his face, and from it makes judgments about character, friendliness, sense of humor, and a host of other attributes. Notions of beauty center there, especially in a culture that emphasizes beauty contests and glamorizes the motion picture and television star. Persons with facial deformities, therefore, could be expected to view social situations somewhat differently from their friends with unmarred faces. These were precisely the findings of Macgregor in her study of 115 patients undergoing plastic surgery. She concluded that:

> The complaints of the majority of patients with reference to their appearance centered around the patterns of interaction between themselves and others. Not only were they daily dismayed by the

reflection of their own mirrors, but, more damaging to their ego esteem, they saw their handicaps reflected in the reaction of others toward them.[10]

Another important constitutional alteration occurs when a woman loses one or both breasts through a radical mastectomy. Not only has she lost part of her body and, therefore, is not a whole person, she has also lost something which in our culture is invested with highly charged emotion. Emphasis on the breast in dress, in advertising, in Hollywood productions, puts to a psychological disadvantage the woman who cannot meet the norm or standard. The implication in loss of breast is more than the feeling of being an incomplete woman; it also involves a deficiency in sexual allurement. Perception of interpersonal situations is bound to change under these conditions, and initially the reaction may be one of depression and bitterness toward those close and dear.

Loss of arms and legs, or crippling through poliomyelitis, blindness, and other kinds of altered physiologic state affect perception. Again, the degree of effect will be due to the extent of loss, the amount to which it interferes with daily living, and the attitudes of society toward the particular kind of disfigurement.

In concluding this discussion of the physiologic determinants of perception, it should be pointed out that physicians and nurses, and in some cases medical social workers, work much of the time in situations where there is a maximum possibility for physiologic factors to play a part in perception, and perceptual distortion. Merely because of the commonness of these situations it is easy to overlook the importance of physiologic factors in helping to explain behavior of patients. There are other variables, however, that are of equal importance; we now turn to the next set.

PSYCHOLOGIC DETERMINANTS OF PERCEPTION

Personality factors provide one set of limits on the perceptual range that is available to the individual in any given situation. Although the range will vary from one person to another, there are broad analytic categories that taken together enable us to understand the dynamics of personality. Three in particular affect the process of perception: psychogenic needs; adaptive and defense mechanisms; and beliefs, attitudes, and values. The first deals with motivation, the second with mediation and control, the third with order and meaning, all of which are pertinent to perception in situations of illness or injury.

Psychogenic Needs

The problem of motivation is far from simple and, indeed, constitutes a lively controversy in the field of psychology.[11] However, from the various concepts that have been advanced to explain the springs of action, psychogenic need is especially pertinent as a determinant of perception. Furthermore, it is a concept that can give meaning to much of the behavior we see in situations of disease or illness, and it articulates well with social and cultural determinants.

Among academic psychologists, Murray and the group at the Harvard Psychological Clinic have presented a systematic scheme of psychogenic needs, accompanied by extensive case history data. "The Case of Ernst," for example, is still a classic exposition of the analysis of ongoing behavior in the service of basic psychogenic needs.[12] The following paragraphs will lean heavily on the theoretical formulations of Murray, with illustrations drawn from the experimental literature or from life experiences.

Murray defines need as a concept that stands for a force of some nature in the brain region, an organizing force that affects thinking, knowing, perceiving in such a way as to change an existing, unsatisfying situation in certain directions. Each need is accompanied by a particular feeling or emotion, and even though sometimes weak or momentary, it usually persists and gives rise to overt behavior or fantasy, which may change the external circumstances sufficiently to appease or satisfy the organism and still the need.

A person can usually describe his wanting and striving for a certain end, can tell what attracted his attention and what the stimuli meant to him. He can relate his inner feelings, the emotions that are aroused, whether he is pleased, or unhappy, or angry, or scared. In these cases we can speak of a *manifest need.*

At other times a need may not reach conscious awareness, may be evidenced in a vague restlessness, or be hidden altogether under the guise of other conscious needs. It may become objectified in play or artistic composition, in dreams, or free association, or in fantasies, and its presence determined only by oblique observation. Under these circumstances we are dealing with a *latent need.*

Both manifest and latent needs affect perception and consequent behavior, and both may be operating at the same time, though to pinpoint the latter special techniques are usually necessary. From a conceptual point of view, however, it is important to emphasize the relevance of both in understanding behavior.[13]

In any given person needs come and go. Some operate for but a brief interval, others endure and recur with consistency and frequency. Mr. Jones may characteristically show needs for achievement, autonomy, dominance, and sex; Mr. Smith may be more likely to exhibit the needs for affiliation, deference, infavoidance, sentience, and nurturance; and for Mr. Brown the needs may be for defendence, harmavoidance, order, seclusion, and superiority. In other words, there are certain patterned regularities in the expression of needs that lend predictableness to human behavior. Part of the process of getting to know a person is an awareness of those needs that are likely to occur under given circumstances.

Turning now to a consideration of the way in which needs influence the process of perception, there is evidence from a number of sources in the experimental literature, of which the work by McClelland and his associates is most relevant. Their concern has been with the need for achievement, or the achievement motive. In one study McClelland and Liberman[14] presented subjects with a series of words in a tachistoscope at .01 second exposure, and with increasing illumination until each word was recognized. Ten of the words were neutral, ten were security related, and ten achievement related. Corresponding measures of the need for achievement were obtained from stories written to pictures like those included in the Thematic Apperception Test.

Results showed that subjects who were rated high on the need for achievement recognized the achievement-related words more quickly than did the subjects who were rated low.

In later studies McClelland and his associates[15] sought to manipulate the achievement motive experimentally in the laboratory much as one might work with the hunger motive. By altering the features of a situation in which subjects found themselves, they hoped to elicit the need for achievement, which then could be measured in the production of stories to the TAT and other pictures.

The "achievement-oriented condition," as the experimental situation was called, began with the introduction of the experimenter as a university instructor who was conducting a serious psychological investigation. He indicated that the tests which the subjects were about to take measured intelligence and a person's ability to organize material and to evaluate situations quickly and accurately. He said that they had been used to select Washington administrators and that the tests were being used to find out which individuals possessed the leadership qualities shown by superior performance on the tests. The subjects were then given a twelve-minute anagrams test and a TAT-type of test in group administration.

The achievement-oriented condition was compared with two previous experimental situations, relaxed and neutral, in which environmental cues toward achievement had been kept to a minimum. As each subject went from the relaxed to the neutral, to the achievement-oriented situations, there was an increase in the achievement motivation, the effect of which could be seen in the TAT stories which the subject wrote in each of the situations. McClelland and his associates sum this up by saying:

> Generally speaking, we are justified in saying that as achievement motivation is experimentally increased, the imaginative stories that subjects write become increasingly more concerned with achievement, the need for achievement, anticipations of success and failure, acts instrumental to success and the avoidance of failure, affective states associated with succeeding and failing, blocks in the way of achieving, and help from other persons in the direction of achievement.[16]

Carrying the study to its logical conclusion, the experimenters found that subjects with high achievement imagery in the stories demonstrated in other ways the presence of achievement motivation. For example, they completed more tasks under achievement orientation, solved more arithmetic problems in a timed test, improved faster in the ability to do anagrams, set a higher level of aspiration if reality factors were ruled out, tended to recall more incompleted tasks, and tended to get better grades.

In the area of one need, that for achievement, we find, therefore, that its arousal has a definite effect on the way a subject perceives situations. His TAT stories are different from those evoked when the need is not aroused. Furthermore, not only does the need for achievement affect perception but is also associated with subsequent behavior.

If we turn to the world of everyday experience, many examples come to mind of the effect of other needs on perception and behavior. The physician who has a strong need for nurturance is likely to perceive an alcoholic patient as one requiring help rather than one to be avoided or pushed out of mind. The chief nurse with a need for dominance may perceive interns who disregard her medical suggestions as insubordinate young upstarts. The young physician with needs for deference and affiliation may prefer to work entirely within the framework of a hospital research staff, while his friend who has strong needs for autonomy would probably perceive that role as undesirable (unless perhaps he is the project director).

One final word—people who visit their family doctor or are patients in hospitals, or who are interviewed by the medical social worker have strong needs as well as presenting symptoms. The needs will vary from one individual to another, but in each case they will affect the person's perception of the illness and his relation to the physician, nurse, or social worker. Awareness of the needs that motivate patients can often facilitate the therapeutic relationship with them and thus be conducive to better medical care. At the same time, needs that motivate physicians, nurses, and other personnel have important effects on relationships with patients. A physician with high needs for dominance and autonomy may have a very difficult time treating a patient with a similar pattern of needs, and a much easier time with a patient characterized primarily by needs for deference and passivity.

Adaptive and Defense Mechanisms

The smooth functioning of the human organism, from both a physiologic and a psychologic standpoint, is a matter of balance among forces, a striving for homeostasis. When imbalances occur, for whatever reason, adaptive mechanisms come into operation. In this section the discussion centers on imbalances brought about by conflict, the resulting ego adaptive and defense mechanisms, and the effect of these mechanisms on perception.

It was noted in the preceding section that different needs may be operating at the same time, some manifest, some latent. Often they operate at cross purposes, wherein the satisfaction of one constitutes the rejection of another. A businessman with high need for achievement has an opportunity to make a sizable profit on a land transaction, but at the expense of a close friend, and need for affiliation. The adolescent, with growing need for autonomy from parental ties and controls, has a strong need for sympathetic help when he doesn't make first string on the basketball squad, and is baffled by which way to turn. Conflicts among competing needs constantly occur. Usually resolution is quick and relatively painless, for by the mere frequency of conflict we learn how to deal with it. When the competing needs are strong, especially when they are from different levels, manifest and latent, and no clear resolution evident, then important ego maneuvers are necessary.

Also to be considered as the cause of conflict is competition among physiologic imbalances, psychogenic needs, and the pressures of the social milieu. The human organism cannot always adjust its physiologic pressures immediately; often they must be delayed in gratification, sometimes deferred entirely. Psychologists, especially the Freudians, have made much of the thwarting of the sexual urges by the pressures of society or by psychogenic needs that are counter to free sexual gratification. Certainly in this area many of the most dramatic examples of conflict are to be found, but conflicts occur from the pressures of other kinds of physiologic imbalances as well, those involved in hunger, thirst, and fatigue. Again resolution of the conflicts thus engendered, and they occur frequently, is usually carried out without great cost. From time to time, however, competing needs and imbalances find no easy solution.

When conflicts occur between needs or between physiologic imbalances and needs, and the potential solutions are within the allowances of the social milieu, the resolution will be largely one of strength. If the feeling of hunger is stronger than the need for affiliation, Dr. Jones will probably excuse himself from the case discussion in the residents' lounge and head for the cafeteria. Contrariwise, when Dr. Jones has the prospect of making an interesting or unusual diagnosis, he will cheerfully forgo lunch in order to be prompt for his appointment with the chief of the medical service. Need for achievement in this case is stronger than the pangs of hunger. In such situations the problem of conflict is of no great consequence.

When competing needs are of equal strength, when the limits of the social milieu are restrictive, or its conditions such that needs, especially latent needs, cannot be satisfied, resolution of the conflict thus engendered is painful. We must remember, too, that the limits of the social milieu need not be physically present in the form of a policeman or disapproving members of one's family or social group, but operate as effectively when they are internalized in the conscience or superego. Competition and conflict are productive of unpleasant feelings, anxiety, and tension, to which the ego responds with adaptive and defense mechanisms.

Action of the ego in handling anxiety can proceed with conscious, flexible mechanisms that serve to channel energies into safe areas, satisfy needs in socially acceptable ways, avoid future conflicts of like type, or reorganize perception in such a way that conflict no longer exists. Because these mechanisms are conscious or close to consciousness, are not rigid and repetitive, they can be called *ego adaptive mechanisms*. On the other hand, if the individual faces a situation of severe anxiety and his experience with satisfying adaptive mechanisms is limited, then more rigid, unconscious, repetitive mechanisms come into play. Here we have the situation of neurotic defenses: repression, projection, denial, reaction formation, and undoing, traditionally labeled *ego defense mechanisms*.

The distinction between adaptive and defense mechanisms as outlined here is one of degree rather than sharpness, but it is a distinction that is often not made at all. It is true that defense mechanisms even of a neurotic nature have an adaptive value inasmuch as they do provide a solution to the conflict, although the solution may not be efficient or permanent. However, distinguishing between adaptive and defense mechanisms has several advantages. In the first place, neurotic behavior can be separated from normal reactions, pathology from health. All too frequently the language of psychological pathology provides the framework for describing normal adaptive behavior with consequent distortion of the perception of that behavior by professional observers. Secondly, the distinction allows us to place emphasis on the strengths possessed by the personality rather than its weaknesses, on the potentialities for growth and change, on the energy available for meeting problems. Most personalities have a balance sheet of debit and credit factors and the process of differentiating adaptive and defense mechanisms keeps this in perspective.

One adaptive technique for handling conflict is avoiding situations that produce tension. Some people, for example, learn that a certain constellation of events will be frustrating to them, will make them angry but provide no means for releasing the anger. For them, avoidance may be the healthiest maneuver. Handling situations by denying the presence of a given need or emotion is more likely to be a defense mechanism. An intense need for aggression can be kept from consciousness, even cloaked in a superficially pleasant manner, because the anxiety over hostile impulses is great. In like manner, signs of illness can be ignored and long delay incurred in visiting a physician because the anxiety about cancer and death causes such pain.

Another adaptive mechanism is transferring the object or outlet for strong needs when the object or outlet in one direction is blocked by other needs or pressures from the social milieu. One research administrator had a load of oak logs delivered to his yard every fall, for he knew that the exercise of swinging a sledge hammer or ax was an excellent outlet for the aggressions engendered in the course of dealing with difficult but important people. Some social organizations have a built-in structure for transfer of object in the face of conflict of needs. The Army sergeant, unable to talk back to the captain when he is "chewed out" by him, and hence unable to find an outlet in that direction for his aggression, is entitled to "chew out" his squad for minor infractions of code or to assign them extra duty.

The unconscious, repetitive act of displacement of energy in the face of conflict is a corresponding defense mechanism. The stereotype of the neighborhood bully often represents the resolution of a conflict between hostile impulses and a strong feeling of inferiority. The hostility is displaced onto weaker individuals and the ineffectiveness of the defense comes to light only when someone who is stronger than the bully calls his bluff.

At times conflict may be resolved by making acceptable the expression of a need which hitherto had been considered unacceptable, especially in the face of blocked goals. Krech and Crutchfield treat this topic in their *Theory and Problems of Social Psychology*,[17] in which they postulate that cognitive reorganization takes place in the face of blocked goals, causing a change in perception and opening up new avenues for tension reduction. The years of adolescence and early childhood constitute the time when many of these cognitive reorganizations occur, appearing at first perhaps under the guise of rationalization and later as genuine alterations in outlook. Yet none of us ever gets beyond the time when we can change our ideas and the possibility of cognitive reorganization is one of the strengths of personality. The physician hopes he can mobilize this mechanism when he has discouraging news for a patient and his family, so does the teacher when he has to inform a student that he has failed an important examination.

Sublimation still remains one of the classic adaptive mechanisms, essentially a process where socially acceptable outlets are found for strong needs. The process is not conscious but it lacks the rigid, repetitive quality of a true defense mechanism and in the course of years may prove an integrative rather than a disruptive force within the personality. Anna Freud[18] describes a young governess who as a child had strong wishes for beautiful clothes and a number of children, who wanted to do everything that her friends did, and was eager to be admired for her cleverness. As an adult she appeared to be unassuming and modest in her demands on life, dressed soberly, and was not willing to compete with people unless forced to do so. At first, it appeared that her need for exhibition and strong sexual drive had been repressed and replaced by reaction formations; on closer investigation, however, it was clear that her original needs were being affirmed, but in ways that did not conflict with her superego and other strong psychogenic needs. She took an affectionate interest in the love life of her friends and colleagues, becoming a confidante and matchmaker. She displayed a lively interest in her friends' clothes, adored children, and devoted her life to them. She sublimated her needs and desires in the lives of other people rather than giving expression to them in her own.

Because of its effect on perception, some attention should be given to one of the major defense mechanisms, that of projection—imputing to a person or situation in the environment the very need over which the personality is in conflict. Projection is often called into play when the need for aggression is strong yet its expression is blocked by the presence of other strong needs or the conscience. Strangers, or even friends, may be perceived as hostile or aggressive without adequate objective grounds for such feeling. Illness is a fertile ground for conflict that can lead to the use of projection in certain patients. Given the right kind of psychodynamic background, a patient may have strong aggressive needs arising out of the dependence occasioned by illness and hospitalization, loss of income, and disruption of normal activities. Yet competing with aggression is the need for sympathetic help and the pressures of the environment that have negative sanctions against the expression of aggression by patients. If projection is used to handle the ensuing conflict, the patient will perceive the nurses and physicians as critical and uncooperative, even openly hostile to him in spite of the fact that there may be little if any objective support for that perception.

In the experimental literature there is evidence that the kind of psychological conflict we have been describing and ensuing adaptive or defensive mechanisms can affect perception. Presenting words to subjects in a tachistoscope, McGinnies[19] gradually increased the exposure time until there was correct identification. Eleven of the words were neutral and seven were emotionally toned. In addition, galvanic skin response recordings were made during the prerecognition presentations. Results showed that subjects required longer exposure time to recognize the emotionally laden than the neutral words, which indicated a resistance to recognizing the words. Galvanic skin responses were higher in the prerecognition period for the emotionally toned words than the neutral words, in this case a condition indicative of anxiety. The longer recognition time could be interpreted as avoidance or denial of the stimulus in the face of anxiety.

In a different experimental design, Bruner and Postman[20] used regular and incongruous playing cards in a tachistoscope, the incongruity being introduced by switching the color on some cards, red clubs and black hearts, for example. As one might expect, they found that recognition times for the incongruous cards were much higher. In the face of a visual field that was different from their expectations, some subjects would use a form of perceptual denial; that is, they would be bound by either the color or the suit and not see the incongruity. Others would try to effect some sort of compromise; some were completely disrupted; and some showed a startle pattern of recognition.

Summarizing much of their work on perceptual adaptation, Bruner and Postman state:

> When a subject is presented stimuli which are known to be threatening or otherwise anxiety-provoking, he may misperceive the stimulus on tachistoscopic exposures preceding correct recognition in one of several characteristic ways. First, he may fail to perceive anything at all, a kind of perceptual blocking. This may occur at exposure levels above his "normal" threshold. Or he may report seeing stimuli which are jumbled and nonsensical or incomplete. Finally he may report seeing material which is either derogatory or contrary to the nature of the actual stimulus.[21]

Ordering Mechanisms: Beliefs, Attitudes, and Values

Needs are inclined to be transitory but human personality has permanency and continuity. In addition, therefore, to motivating forces and to mechanisms for resolving conflict, we need to consider the factors that bind together the impressions of everyday experience. Beliefs, attitudes, and values serve to provide continuity from one situation to the next, to give a structure to one's psychological world. They aid the individual in his attempts to find meaning in the events that occur around him, providing ready-made answers for situations that would otherwise be ambiguous and disconcerting. Furthermore, they assist in the achievement of various goals by defining courses of action that are open to the individual.

These functions in personality of beliefs, attitudes, and values lead us to call them *ordering mechanisms*. In common they have the feature of being enduring cognitive organizations of previous perceptions and knowledge about the world, but at the same time each provides a different kind of ordering procedure. Beliefs tell us how things are related to each other, attitudes tell us how we relate to them, while values tell us how to choose from among objects and events. Beliefs include knowledge, opinions, and faith about aspects of the world; they are the pattern and meaning of a thing. In their clear state beliefs are emotionally neutral. Attitude has been defined as "an [enduring] syndrome of response consistency with regard to [a set of] social objects."[22] Attitudes are in part a readiness to act; in addition to cognitive properties there are affective or emotional qualities which we often call *pro* or *anti*. Values are the principles by which we establish priorities and hierarchies of importance among needs, demands, and goals, helping us to decide where our emotional investments will be made and the extent of these investments. Clyde Kluckhohn defined value orientation as "a generalized and organized conception, influencing behavior, of nature, of man's place in it, of man's relation to man, and of the desirable and non-desirable as they may relate to man-environment and interhuman relations."[23]

We may believe that germs cause disease, and more specifically that the tubercle bacillus causes tuberculosis; and this may help to make meaningful much of the everyday experience of physicians or nurses. On the other hand, we may have an attitude toward those who believe that magic causes disease, probably a negative or anti-attitude, which leads us to scoff at them or even lobby for legislation against them. Finally, we may hold the value that human life has great worth and should be guarded at all costs, which impels us to spare neither money nor energy in the fight against disease or for prolonging life.

To take another example, we may believe that capitalism and free enterprise are the most efficient economic procedures and around this belief organize the structure of our medical practice. Our attitude toward the activities of the American Medical Association in condemning socialized medicine may be positive and lead us to write letters to the Association in support of its pronouncements. At the same time we may place great value on individual self-determination and striving, which leads us to hold in at least mild contempt those patients who seem to prefer the comforts of prolonged convalescence in the hospital to a return to work.

Beliefs, attitudes, and values are intimately related but for purposes of exposition we will separate them in the following paragraphs, discussing first some of the characteristics of beliefs and attitudes which are important for behavior in health and disease, then consider important aspects of value orientations as a conceptual tool for those in the health professions.

Characteristics of Beliefs and Attitudes. Beliefs and attitudes are sometimes clear, explicit, and highly differentiated, or conversely they may be vague and poorly structured.[24] For those in the health professions, belief in the germ theory of disease will be highly differentiated, with specific diseases and specific organisms associated, and with the psychosomatic disorders held separate. For the same individuals, belief in the immortality of the soul may be quite vague with no clear idea of the form or process of immortality at time of death. In the first case, the belief will be compounded of much knowledge and relatively little faith, while in the latter it will be almost completely a matter of faith. This is not to say that beliefs which involve a great deal of faith are vague and poorly structured, for as we shall see in Chapter 4 much of primitive beliefs about disease is based on faith but is often highly differentiated. Faith, knowledge, and opinions all enter into our varied beliefs and attitudes with equal weight.

Some of our beliefs and attitudes are an intricate part of systems of beliefs and attitudes, while others are relatively isolated. Not all are equally important for daily behavior. Some are fundamental "givens" about the world which we use all the time. In Smalltown and Central City, U.S.A., the fundamental beliefs that will be shared by most people include the following: God exists, communism is a danger to world peace, and democracy is the highest form of government yet achieved. In like fashion most people will hold that the earth has arrived in its present state through a process of evolution, that natural cause and effect relationships govern most of our behavior, that man can exert increasing control over nature, and that disease can be understood and controlled through scientific experimentation. Some people in Smalltown may believe that the width of the band on woolly caterpillars in the fall foretells the severity of the approaching winter, or that eating fish increases a person's intellectual powers, but such beliefs are relatively isolated and enter into daily behavior to a much less extent than other beliefs.

The really important beliefs and attitudes for any given person are those that are functionally related to the more central characteristics of the individual's personality structure, are well organized and generalized, and based on needs for identification with other people and groups. The beliefs and attitudes of the ardent racist will probably be related to important psychogenic needs like those for dominance, aggression, inviolacy. They will be well differentiated, with quite specific beliefs about level of Negro intelligence, about the habits and motivations of the Negro, with strong attitudes toward northern liberal Democrats, *Time* magazine, and the Supreme Court. They will be part of other systems of beliefs and attitudes—religious, political, and social. They will be generalized to different minority groups, including Jews and "foreigners." The need for identification with others will be evidenced in membership in White Supremacy councils, or even the Klan, where friends hold similar beliefs and where there are periodic occasions for reaffirming and strengthening the beliefs and attitudes.

We have noted that beliefs and attitudes are compounded of knowledge, opinions, and faith. The strength of a belief or attitude does not necessarily depend on its degree of correspondence with objective fact, or upon its lack of contradiction with other beliefs and attitudes which the individual may hold. For example, the individual who believes that natural cause-and-effect relationships are necessary to explain disease may also believe that copper wire around the wrist or ankle can prevent rheumatism, that "sinful living" leads to insanity, that heartburn during pregnancy is associated with a heavy head of hair on the newborn, and that frightening experiences during pregnancy can mark the baby in peculiar ways. Another example, directly relevant to those in the health professions, concerns a group of public health nurses who were interviewing a mother and child from India during a teaching institute. The mother, being a good Hindu, did not eat meat. Reared in the western tradition, the nurses believed that meat was an essential part of every diet. Both mother and baby were healthy individuals but the nurses were quite aghast at their lack of success in convincing the mother about "proper" dietary prescriptions. In both cases, that of the Indian mother and of the American nurses, the correspondence of belief and objective facts was not completely clear, and certainly was in contradiction with other beliefs and attitudes they held, yet there was no question about the strength of those beliefs and attitudes. The presentation of new "facts" will not necessarily change the kinds of beliefs and attitudes illustrated above; hence, their very tenacity makes them doubly disturbing to others who have different beliefs.

Beliefs, Attitudes, and Perception. The experimental literature in the behavioral sciences abounds with the effects of beliefs and attitudes on perception, even though the reports may not be couched in the terms used here or the projects specifically designed to show variations in perception with variations in belief and attitude. Everyday experience also provides a multitude of pertinent examples. Chapter 4 will present examples of beliefs and attitudes about disease as they affect perception of illness, but for the present some simple examples will suffice.

Take the case of an American businessman who is a staunch member of the Republican party. He reads in his morning paper that the President of the United States, who is also a Republican, is on a ten-day vacation in Florida. Our businessman thinks little about it, for he feels the country is in good hands and the strains of that high office require periodic vacations so that the President can keep fit and alert. The same man four years later may read the same kind of item in his newspaper, except that political fortunes have changed and a Democrat is now President. Our businessman has strong attitudes toward Democrats, regarding them as too socially minded and wasteful of the taxpayer's money. He is fearful for the future of the country while in their hands. This time he sees the vacation in quite a different light and tells his wife that the President always seems to be taking a vacation. He wonders how much it costs to fly the President to his vacation retreat and feels that the government cannot run efficiently with a "part-time" Chief Executive. His political attitudes have led him on two different occasions to very different perceptions of the same kind of event.

Consider two patients coming to Smalltown General Hospital for surgery. One comes from an isolated rural area where there has been little if any formal education and where illness has been treated by remedies passed down from generation to generation. He comes to the physician and to the hospital only as a last resort after all other treatments have failed. The other patient comes from an urban area where there has been extensive formal education and where contacts with modern medical procedures are routine. He comes to the hospital readily when stabbing abdominal pains and nausea tell him that he has more than an upset stomach. The first patient is likely to perceive the surgeon and hospital procedure with suspicion, having in mind that doctors often experiment on people, especially if they are strangers. The thought of being unconscious during the operation may be quite terrifying. The second patient will perceive the hospital as a source of help and though fearful that he may die, will submit to surgery with fortitude and trust. Again, differing sets of beliefs and attitudes produce strikingly different perceptions and behavior and call for variation in the psychological approach to each patient.

The Foundations of Values. Bearing in mind that values tell us how to choose between objects and events and establish hierarchies of needs, demands, and goals, we need to look for the basis of value orientations. One approach is that taken by Florence Kluckhohn in outlining the basic human problems to which all people must find some solution.[25] Phrased in terms of questions, these are: (1) What are the innate predispositions of man? (2) What is the relation of man to nature? (3) What is the significant time dimension? (4) What is the valued personality type? (5) What is the dominant modality of the relationship of man to other men?

In seeking solutions to these questions, a system of values emerges, and for each question certain alternatives have been utilized by different groups of people. Considering the nature of man, it can be regarded as inherently evil, a state that may be unalterable or perfectable. The doctrine of original sin fits this, with the possibility of salvation through faith or the sacraments of the Church. There is a midpoint where man is basically neither evil nor good, and another extreme where man is essentially good, unalterably so or subject to corruption.

The man-nature relationship can view man as subjugated to nature, at the mercy of natural forces; as man in nature, a harmonious whole; or man over nature, the harnessing of the power of the elements. The last orientation is characteristic of most Americans. Fatalism and acceptance of the inevitable, as when man is subjugated to nature, may thwart the best intentions of those who practice scientific medicine and see man as master of nature.

Time orientation breaks down easily into reference toward the past, the present, or the future. The ancient Chinese looked toward the past with ancestor worship exemplifying their value orientation. Many Spanish-Americans are oriented toward the present and the things that interest them at the moment. For them an appointment by the clock has a meaning that is quite different from that given to it by the future-oriented, time-conscious Anglo-American.

The question about valued personality type is answered with three possibilities: what Kluckhohn calls the Being, the Being-in-Becoming, and the Doing orientation. The first stresses spontaneous expression of the "given" in personality, not spontaneity in the form of pure license, but spontaneity controlled by the other value orientations. The second stresses development as well as concern with what the human being is, self-realization and self-development of the integrated personality. The third is distinguished by its demand for action and accomplishment in accord with standards which are external to the individual. What the individual does and what he accomplishes are of primary importance.

Man's relationship to other men can also have three different emphases, termed by Kluckhohn as Lineal, Collateral, and Individualistic. All societies must give some attention to each of these, but values cluster around the one that receives greatest emphasis. Where the Lineal principle is heavily stressed, group goals are of primary concern to the individual, and one of these important goals is continuity of the group through time. When the focus is on the Collateral, the goals of the laterally extended group—that is, one's family or close associates at a given point in time—have primacy and continuity is not critical. In the third principle, individual goals will have primacy over those of the group, either at the present or through time. This is true of the United States with scattered exceptions.

The manner in which these five basic questions are answered provides the foundation for constructing an intricate value system. For example, if the valued personality type is that of the "Doing," then there will be subsidiary values on hard work, success through accumulation of objects or ideas, and activity of all kinds. If, in addition, the time orientation is future, there will be acceptance of the value of deferred gratification, the importance of scheduling, and emphasis on detailed planning. As the reader will be aware, these patterns are characteristic of the contemporary United States and even a little thought will indicate how much this system of values influences our daily perceptions and behavior. Suffice it to say that other people may erect alternative systems of values on the basis of different answers to the five questions, a fact that can do much to hinder the process of communication between them and someone from the contemporary United States.

Values and Perception. Although it is not easy to take the step from a theoretical discussion of values, as in that by Florence Kluckhohn, to the laboratory, there is merit in looking at the experimental literature for the effect of values on perception. In one of the early social perception studies Bruner and Goodman[26] used two groups of children to judge the size of coins: one group from a settlement house in a slum area, and one group from a progressive school in which sons and daughters of successful business and professional people were enrolled. The poor group overestimated the size of the coins to a greater extent than the rich group. Carter and Schooler[27] repeated the experiment but had the subjects judge the coins when present and from memory. Only when the subjects judged from memory were there significant differences, and the experimenters concluded that values play a role in perception when the stimulus object is equivocal or not present. In much of our social perception, ambiguity and equivocality certainly are present.

McGinnies and Bowles[28] asked subjects to identify 12 unfamiliar faces by occupational titles that were comparable to the six value types of Spranger: religious, esthetic, theoretical, economic, social, and political. The number of exposures required for each person to fixate, or identify correctly, the two faces representing each value were correlated with his scores on the Allport Vernon Scale of Values, which measured strength of values in each of Spranger's six areas. The correlation was significant, showing that subjects fixated more readily on faces symbolizing their highest value orientations than those representing their lowest.

In an experiment somewhat similar to that of McGinnies and Bowles, Vanderplas and Blake[29] presented to subjects 36 words that matched the six value areas on the Allport Vernon Scale of Values. The words were given orally at increasing intensity until recognized. Recognition threshold scores for each group of six words were then correlated with the scores on the value areas of the value scale. Subjects perceived words representing their high value areas at significantly lower intensity levels than they perceived words that represented their lower value areas.

Again turning to everyday experience, there are many illustrations to be found concerning values and perception, especially in situations of health and disease. For example, the person or group with a time orientation toward the present will have difficulty in seeing the value of inoculations against disease, a future occurrence. Emphasis on collateral relationship to others in distinction to individualistic will cause difficulty in perceiving the importance of taking a person out of a family and putting him in a tuberculosis hospital miles away. The view that man is subjugated to nature may lead an individual not to seek medical help in time of disease, in the belief that the inevitable or fate cannot be overcome. In like vein, this person may not see health as a positive value, much to the dismay of the highly educated physician or public health specialist, who views man as overcoming nature and as able to reach levels of health beyond those of the past.

At the beginning of this section we defined beliefs, attitudes, and values as ordering mechanisms in personality, techniques for providing continuity and giving meaning to everyday experience. In the course of fulfilling that function they enable the individual to be selective in his perceptions, with consequent effects on his overt behavior. We have tried to show through the use of illustrations that these ordering mechanisms affect perception in matters of health and disease and that the behavior of patients can be made more meaningful by knowing something about their beliefs and attitudes, and their value systems.

Though an individual matter in terms of their action, beliefs, attitudes, and values also reflect the effects of social groupings to which the individual belongs. We share our beliefs, attitudes, and values with others who are members of our church or political party, who have the same kind of educational background or are in the same occupational group, who recognize common ethnic origins or share the same cultural traditions. Sociocultural factors therefore become important determinants of perception, a topic to which we must devote our attention in Chapter 3.

NOTES TO CHAPTER 2

1. A number of books are available that deal with perception in psychology as the term is used here. For one account the reader is referred to Blake, Robert R., and Glenn V. Ramsey, editors, *Perception:* An Approach to Personality, Ronald Press Co., New York, 1951. The chapter entitled "Perceptual Processes as Basic to an Understanding of Complex Behavior" by Blake, Ramsey, and Moran, is pertinent for a fuller and more technical discussion of perception as an important psychological process. An application of the perceptual approach to medical problems can be found in an article by Hadley Cantril, "Perception and Interpersonal Relations," which appeared in the *American Journal of Psychiatry*, vol. 114, August, 1957, pp. 119–126.

2. For those readers who are not familiar with the Thematic Apperception Test, commonly referred to as TAT, a brief description is in order. The test was developed by Henry Murray and his colleagues as part of the studies reported in *Explorations in Personality*, Oxford University Press, New York, 1938. The subject is asked to tell a story about each of a series of pictures. He is instructed to make the story creative, and to tell what happened in the past, what is presently taking place, and what may occur in the future. The results can be analyzed in a number of ways: by scoring the various themes that appear throughout the stories, by analyzing the actions of the "hero" relative to other people, or by interpreting material from the stories in symbolic form. Psychodiagnosticians use the TAT as part of a test battery; in addition it has been used extensively in research. Also variations of the test have been developed where different pictures are presented that relate to specific goals of an investigation, or where the pictures are projected on a screen for a short interval rather than given to the subject to examine.

3. Levine, Robert, Isidor Chein, and Gardner Murphy, "The Relation of Intensity of a Need to the Amount of Perceptual Distortion," *Journal of Psychology*, vol. 13, April, 1942, pp. 283–293.

4. McClelland, David C., and John W. Atkinson, "The Projective Expression of Needs: I, The Effect of Different Intensities of the Hunger Drive on Perception," *Journal of Psychology*, vol. 25, April, 1948, pp. 205–222.

5. For research relating the activity of the sympathetic nervous system to perception, the reader is referred to Callaway, Enoch, III, and Samuel V. Thompson, "Sympathetic Activity and Perception," *Psychosomatic Medicine*, vol. 15, September-October, 1953, pp. 443–455.

6. Costeau, Jacques Y., with Frederic Dumas, *The Silent World.* Harper and Bros., New York, 1953, pp. 111–113.

7. Jellinek, E. Morton, and Ross A. McFarland, "Analysis of Psychological Experiments on the Effects of Alcohol," *Quarterly Journal of Studies on Alcohol*, vol. 1, September, 1940, pp. 272–371.

8. Fabing, Howard D., "On Going Berserk: A Neurochemical Inquiry," *American Journal of Psychiatry*, vol. 113, November, 1956, pp. 409–415.

9. *Ibid.*, p. 410.

10. Macgregor, Frances Cooke, "Some Psychosocial Problems Associated with Facial Deformities," *American Sociological Review*, vol. 16, October, 1951, pp. 629–638. Another report, covering many kinds of disfigurement and disability, includes some good examples of altered or limited constitutional state on perception: Wright, Beatrice A., *Physical Disability:* A Psychological Approach, Harper and Bros., New York, 1960.

11. A detailed review of some of the shortcomings in major theories of motivation is to be found in White, Robert W., "Motivation Reconsidered: The Concept of Competence," *Psychological Review*, vol. 66, September, 1959, pp. 297–333. Professor White reviews the two classic theories, of drive reduction and of psychoanalytic instincts, and discusses the factors that these theories do not encompass. He then proposes a new concept in motivation, that of competence, the biological capacity of the organism to interact effectively with its environment. He argues that the motivation needed to attain competence cannot be derived completely from energy which is currently conceptualized as drives or instincts. The interested reader will find in this discussion a review of the changes that have occurred in both drive reduction theory and psychoanalytic instinct theory and of the newer research findings in motivation that call for further changes in theory.

12. Murray, Henry A., *Explorations in Personality*. Oxford University Press, New York, 1938. The concept of need is described in great detail, and it provides a theoretical framework for a variety of studies by staff members at the Harvard Psychological Clinic, among which is the development of the Thematic Apperception Test, referred to in note 2. "The Case of Ernst," by Robert W. White, is described on pp. 604–702.

13. The needs listed by Murray, the basic ones used in the studies at the Harvard Psychological Clinic, are as follows: abasement, achievement, affiliation, aggression, autonomy, counteraction, deference, defendence, dominance, exhibition, harm-avoidance, inviolacy (a composite of infavoidance, defendence and counteraction), nurturance, order, play, rejection, seclusion, sentience, sex, succorance, superiority, and understanding. Many of these will be familiar to the reader, others will not. Infavoidance, for example, is defined as the need to avoid failure, shame, humiliation, or ridicule; and succorance as the need to see aid, protection, or sympathy. Deference is the need to admire and willingly follow a superior person with whom one is allied, and sentience is the need to seek and enjoy sensuous impressions.

14. McClelland, David C., and Alvin M. Liberman, "The Effect of Need for Achievement on Recognition of Need-Related Words," *Journal of Personality*, vol. 18, December, 1949, pp. 236–251.

15. McClelland, David C., and others, *The Achievement Motive*. Appleton-Century-Crofts Co., New York, 1953.

16. *Ibid.*, pp. 145–146.

17. Krech, David, and Richard S. Crutchfield, *Theory and Problems of Social Psychology*. McGraw-Hill Book Co., New York, 1948.

18. Freud, Anna, *The Ego and the Mechanisms of Defense*. International Universities Press, Inc., New York, 1946.

19. McGinnies, Elliot, "Emotionality and Perceptual Defense," *Psychological Review*, vol. 56, September, 1949, pp. 244–251.

20. Bruner, Jerome S., and Leo Postman, "On the Perception of Incongruity: A Paradigm," *Journal of Personality*, vol. 18, December, 1949, pp. 206–223.

21. *Ibid.*, p. 25.

22. The definition is by D. T. Campbell and is taken from the discussion of attitudes by Bert F. Green in his chapter entitled "Attitude Measurement" in the *Handbook of Social Psychology*, edited by Gardner Lindzey, Addison-Wesley Publishing Co., Cambridge, Mass., 1954, pp. 333–369.

23. Kluckhohn, Clyde, "Values and Value Orientations in the Theory of Action," in Talcott Parsons and Edward A. Shils, editors, *Toward a General Theory of Action.* Harvard University Press, Cambridge, Mass., 1951, p. 409.

24. For a systematic treatment of beliefs and attitudes as important concepts in social psychology, the reader is referred to Krech, David, and Richard S. Crutchfield, *Theory and Problems of Social Psychology.* Chapters 5, 6, and 7 are devoted specifically to this topic.

25. Kluckhohn, Florence R., "Dominant and Variant Value Orientations" in Clyde Kluckhohn, Henry A. Murray, and David M. Schneider, editors, *Personality in Nature, Society, and Culture.* 2d ed. Alfred A. Knopf, Inc., New York, 1955, pp. 342–357.

26. Bruner, Jerome S., and Cecile C. Goodman, "Value and Need as Organizing Factors in Perception," *Journal of Abnormal and Social Psychology*, vol. 42, January, 1947, pp. 33–44.

27. Carter, Launor F., and Kermit Schooler, "Value, Need, and Other Factors in Perception," *Psychological Review*, vol. 56, July, 1949, pp. 200–207.

28. McGinnies, Elliot, and Warren Bowles, "Personal Values as Determinants of Perceptual Fixation," *Journal of Personality*, vol. 18, December, 1949, pp. 224–235.

29. Vanderplas, James M., and Robert R. Blake, "Selective Sensitization in Auditory Perception," *Journal of Personality*, vol. 18, December, 1949, pp. 252–266.

Chapter 3

A Conceptual Framework—II

SOCIOCULTURAL DETERMINANTS OF PERCEPTION

THE SOCIAL MILIEU IN which individuals are reared and in which they live provides another set of factors that limit and determine the process of perception and of subsequent behavior. The first section below deals with concepts that are important to an understanding of the broad social matrix, that is, culture and subculture. Subsequent sections will consider the anchoring points around which people organize their lives, roles, and positions; the variables that stratify or divide people, social class, and ethnic group; and the guides for behavior, folkways, and mores. Like the psychologic determinants, those chosen from the sociocultural realm are especially pertinent to problems of perception in health and illness.

The Social Matrix: Culture and Subculture

Although of common currency in the behavioral sciences, culture as a concept is difficult to define precisely. A number of definitions by different authors may be useful in pointing up the central characteristics of the term. Kroeber calls it the mass of motor reactions, habits, techniques, ideas, and values that are learned and passed on from one member of society to another, and he includes the behavior that these things induce.[1] Walter defines it thus:

> Culture is the learned ways of acting and thinking which are transmitted by group members to other group members and which provide for each individual ready-made and tested solutions for vital

life problems. Every human culture is a historical growth, and only as such can it be explained or understood. Since the very essence of culture is its transmission through generations, a culture may be thought of as the experience of the past entering as a determinant of thought and action in the present, and carrying, of course, important relation to the future of a group.[2]

Finally, as used by Margaret Mead, culture is:

. . . an abstraction from the body of learned behaviour which a group of people, who share the same tradition, transmit entire to their children, and, in part, to adult immigrants who become members of the society. It covers not only the arts and sciences, religions and philosophies to which the word culture has historically applied, but also the system of technology, the political practices, the small intimate habits of daily life, such as the way of preparing or eating food, or of hushing a child to sleep, as well as the method of electing a prime minister or changing the constitution.[3]

Each society has a characteristic culture, and we are able to differentiate not only the culture of Bali from that of the United States but also that of England and France from the United States.[4] The man in the latter society has a distinctive language and accent, form of government, set of historical traditions, way of dress, and many other characteristics that differentiate him from the Englishman, Frenchman, or Balinese. These are the things that we have in mind when we talk about culture.

As one would expect, subcultures are smaller groupings within a total culture, reflecting variations from the overall pattern in certain, but not all, respects. In a complex society such as we have in the United States there are any number of subcultures, some more distinguishable than others. For example, the term "upper-upper class" has come to mean the cream of top society, and is identified by names in the Social Register, membership in certain clubs, and residence in certain areas. Members of this group are part of American culture, but within this form a subculture. Their manner of speaking may be somewhat different from their fellow citizens, their values will emphasize tradition more than novelty, their customs will include things like "coming out" parties, polo matches, and horse shows, and the choice of eligible bachelors for marriageable women will be restricted. Other examples of subcultural groups that come to mind are the Mormons, people in show business, members of the underworld, the Puerto Ricans in New York City, the mountain folk of Arkansas, and college professors.

Culture and Perception. The relationship of culture to perception has been pointed out by Benjamin Paul: "One of the functions performed by culture is to serve as a subtle and systematic device for perceiving the world. Since cultures vary, perceptions of the world vary correspondingly."[5] People in a given culture classify events in certain ways, but the same events may be classified differently by people in other cultures. Paul cites color perception as an illustration, showing that in the studies of American Indian tribes, no two of them divided the spectrum in the same way. The number of standard colors ranged from three to eight, in comparison with our own division of six; red, orange, yellow, green, blue, and violet. Some cultures regard blue and green as the same, as in the case of the Zulus, but differentiate a number of shades of brown because of the importance of cattle in every aspect of their lives.

Differences in classification and association of events occur in many fields of experience. The Navajo Indians have few classifications of pain in contrast to our complex system of sharp, throbbing, dull, gripping, searing, and so forth, and the physician who is trying to establish a diagnosis of appendicitis in a Navajo may have difficulty in getting the kind of information he needs. Cultures and subcultural groups vary in the extent to which they perceive a set of circumstances as constituting illness or health, abnormality or normalcy, as calling for action or for disregarding. For example, in some South American countries at one time yaws was virtually a universal disease. People believed it to be a normal event and those who did not have it were thought to be abnormal. In a lower-class Negro subculture an illegitimate pregnancy may be perceived as an annoyance but not as a grievous sin, while the same event in an upper-middle class white subculture would be viewed as a catastrophe in moral laxity.

Among certain groups in our society alcoholism is regarded as a disease, and thus to be treated by medical means. Among other groups it is still regarded as a moral problem, and approached emotionally rather than rationally. Someone from a poorly educated working class group may perceive the chiropractor as a legitimate specialist for all kinds of illness, yet a well-educated person from upper-middle class may regard the chiropractor as useful only for back or neck pains and is careful not to tell the family physician about consulting him. Perception of important events varies markedly from one subcultural group to another.

The concepts of culture and subculture as important determinants of perception will be useful to those in the health professions in two ways. First, they can bring about a better understanding of patient behavior. Patients come from a variety of subcultural backgrounds, many of which may be quite different from the background of the physician, nurse, public health specialist, or medical social worker. As a consequence, these patients may have a different perception of the disease process and the manner in which forces should be brought to bear in treating disease. Tied in with the perception of illness will be a number of other factors, all part of cultural tradition, that affect the treatment situation. For example, food preference and beliefs about the value of food in sickness, methods of emotional expression, and the extent to which one is expected to show emotions in sickness, decision-making, and the emphasis on individual or collateral decisions; all these will be part of cultural tradition and may be at variance with the background of the medical care specialist. Knowing something of the patient's cultural background can lead to a better understanding of the way he perceives his illness situation and in many instances can lead to a more realistic treatment plan. By altering the treatment situation even in small ways the patient may be aided in making a more adequate adjustment.

In the second place, the health professional may come to a fuller understanding of himself, of relationships with colleagues, and thus use his energies more effectively in his work. Culture is not something that only *other people* have. The medical care and public health fields represent subcultures themselves in which the health professional participates but which he may never have tried to analyze in an objective sense. Later chapters in this book will deal with aspects of these subcultures and will utilize studies that have been made by behavioral scientists of the customs, traditions, behavioral expectations, and other cultural features of the world of the health professional. Knowing about his or her own cultural background enables the physician, nurse, medical social worker, or other health specialist to deal more realistically with colleagues and to be more flexible in treatment plans or health programs.

Anchoring Point: Position and Role

Activity patterns in social interaction can be understood in large part through the use of one of the major concepts in the behavioral sciences, that of role, and its counterpart, position. Role serves as an important mechanism in social coordination, giving the individual anchoring points in society and facilitating his relationships with other people. By knowing what to expect when one meets a person who fills a certain role, much probing of the environment is eliminated, ambiguity reduced, and the business of social transactions made easier. A case in point would be the interaction of one physician with another at a medical meeting, both strangers to each other. As soon as they identify each other as physicians, a whole set of behaviors appropriate to that role are immediately put into effect. If, however, one of the physicians had been introduced to a medicine man from the Navajo tribe, the situation would be quite different. Some time would be necessary to find out what a Navajo medicine man does, what subjects one discusses with him, whether or not he is expected to marry and have children, whether he falls into trances, practices sorcery, and a whole host of other things. In order to act correctly toward him the other person has to know something about his role.

Role theory is especially pertinent to the health professions in analyzing the perceptions and behaviors of both the health specialist and patient; hence, a fairly detailed exposition is in order here. First there is the problem of adequate definitions, for which we turn to a quotation from Sarbin:

> Moreover, persons are always members of a society (defined as an aggregation of persons with common goals), and these societies are structured into *positions* or statuses or offices. The positions are collections of rights and duties designated by a single term, e.g., mother, village chief, teacher, etc. The actions of persons, then, are organized around these positions and comprise the *roles*. Role and position are conjoined. Roles are defined in terms of the actions performed by the person to validate his occupancy of the position. In sum, all societies are organized around positions and the persons who occupy these positions perform specialized actions or roles. These roles are linked with the position and not with the person who is temporarily occupying the position.[6]

Position is location in a social system, while role is the set of attitudes, values, activities that constitute the behavior of the person occupying that position. Role is the dynamic concept, position the static one. The concept of role needs further elaboration, however, than "actions performed by the person to validate his occupancy of the position." Three aspects of role can be delineated, *expectations*, *conceptions*, and *performance*, each of which deserves brief description.[7]

The social system has a set of expectations for the incumbents of each particular position, the demands for behavior, what the person occupying that position should do. Furthermore, these expectations have an aspect of *reciprocity*. They are obligations with respect to other roles; for example, physician to patient, physician to nurse, or physician to hospital administrator. Roles interlock much as pieces in a jigsaw puzzle. The medical student, for example, is very much aware of role reciprocity the first time he puts on the white coat when going to see a patient. He is treated like a doctor, not like just plain John Jones. Consensus existing in the social system for the expectations of a particular role becomes an important question. It is important to know who establishes sets of expectations, the *role definers*, and what degree of consensus there is among role definers. Also, there is the problem of the amount of coherence and clarity in the role expectations, a factor of some magnitude for the individual who tries to carry out a particular role. Later chapters will discuss the roles of the physician, nurse, and medical social worker, where it will become apparent that coherence and clarity in the expectations for the medical social worker is not high among certain of the sets of role definers—quite the opposite situation from that for the physician.

What an incumbent understands his role to be is a matter of role conception. Does he perceive the expectations as coherent and clear and do other incumbents of the position perceive the expectations in the same manner? From the sociological standpoint this is a matter of consensus among the incumbents. We can also approach role conception through individual psychodynamics and look for the extent to which psychogenic needs or ego defense mechanisms may alter perceptions of the role for a particular person.

Conformity to expectations, the actual behavior of the person as he fulfills the role, is a matter of role performance. The degree of congruence in expectations and conceptions contributes a great deal to role performance but again individual psychological factors enter the picture. When an individual conforms to expectations social interaction will be enhanced; when he conforms only in part there will be disturbance.

Society has simplified the procedure of assigning roles in that some of them are *ascribed* while others are *achieved*. Linton[8] describes the former as those that are assigned to the individual without reference to innate differences or abilities, that can be predicted from infancy and training for them instituted at an early age. Achieved roles require special qualities and are left open to be filled through competition and individual effort. In simple societies much of the business of everyday living is taken care of by ascribed roles, but in the more complex and fluid societies achieved roles play an increasingly important part.

The important variables, or reference points, in determining ascribed roles are age, sex, race, caste or class; and in some cases, membership in family group, or blood relationships. To take a simple example, using the sex reference point, boys and girls are reared differently, and the mere fact of biological distinction means characteristic sets of demands and expectations. It begins with dress, blue for boys and pink for girls, shorts for boys and dresses for girls, crew cuts for boys and curls for girls. It continues in the kind of behavior that is rewarded, daintiness for girls, "toughness" and aggressiveness for boys, the kinds of games that each sex is expected to play, the kinds of chores that will be assigned to them around the house, and the amount of social freedom each will have. As a result, most boys will perceive doll play for themselves as sissy behavior; most girls view as tomboys those of their sex who play ice hockey.

In the days of the feudal system in Europe, or the rigid caste system in India, the group into which one was born was as important as sex as a reference point. The son of a miller could never hope to become one of the nobility, while the son of the lord of the manor would naturally be expected to assume leadership and receive the rewards due his station. In India a person born as an Untouchable began from the moment of birth to learn the intricate series of deferences and behaviors due all of those who were in other castes, and an Untouchable he would always remain. The situation in present-day United States is not so rigid, but the importance of social class for roles will be discussed shortly.

Ascribed roles are also important in determining which persons in the social structure will have the possibility of achieving certain roles. The Constitution of the United States does not forbid a woman from being elected President, an achieved role, but the informal social sanctions against such a possibility are most formidable. Furthermore, until the present time it was almost inconceivable that a Roman Catholic or Jew could be elected President. Although women play a part in business, it is well nigh impossible for one to be become chairman of the board of a large manufacturing industry. The number of men who are manicurists is indeed small, if there are any at all. Later in the section on membership in the various health professions we will see the effect of ascribed roles on achieved roles.

The chief vehicles to achieved roles in the United States are special abilities, such as muscular strength and coordination, high intelligence, education, a "good personality," and willingness to work hard. The worlds of professional sports and show business provide examples of ways that natural abilities can be transformed by hard work into achieved roles of high prestige. Politics, especially in the form of elective offices, provides openings for those who are shrewd, have likable personalities, and are also willing to work hard. Perhaps the most important mechanism today, however, in achieving a role is education, an essential for becoming a physician, nurse, psychologist, biochemist, or medical social worker. In fact, education is an important route which those of low estate can follow in achieving roles of considerable prestige, the son of a mill hand to a doctor being a case in point. Thus, achievement factors in role have for some people in the United States become as important as ascription in determining their position in society.

The complexity of the system of roles, especially where many are achieved, opens up the possibility of *role conflict*. This occurs in a number of ways, one of which is when a person finds himself filling two different roles at the same time, the demands and expectations of each being contradictory to the other. The career woman who is also the mother of three small children will often have contradictory demands because of her two roles. So will the physician who is the father of a desperately ill child, a situation discussed in more detail in Chapter 6.

Role conflict may also occur when the rewards that ordinarily accrue to the performance of a certain role are not forthcoming. For the actor the applause of the audience is meat and drink. When it is withheld he is dejected and miserable; and should it not be given in accustomed amounts over a period of time, he might begin to have serious doubts about the stage as a career. Rewards for a role, therefore, may not necessarily be monetary in nature, although this is one form of reward. The deference, respect, acclaim, publicity, actions of other members of society are the big factors, and when these are missing or diminished, role conflict readily appears. In this vein, an ungrateful, hostile, or resistant patient, regardless of whether he pays, can be upsetting to the physician.

Conflict can also ensue through the overlapping of roles, when two different roles have some of the same expectations for a particular situation. At the present time a conflict of this nature exists between clinical psychology and psychiatry in the practice of psychotherapy where both feel qualified to perform that function. Conflict can also appear between the public health nurse and social worker in a health department in counseling patients and making decisions for referrals to other agencies. Within medicine conflict often occurs between general practitioners and surgeons about performing appendectomies, and the general practitioner may feel he is being denied both money and status if prevented from operating. As roles change, the overlapping of expectations can lead to serious problems.

Role conflict is a problem of some magnitude in the western, highly industrialized societies, especially those in rapid change, and is important for perception in that it makes difficult the clear meaning of a given set of social stimuli. For example, the career woman with small children may have difficulty in perceiving what to do when they develop the mumps. The expectations of her mother role would lead her to see her place as at home, yet the expectations of her career role, especially if it is in the business world, would lead her to define the situation as one requiring a good nurse and baby sitter but not an interference with her career life. The conflict between the competing expectations may give her a distorted view of the pressures on her and of the intentions of those people who are important in her life.

Stratification and Division: Social Class and Ethnic Group

A society like the United States is segmented along a number of lines, of which two are social class and ethnic group. These large social groupings or divisions provide the framework for common values, customs, ways of rearing children, use of leisure activity, and many other things. As a consequence, they influence the manner in which an individual within the group will perceive social situations, including those that are concerned with disease and injury. Throughout the book there will be numerous illustrations that utilize the concepts of social class and ethnic group, thus highlighting the following theoretical description.

Social Class. Stratification by social class is well understood but its occurrence not always admitted, at least not in the United States. This country has prided itself on being the land of the "common man" and has pointed to the possibility of following a path from log cabin to White House as vindication of the equality of all citizens. When sociologists cited the existence of social classes in the United States, the idea was accepted, but grudgingly, by most people and its importance minimized. Steady research has indicated, however, that there are distinguishable social classes in the United States, that each class has characteristic values and modes of behavior, and that people in different social classes tend to perceive certain aspects of the social environment in diverse ways.

Variables that are useful in identifying the social classes are education, occupation, income, prestige, interaction (who invites whom to dinner), and place of residence. Frequently sociologists have divided communities into strata by the use of these variables, then asked persons in the community to rank other members of the community in terms of social class position. Invariably the correlation between the ranking by the community member and the sociologist has been high, indicating both that the variables are valid and that people in the community recognize the existence of social classes.

A recent book by Kahl has synthesized previous studies on social classes in the United States and presents a comprehensive picture of the major divisions. From his work the following descriptions have been constructed.[9]

The *upper class* can be characterized by *gracious living*. Membership depends on a high income and an honored family tradition, or a high position in the commercial hierarchy. Often one finds there the self-made man who cannot be ignored by society as well as the man who has inherited wealth and position. People in the upper class are intertwined in networks of kinship, common club affiliations, and interlocking memberships on committees and boards.

One of the dominant values concerns wealth, and the manner in which it is spent, for it is crude and boorish to display one's wealth. It is no surprise that the boom for the small, economical foreign cars began in the upper class. The art of graceful living, exemplified in comfortable houses, simple entertaining, travel, interest in the arts, and in many subjects besides one's business life, distinguishes people in the upper class from others. Leisure and income, as well as motivation, enable a person to be a dilettante, in the best sense of the word.

Much emphasis is placed on family tradition, on devotion to old people and to old things, and family solidarity through generations. Events that emphasize family tradition, christenings, weddings, and the like are important events, and serve to pull people in this class together and give them a consciousness of kind.

Career is the word to distinguish the *upper-middle class*. Here are the active people who are the leaders of the American work world, the trained specialists in business or professional pursuits who make the daily decisions that guide the work of the "little" people.

A career involves education, often considerable education, but personality, intelligence, and motivation are also important. The difference in success between equally educated men often rests on personality characteristics of geniality, ambition, and ability to make decisions quickly and wisely. Once a career has begun, it must be nurtured. It does not stop when the man leaves his office. A wife is an important asset because the contacts that can be made through entertaining are essential. Participation in community affairs, fund drives, and civic betterment projects also foster advancement.

The upper-middle class is characterized by an interest in the latest styles for houses, clothes, cars, and thoughts. There is more emphasis on consumption behavior than on gracious living.

Work at a career is satisfying in itself, and in some cases the career becomes the most important thing in life. Members of the upper-middle class are expected to be alert and ever competing, because there is strong belief in the existence of free competition and individualistic effort.

The class contains many newcomers, inasmuch as it is filled with people who have achieved roles. It is also a mobile group, families moving to new parts of the country on short notice, roots staked in the career and the future rather than in the past, the important symbols of position being external rather than resting in a tradition.

Those in the *lower-middle class* emphasize *respectability*. Here are the semiprofessional, the semimanagerial, the small businessmen, the small farmers. They work with the "big" people in the upper-middle class but live with the "little" people. Foremen and skilled craftsmen also belong here. It is a middle-income group. constantly striving to get ahead. Most, however, never get very far, and after they have outlived the romantic dreams of youth, they know they never will. At the same time it is a stable group, placing high value on education, home ownership, religious values, and respectability.

The *working class* is characterized by the phrase "get by," where it is important to "hold your own," not lose ground. Here are the semiskilled people who have no particular specialty, who find few differences in pay and responsibility from job to job, or from year to year, and there is not much point in working hard to get somewhere because there is no place to go. As a matter of fact, the work group is likely to determine just how much work will be done.

A working-class job is something one does in order to earn a living and one accepts unpleasantness in the job in order to bring home a good paycheck. Careful study has shown that large numbers of persons employed in monotonous assembly-line types of jobs do not expect to find satisfaction or even mild interest in their work. Thus, we find here the opposite of the career orientation and sometimes an alienation of the man from his work.

In the face of this kind of job situation, the worker tends to concentrate on steady pay and growing seniority, looking for satisfactions in life from outside the factory. The satisfaction comes from the money he earns and what it will do more than from the work he performs.

People in the working class tend to lack interest in public affairs, because they feel less sense of participation and control. They read less, understand less, and generally live in a world that is narrower in psychological space.

Resigned to a life of frustration and defeat, the *lower class* is marked by *apathy*. Living in decrepit housing, with irregular work and poverty, the people in the lower class find themselves caught in a vicious cycle. Their average IQ is low, their health and physical stamina poor, their education meager, the kind of people on whom employers frown.[10] In the face of a hopeless situation, the response is not hard work and saving, but helping one another. A large family, a feature especially common in the lower class, means that one has a source of help and protection in his trouble.[11]

It is easy to feel that a steady job is not important even when it may be available, and when a job is undertaken, there is likely to be little sense of responsibility toward the employer. Under these circumstances specialists in the health professions may experience real difficulty in helping someone from the lower class plan constructive behavior in a disease or illness situation, a difficulty due in large part to differing perceptions of constructive behavior.

Quite naturally, the descriptions just given represent average types from which there are many variations and subtypes, yet in their broad outlines these descriptions are useful. The important thing about them as determinants of perception is that each class has a somewhat different way of regarding social events, of assigning priorities to things. Many of the values are different, modes of behavior, expectations about life. A simple example: To the worker who is covered by health insurance plans and seniority protection, an average stay in the hospital may be regarded at worst as an uncomfortable experience and at best a welcome relief from the job. But to the fast-rising young executive in the same industrial organization, a similar hospital stay could mean a serious setback to his career, a frustration that might prove as painful and damaging in the long run as the physical illness he fights. Social class distinctions are real to the physician as well. Whenever the doctor reads a patient's record before going in to examine him, he is likely consciously or unconsciously to make a social class estimate of the patient. Furthermore, without a systematic knowledge of social class differences the physician may form some erroneous impressions.

Ethnic Group. Common backgrounds in language, customs, beliefs, habits, and traditions, frequently in racial stock or country or origin characterize people in ethnic groups. Of paramount importance is another feature, a consciousness of kind.

The United States is composed of many ethnic groups who came primarily in the great migrations of the past century. Although most people in these groups have taken on the broad outlines of the American way of life, striking features of ethnic group membership remain. There has been a tendency to marry within the group—the Irish with the Irish, the Italians with Italians—and to keep many of the customs, traditions, and patterns of family life. Unconsciously many attitudes have been maintained as well. It is these things that make the concept an important one for perception.

Perhaps the implications of ethnic group for matters relating to health and disease can best be further elucidated by some illustrations. Irishmen and Jews have different attitudes toward alcohol. In the case of the Jews, alcohol is used by all the participants in religious ritual. Excessive use of alcohol even in social activities, however, comes in for serious disapproval. Most Jews drink liquor but few become intoxicated, and it is rare to find a Jew who is an alcoholic. Among the Irish and Swedes, drinking is more a man's habit; much of it is done outside the family and intoxication is frequent. Alcoholism rates for the Irish and Swedes are high.

The family structure of the traditional Italian and Irish families is different. In the Italian, the father or elder male siblings are authoritarian figures, the mother nurturant and expressive. In the Irish the father is often evanescent, while the mother is the controlling figure. Italian families encourage direct expression of feelings, especially sexual. Irish families repress it, postpone it, and rigidly define it for marriage. Opler and Singer[12] have shown that these ethnic group differences are related to variations in symptom patterns for Italian and Irish schizophrenic patients. Italian patients showed acting-out behavior, little sin-guilt concern, noncompliance with authority, somatic preoccupation, and overt homosexuality. In Irish patients, there was a utilization of fantasy, compliance with authority, fixity of delusions, latent homosexuality, sexual misidentification, and sin-guilt ideology.

A final brief illustration. German and Spanish groups show different attitudes toward modesty and exposure of the body. Germans regard nudity and sunbathing as beneficial and see little harm in children of opposite sex disrobing in front of each other. The Spanish look upon exposure of the body as immoral, separate boys and girls as much as possible, and chaperon girls until marriage.

Again, as with the description of social classes, the pictures here of ethnic group differences are broad generalizations, more true of some members of each group than others. By and large, however, they hold as influences on perception.

The other aspect of ethnic group behavior and perception is that there are stereotypes about the behavior of people in various ethnic groups that are held by outgroup members. The Irish expect the Poles to behave in a certain way; the whites expect characteristic patterns from the Negro; the Jews look for particular actions by the Yankees. In the United States we use ethnic group to sort out the people in our social environment and base our perception of them and actions toward them on firm expectations we hold about them.

From the medical point of view there are differences in the incidence of disease among ethnic groups, as well as expectations for differences in behavior. When the physician is incorrect in his appraisal of the patient, for either reason, a distortion of medical judgment conceivably can result.

One final medical illustration is pertinent. In a study of medical students Devereux[13] reports that white male students almost never examined Negro males for hernia but did examine whites. Ethnic group perceptions on an unconscious level may well lie behind such a difference in behavior.

Guides for Behavior: Folkways and Mores

Custom and habit are well known in terms of their effect on behavior and can be said to characterize social life as well as that of the individual. Behavioral scientists refer to customs and group habits as folkways and mores, factors that appear to be commonplace things in life but exert a considerable influence on perception and behavior.

Folkways are the accustomed and time-honored ways of doing things, the social habits that become routine and often are performed without thinking. The reason behind given folkways may be lost on the majority of people who carry them out but they continue to make these individuals feel related to an understandable environment. Few if any of us know the reason for the seventh inning stretch at a baseball game but we would feel cheated if it did not occur. Americans generally hold the fork in the right hand when they eat meat, in contrast to the use of the left hand in England; Americans wear a coat and tie when they go out to dinner, send cards at Christmas, and eat "hot dogs" at all kinds of sporting events. By participating in folkways they feel an integral part of the group and their perception of the demands of a given social situation will be so guided.

An interesting illustration of the action of folkways in the health field comes from an analysis of behavior in a tuberculosis hospital by Julius Roth.[14] Protection against the spread of the tubercle bacilli took many forms, one of which was the use of protective clothing by hospital personnel when they entered a patient's room. However, not all personnel wore a mask and gown, the use of this clothing being inversely related to occupational status level. Doctors hardly ever wore cap, gown, or mask; students always wore them. When patients left their rooms to go to other parts of the hospital, they were required to wear masks on some occasions, not on others. Roth found that when the activities were "business," masks were required; when they were "pleasure" no masks were needed, even though contact with people who did not have the disease was just as close under both circumstances.

Other familiar illustrations concern the manner in which nurses are taught to make beds, or the sorts of uniforms worn by various staff members in the hospital. The utilitarian aspect of the former is less emphasized than is the tradition, while the variety of the latter is fiercely guarded. In both cases the world of the hospital staff member is given form and order through these customs, his perceptions have guidelines for what is right and proper.

Mores differ from folkways in that they are customs which are regarded as particularly sacred and necessary to social welfare. Although they are not formalized into law, violation of them brings social censure and sanction. They are, therefore, a form of social control in which ridicule, threat of physical punishment, and ostracism come into action. Mores have an aspect of sacredness or sanctification which is not true of folkways. All Americans stand and the men uncover their heads when the Star Spangled Banner is played; the male Jew wears his hat when he attends services at the temple; children, in general, and a sick child, in particular, have first claim over everything. These are all familiar unwritten rules we are not likely to break even though people in other societies may think any one of them strange. They are expectancies about the world around which we organize many of our perceptions.

Mores operate in the field of health and disease with as much force as in other kinds of behavior. Birth-control information is freely dispensed, but not to unmarried young women. The nurse may know a great deal about a patient's diagnosis and condition but she is expected to refer all questions on these matters to the physician. Criticism of each other in public or before patients is regarded by doctors as unethical and damaging to good relationships with patients. Should these mores be broken, reprimands, possible loss of job, hesitation about referrals, all might be forthcoming. Finally, in taking a history from an unmarried patient who is a woman, a physician will ask her about menstruation but is not likely to ask about intercourse. He will not hesitate, however, to ask a man about such experience.

As guidelines for behavior, folkways and mores play an important part in the routine of everyday living, and they vary from one subcultural group to another. Having the force of habit or the backing of social censure they carry an emotional impact that makes them resistant to change. Being almost automatic in operation they are also unobtrusive. Finally, they exert a strong influence on the perception of situations involving illness, both on the part of the patient and those who are responsible for his care.

INTERACTION AMONG THE DETERMINANTS

Only at some peril can a dynamic system of behavior be pulled apart into its components for didactic purposes. Perception of the world is a dynamic process in which a number of determinants contribute, each interacting with the other and the importance of each varying from situation to situation. In predicting the way someone will perceive a situation and behave in it, we find it necessary to use the phrase "other things being equal" to indicate our difficulties in knowing precisely the weight to attach to each determinant. This is not to discourage attempts at predicting but merely to caution against undue emphasis on one determinant or another.

In real life where the factors that have been discussed in these two chapters operate, it is possible on thoughtful reflection to identify them and to gauge in at least a rough way their interaction. Let us examine what may happen, for example, in an imaginary (but not very unusual) patient-physician contact. Dr. Johnson, a young physician, is called from his suburban office to see a new patient in the city; the call comes from the patient's neighbor who works as a ward aide at the local hospital and knows the doctor, since the patient herself is too ill and has no telephone. A few hours later the physician arrives to make his house call, finding himself in a neighborhood of small and old, but generally neat, two- and three-family frame dwellings. The neighbor guides him to a third-floor apartment, where he finds his patient—Miss Reilly, a seventy-one-year-old woman who had never married—propped up in bed, uncomfortably short of breath, and complaining of the "pounding and racing feeling" in her chest.

The neighbor draws the doctor aside to whisper that the old lady has been ill for several months, and has been increasingly unable to get out of bed, cook, clean, or do any shopping. Inasmuch as she has lived in the neighborhood for thirty years, friends and neighbors have come in to help her, but recently her condition has caused them concern.

The patient, however, maintains that she just has a little shortness of breath and "all old people have that, so there's hardly any use in bothering a doctor." What is more, she adds, a doctor will probably want to send her to a hospital—and she cannot afford that; she will *never* be a charity patient, and hospitals are just places for people to die, anyway. What she really wants is "a little medicine to fix up my chest right now."

The physician examines her—with some difficulty since she refuses to remove her nightgown. After Dr. Johnson has listened to her heart, Miss Reilly asks, "Am I going to die?" When the physician palpates a swollen knee joint, the patient cries out in pain; but when he asks whether the pain is dull or sharp, steady, or intermittent, the patient can only explain that the pain is "about like the pain from kneeling at Mass."

With history and examination completed, the doctor announces that his patient has congestive heart failure, that she should have seen a doctor long ago, that she was unwise to wait so long, and in any case, she will have to be moved to a hospital at once. There, he explains, she can get the necessary x-rays, an electrocardiogram, blood tests, oxygen, and digitalis; and her diet can be regulated. She must cut out salt and salty foods. Afterward, he explains, she will have to find a new apartment—something on the first floor, so that there will be no more climbing of stairs.

But the patient resists, and tells the doctor that she must know more about her condition before she can decide. The doctor explains that her heart is too big and will not pump blood properly, and warns that without treatment "you will drown in the water in your lungs." He adds that an electrocardiogram is just an electrical tracing of the heart action.

The patient decides. She wants some medicine now, but wishes to be treated at home, where her friends and neighbors will take better care of her than any strange nurse; anyway, her old family doctor (now dead) always treated his patients at home, even if they were very sick. With some exasperation, the doctor tells her that it is up to her—but he warns that he cannot help her if she is not willing to cooperate, take orders, and be reasonable. Reluctantly, Miss Reilly allows him to send for an ambulance—but asks that a priest be called before the ambulance arrives.

In terms of interaction among the variables, the following observations can be made. On the physiological level the patient has been experiencing pain in her chest and knee, and marked shortness of breath. At times she must have wondered if she was going to get her next breath. As a result she has not been able to lie flat in bed and, therefore, has not been sleeping well. When the doctor arrived she undoubtedly felt tired and irritable. Thus, her perception of the situation would be influenced by the physiological effects of her illness. Accompanying these determinants are certain psychogenic needs that can be inferred from the data. Among these would be autonomy, or a wish to keep in control of the situation, dependence in the form of reliance on her neighbors, deference in her interaction with the doctor, succorance and the recognition of her need for help, and, finally, affiliation, as evidenced by her ties to the neighborhood and the wish to stay there. Along with these needs there would appear to be anxiety, fear that she might have to go to the hospital, but more basic, the fear that she might die. These fears, as well as the conflict between the various psychogenic needs, were probably heightened by the physiological reactions she was experiencing.

When the physician came into the situation, various needs and psychological reactions can be observed in his actions as well. Dominance would be one of these, shown in his irritation with her lukewarm cooperation in terms of his orders. However, one might also discern the need for nurturance, to help and care for his patient. In addition, there is the need for energy and action and that for order, the careful delineation of a plan of therapy to control her illness.

The patient reacted to her pain, fear, and conflict by certain defensive and adaptive reactions. In terms of the latter, she was willing to have the doctor called, and eventually to follow his suggestions. Previously, however, she had tended to deny the serious nature of her condition and to rationalize her behavior by expressing the opinion that older people are bound to have shortness of breath. One would expect that these reactions would continue during her hospitalization and that she might have difficulty in adjusting to the hospital routine. Withdrawal and depression might also occur. At the same time, the doctor also exhibited some ego mechanisms. He tended to withdraw from involvement in the situation by aloofness, especially in the face of some resistance by his patient. His irritation took the form of indicating that he could not help her if she was not willing to cooperate.

Other variables also enter the picture, particularly in the form of beliefs, attitudes, and values that are associated with social class, ethnic group, and role. The patient emphasizes thrift and respectability; she does not want to be a charity case. Along with this goes an emphasis on independence and also on modesty. Personal relationships are important, especially those built up over the years. Values like these are often found in lower-middle-class groups in the United States. The patient also reflects some of the beliefs of her childhood, namely, that hospitals are a place where people go to die. She prefers to be treated at home, in line with her past experience and traditional orientation. Such values and beliefs would affect her perception of the illness situation in terms of seeing it as more threatening than otherwise might be warranted. From the physician's point of view, hospitals are the appropriate place for scientific treatment, especially for adequate long-term treatment. In this situation he perceived his role as that of designating the treatment to be followed and viewed the role of the patient as unquestioning or submissive, or at least responsive to "reason." Some problems of communication because of the differences in background could also be inferred. Patient and doctor might have different ideas about what constitutes salty food, what is dull or radiating pain, what image arises from the phrase "drown in the water in your lungs," what is implied by an electrical tracing of the heart, and what is digitalis.

Physiologic, psychologic, and sociocultural determinants were all at work, determining the manner in which both the patient and the physician perceived the situation in which they were interacting. The case was oversimplified in presentation, to be sure, but variation in one or more of the determinants of perception might have contributed to a different outcome if the case were followed for some months. In assessing patients, and the reaction of physician, nurse, or other health professional to these patients, a careful weighing of determinants from the various areas and a reflection on their dynamic interaction in the situation will be necessary.

Having outlined the major concepts in the behavioral sciences that are pertinent for the work of those in the health professions, we now turn to the application of this conceptual scheme to three major areas: disease and its manifestation, the people who treat disease, and the place where disease is treated.

NOTES TO CHAPTER 3

1. Kroeber, A. L., *Anthropology:* Race, Language, Culture, Psychology, Prehistory. Rev. ed. Harcourt, Brace and Co., New York, 1948.

2. Walter, Paul A., Jr., *Race and Culture Relations*. McGraw-Hill Book Co., New York, 1952, pp. 17–18.

3. Mead, Margaret, editor, *Cultural Patterns and Technical Change*. UNESCO, Paris, 1953, pp. 9–10.

4. The terms "culture" and "society" are often used interchangeably, yet behavioral scientists do recognize a distinction between them. Society is the term that is applied to the organization of activities and relationships; culture to the material that is transmitted from one generation to another. In this sense, certain of the insects, especially the ants and bees, have societies, with division of labor and organization of function. Insects do not have culture, because they are not able to transmit these social relationships except through genetic inheritance in the form of instincts. Human beings have both societies and culture, both social structure and knowledge about that structure which can be passed on to new members. Benjamin Paul has phrased the distinction in simple but useful terms as follows: "Where emphasis falls on the ideas shared by a group, the frame of reference is usually cultural. Where emphasis is on the group that shares the ideas, the frame of reference is usually social." Paul, Benjamin D., editor, *Health, Culture, and Community*. Russell Sage Foundation, New York, 1955, pp. 463–464.

5. Paul, Benjamin D., editor, *Health, Culture, and Community*. Russell Sage Foundation, New York, 1955, p. 467.

6. Sarbin, Theodore R., "Role Theory" in Lindzey, Gardner, editor, *Handbook of Social Psychology*, Addison-Wesley Publishing Co., Cambridge, Mass., 1954, p. 224. Professor Sarbin notes at the beginning of his article that the concept of role has suffered from the problem of conceptual clarity, often not being differentiated into its component parts or being used in different ways by different writers. Because the concept occupies such a central place in behavioral science theory, careful definitions

are necessary. Readers will also note that the term "position" has replaced that of "status," inasmuch as the latter term has taken on added meanings, one of which is that of prestige.

7. I am grateful at this point for a paper by John P. Hill, "Role Theory and Personality," which he originally prepared with Carol Friedman for a course in the Department of Social Relations at Harvard. Material on expectations, conceptions, and performance is drawn largely from that paper.

8. Linton, Ralph, *The Study of Man.* D. Appleton-Century Co., New York, 1936.

9. Kahl, Joseph A., *The American Class Structure.* Rinehart and Co., New York, 1953. The reader is referred specifically to Chapter 8, Classes as Ideal Types: Emergent Values.

10. In considering the question of IQ, the below-average scores of people in the lower class could be due to a number of factors. On the one hand, the scores could reflect the true state of affairs. Lower intelligence could be carried through genetic inheritance or by the drift into this class of people from other classes who have less than adequate ability. On the other hand, scores on IQ tests may not reflect the true state of intelligence in this group. Success on most IQ tests varies with the richness of educational and social background, a commodity in short supply for people in the lower class. At the same time there may be a lower motivation to do well on the tests because educational and intellectual activity are not given high value. As an example of what changes might occur with some sort of intellectual stimulation, we need only to remember the studies of IQs among Negroes who moved from schools in the rural South to schools in New York City.

11. For detailed description of an urban lower class culture the reader is referred to three papers by Walter B. Miller: "Cultural Features of an Urban Lower Class Community," Community Services Branch, United States Public Health Service, Washington, mimeographed; "Lower Class Culture as a Generating Milieu of Gang Delinquency," *Journal of Social Issues*, vol. 14, no. 3, 1958, pp. 5–19; and "Implications of Urban Lower Class Culture for Social Work," *Social Service Review*, vol. 33, September, 1959, pp. 219–236.

12. Opler, Marvin K., and Jerome L. Singer, "Ethnic Differences in Behavior and Psychopathology: Italian and Irish," *International Journal of Social Psychiatry*, vol. 2, Summer, 1956, pp. 11–22.

13. Devereux, George, "The Idealized Self-Image as an Obstacle in Interracial and Intersexual Diagnoses." Paper read at the Sixtieth Annual Meeting of the American Anthropological Association, Philadelphia, 1961.

14. Roth, Julius A., "Ritual and Magic in the Control of Contagion," *American Sociological Review*, vol. 22, June, 1957, pp. 310–314.

PART TWO
DISEASE AND ITS INTERPRETATION

Chapter 4

Systems of Beliefs and Attitudes About Disease

ILLNESS AND DEATH are social phenomena as well as biological reactions. They are regularly occurring events that are dismaying and disruptive of social relationships, events that must be explained and dealt with in some manner. The beliefs and attitudes about illness that are held by a particular group, therefore, become important variables in understanding how the members of that group will perceive injury or illness and how they will act toward it. Benjamin Paul has phrased some of the important questions that need to be asked as follows: "What does disease mean to people? How do they define illness? What disorders do they recognize and how do they classify them? What are their notions of prevention and of etiology? What is their knowledge of curing techniques? How is illness tied to other aspects of their culture?"[1] In this chapter we shall provide some tools that will help in answering these questions through a classification scheme for systems of beliefs and attitudes about disease. Before presenting the scheme, however, some general considerations need to be outlined.

First, any set of beliefs and attitudes in the health-disease area will be integrated with other important belief and practice systems, such as kinship relationships, religious beliefs, methods of political and social control, and interest in esthetic pursuits. For example, in the United States beliefs and attitudes toward pregnancy and birth are integrated with religious teachings on contraception, emphasis by psychologists and teachers on the perils of the only child, and social attitudes toward pregnant women appearing on public beaches.

Second, there will be variation from group to group in the way that illness and injury are perceived and handled. The cultural diversity of the United States makes this consideration most important when we discuss our own society, and, of course, variation in beliefs and attitudes occurs when we compare the United States with other societies. The Negro in rural Alabama will have different beliefs and attitudes toward tuberculosis or cancer from those of the professor in an Ivy League university or the member of a splinter religious sect in southern California. Social class, ethnic group, and religious affiliation will be some of the important factors in distinguishing subgroups in the United States that show variation in the perception of health and disease.

Finally, beliefs and attitudes toward disease in any group will be held with tenacity and assurance that they are quite adequate to explain and handle illness. The beliefs of a Navajo from a remote village on the reservation cannot be dismissed as mere superstition; to him they are real and sensible. The diagnostic report of a medicine man to a member of the Thonga tribe, of a naturopath to a coal miner in Pennsylvania, or of a board-certified internist to an upper-class resident of New York in each case is valid to the person making it, the one who is ill, and probably to the significant people in his environment as well. Practitioners of modern medicine find it helpful when a patient shares enough of their beliefs and attitudes to make acceptable a professional or rational explanation of disease, and frustrating when another patient cannot seem to understand or accept their explanations or orders because they are inconsistent with his, the patient's, beliefs and attitudes. Thus, a physician's effectiveness in treatment (or indeed that of a medicine man or naturopath) varies with his understanding of how the patient perceives the situation.

We can characterize beliefs and attitudes toward disease as belonging to any one of three major categories: scientific medicine, primitive medicine, or folk medicine. These are broad types within which considerable variation occurs, yet each type has distinguishing features. Furthermore, more than one type of belief system can and does exist in any one group or individual. They constitute what Straus[2] has called alternative responses to illness. Although one of the systems will be dominant in any group, recourse will often be had to an alternative system under certain conditions, as when the illness is mild or very severe, when the outcome cannot be predicted, or the threat to the individual is high.

The characteristics of scientific medicine are already well known to the readers of this book; hence, it will be described only briefly. Primitive medicine and folk medicine will be described in more detail, showing how they can be meaningful determinants of perception to certain people in times of illness.

SCIENTIFIC MEDICINE

The rational explanation of natural events in terms of cause and effect is the central feature of scientific medicine. Cause is viewed as natural in contradistinction to supernatural cause, for the latter has no place in scientific medicine. Facts in this system of belief are determined by the scientific method, whereby phenomena are observed, described, and classified; then by inductive reasoning general principles or hypotheses are derived. From the general principles, deductions or predictions are made about relationships between events, these predictions being verified or dismissed through experimentation. One of the premises of scientific medicine is that the results of new experimentation can change the basic principles. For example, the belief that premature babies should be given large amounts of oxygen was changed following the controlled experiments connecting retrolental fibroplasia with excessive oxygen intake at certain developmental stages. Scientific medicine thus depends on objective observation, experimentation, the seeking of natural causes, allowing in all cases for change when demanded by evidence. Although the fact occasionally makes physicians uncomfortable, it must be recognized that scientific medicine and the experimental procedure is a system of belief that is not perfect or complete. However, practitioners and researchers in scientific medicine believe the system to be perfectable.

PRIMITIVE MEDICINE

Magic is the basis of primitive medicine. The malefic action of another human being or intervention by a supernatural power causes disease, which can be cured only by resort to the appropriate magical formula or supplication to the supernatural power. Primitive medicine operates on a completely different set of principles from those of scientific medicine; causal relationship between events is not one of the natural world but of the supernatural. Experimentation is unnecessary; supernatural laws are immutable and need but to be discovered. Tradition is important, not in the sense of empirical experience, but through the social support it grants to the power of the unseen world.

Primitive medicine is so named here for a number of reasons. First and foremost, it is the oldest system, stretching back to the very early days of man's existence. For most of recorded time, man has used magic and only in the very modern eras have whole societies turned away from it. Thus, in terms of time sequence "primitive" here refers to early or first. From another point of view, primitive has the connotation of unsophisticated. As far as understanding the role of natural cause in disease, such as the effect of microbes or viruses as disease agents, primitive medicine is, indeed, unsophisticated. Finally, this system of beliefs and attitudes about disease is found most frequently today among primitive societies, often preliterate in nature, but certainly those in which the scientific approach has made little headway as the basic philosophy of life.

Even in a society that is dominated by the scientific method, magic is not as far away as we might like to think or hope. It is a background to which we are all heir and which we may be tempted to use in situations that are high in ambiguity and fraught with great threat. We may use it in disguised form, clothe it in up-to-date language, but it still exists. Many patients have an unshakable belief in the efficacy of penicillin or any other medicine injected with a needle—a belief that is held in the absence of any rational knowledge of the mode of action or even the general nature of the medicine. The belief is thus in part a magical one. Some physicians may give penicillin or other injections in response to this demand from patients, and at least a few physicians may convince themselves of the effect of these medicines in the absence of any real data.

Some people in our modern society use magic more than do others, but among the patients coming to visit well-qualified physicians in the United States and other countries where scientific medicine holds sway, many will have recourse at times to principles of primitive medicine. A rather detailed discussion of magic in beliefs and attitudes about disease, therefore, is in order here. Although much of the source material comes from "primitive" societies, we will indicate ways in which this system acts as a determinant of perception in situations of disease in our own world.

Though primitive medicine is unsophisticated, it may be both complex and detailed. For the individual living in a society that is bound together by magic, he uses it not only at times of sickness but in hunting, fishing, growing food, making love, and waging war. An invisible network of relationships "ties together" objects and the events associated with them, so that with proper knowledge he can manipulate the network to his own benefit or the harm of others. In this sense magic is mechanistic—if you invoke the right formula you always get results. At the same time, field and forest are the home of supernatural beings, not visible, but whose presence is felt, and the spirits of the departed walk the earth, still interested in the ways of men. Therefore, when we talk about illness and its treatment the term "magico-medical," as suggested by Stayt, is in order.

> It is impossible to consider the intimately associated subjects of medicine and magic except in conjunction with each other. Although a few of the purely medicinal and herbal treatments are of real therapeutic value, nearly all depend for their efficiency upon the inclusion of a magical element. Magico-medical seems to me the most appropriate term to describe the twofold art which is founded on one fundamental concept, the belief that every object, animate or inanimate, possesses a kinetic power for good or evil.[3]

Within the framework of magic, disease is caused by a number of different factors; sorcery, breach of taboo, disease object intrusion, spirit intrusion, and soul loss.[4] Each of these now needs to be considered in some detail.

Sorcery

When one person harms another through the use of magic, this is sorcery. It can be done in a number of ways, one of the most common being called *imitative magic.* An image is constructed of the person to be harmed, a wax or cloth doll perhaps, then the image is maltreated in some manner. By imitation the person who is represented by the image falls ill or is hurt in the same manner as the doll. We are already familiar with this technique through the exploits of Nightmare Alice in Al Capp's *Li'l Abner.*

Disease so induced can only be cured by finding the person who created the image, then forcing or persuading him to remove the spell.

An alternative technique involves utilization of some aspect of the victim's body, fingernail parings, a bit of hair, some saliva, or even excreta. Sometimes clothing can be used. The sorcerer performs the correct magical rite over this "bit" of his victim, whereupon illness ensues. The continuity between the body and aspects of it that become detached, a magical continuity, leads this technique to be classified as *contagious magic.*

Witches or sorcerers who are in good contact with the supernatural world may cast a spell over a victim or cause an evil spirit to come and lodge in his body. The town of Salem in the Bay State Colony during the late seventeenth century became quite famous for its concern with witches. On that occasion barnyard animals were alleged to be affected, as well as human beings; cows refused to give milk and children developed a fever.

In some cultures sorcery is all pervasive, the Dobu of Melanesia being a prime example. Everyone has spells which he uses day by day to ensure that his crops will grow, that his spouse will be faithful, that he can defeat his enemies. Special spells are set aside for disease, and described by Ruth Benedict as follows:

> The disease-charms have a malevolence all their own. Every man and woman in the Tewara village owns from one to five. Each is a specific for a particular disease, and the person who owns the incantation owns also the incantation for removing the same affliction. Some persons have a monopoly of certain diseases and hence are sole owners of the power to cause it and the power to cure it. Whoever has elephantiasis or scrofula in the locality, therefore, knows at whose door to lay it.[5]

The technique for ensnaring an enemy is the following:

> He breathes the spell into the excreta of the victim or into a creeper which he lays across the path of his enemy, biding nearby to see that the victim actually brushes against it. In communicating the spell the sorcerer imitates in anticipation the agony of the final stages of the disease he is inflicting. He writhes on the ground, he shrieks in convulsion. Only so, after faithful reproduction of its effects, will the charm do its destined work. The diviner is satisfied. When the victim has brushed against the creeper, he takes the bit of vine home with him and lets it wither in his hut. When he is ready for his enemy's death he burns it in his fire.[6]

A variation of sorcery is the *evil eye*, so called because the glance of certain individuals is enough to cause illness, especially in children, who are unusually vulnerable. Some of those who possess the evil eye are quite aware of their power, using it to harm their enemies and to wield authority over the community. They are to be treated with respect and avoided as much as possible. Again we are reminded of Eagle Eye Fleagel in *Li'l Abner*, a humorous caricature of a desperately real process in many parts of the world. Others who have an evil eye may be quite unaware of their destructive powers. Only through the divinations of the proper diagnostician can they be sought out and the spell be removed. In many ways those who are unaware that they possess the evil eye are more to be feared, for one cannot take steps to avoid them, one's children may run afoul of the dangerous spell at any time. Among the Spanish-speaking people of the American Southwest or Latin America, the evil eye is called *mal ojo* and in some sections it is a very prevalent disease.[7] Persons *who admire and praise a child* and do not realize the harm they may be doing are often thought to cause the disease. Public health nurses, for example, not knowing the ritualistic techniques for preventing the evil eye, as a result of their actions in admiring children, may have caused as much disease as they cured. The disorder can occur in New York as well. In her study of patients with facial deformities, Macgregor[8] reports that the mother of a child with a harelip said that she had been told by another woman that "somebody must have thrown a 'curse' or 'evil eye' on you."

By and large, belief in the evil eye is confined to rural areas or to sections of our large cities where the influence of old world groups is still strong. For those who believe in it, however, it is not to be scoffed at or derided, else the patient may think twice before consulting that particular doctor or nurse again.

Breach of Taboo

Polynesian culture is the source of the word "tabu," which now has come to be taboo in popular usage. Originally it stood for the threat of a powerful evil influence, comparable in might to our phrase, the wrath of God. The Polynesians believed that a force called mana pervaded the world, people, animals, stones, trees, everything. It was like the concept of electricity in many ways but was spiritual in nature, and life went along on an even keel until something upset the balance of mana. By building up too much mana, or by losing it quickly, a man opened himself to disastrous consequences, even death. A chief, for example, was the repository of large amounts of mana, and a commoner would have to watch his relations with the chief, else he became overloaded. This put the chief's barbers in a difficult situation and necessitated a careful ritual to cleanse themselves of the excess mana before they were harmed. Life was covered by rules, or taboos, concerning the things that one should not do, protections against threat.

Taboo has been broadened to include all rules that define a person's actions in a negative way toward the supernatural, mana, gods, or ancestors. In our world we have taken it to mean something forbidden by convention rather than statute, but in the world of primitive medicine breach of taboo has devastating results. For the trespasser, the power of the supernatural falls on him.

Illness and death can result from breach of taboo, and unfortunately a person may break a taboo without knowing it. Then it is the task of the diviner to determine which taboo has been broken and devise the correct kind of restoration. Many illustrations can be found in the anthropological literature for disease as a breach of taboo, of which one has been selected for presentation here.

Hsu[9] describes an epidemic of cholera in a town in Yunnan Province in southwestern China. A common and dreaded disease in China, cholera struck many of the inhabitants of the town and deeply disturbed everyone. The local medical practitioners who were trained in western medicine knew that the cause of the epidemic was bacterial, that the source of the infection was fecal contamination, and that with stringent sanitary measures the spread of the epidemic could be halted. To this end they worked with great diligence, only to find their efforts largely wasted, the inhabitants preferring their own explanation for the tragedy, and their own countermeasures. The average person believed that the disease was brought by epidemic-carrying spirits who had come from the gods and could only be recalled by the gods. Misconduct and breach of moral code obviously lay behind the epidemic. Action consisted in attempts to propitiate the gods through prayer meetings and sacrifices, and the use of charms and other devices to ward off the disease spirits. The people were urged to purge themselves from evil thoughts and deeds, to abstain from sexual relations, to clean up the town in order to please the gods, and to cease the eating of many pleasurable foods. Large quantities of "fairy water" were consumed as a preventive measure, water that came from a spring that was also the home of a powerful deity.

Disease once again must be viewed in the context of the total culture. In the Chinese town it was the one that emphasized tradition, the importance of filial piety and ancestor worship, honor for spirits and priests, and a sharp awareness of the consequences of moral transgressions. Disease was punishment and could only be cured by propitiation of the gods and moral endeavor.

Not infrequently do we hear people ascribe their illness or that of someone else to punishment by the Deity for wrongdoing. As we shall see in the next chapter, many in our population believe that insanity results from "sinful" living. When someone of good character becomes ill with an incurable disease, those close and dear to him often ask "Why did it happen to him?"—by which they imply that such disease should not strike good people. The idea of breach of taboo as a cause of disease has been pushed from the conscious lives of most of us, but not eliminated.

Disease-Object Intrusion

A harmful foreign substance, somehow embedded in the body, can cause disease. The object need not be intrinsically pathogenic, in the same sense as a rusty nail or a radioactive protein; rather the important element is a spiritual essence in the object that is the real cause of disease. Presence of the disease-object in the body is usually the result of action by a sorcerer or witch. Cure is brought about through removal of the object by the medicine man who has the specialized knowledge of magical ritual necessary for this difficult task.

There has been considerable controversy among students of primitive people over the removal of foreign objects by the medicine man, a controversy that does much to clarify our discussion of the importance of magic. Removal of the foreign object is usually accomplished by the process of palming, whereby a small stone or other object is hidden by the medicine man in his mouth or hand, then produced at the correct time in the course of his ceremony. The stone was never really embedded in the body of the patient, and the medicine man "fakes" its removal. Many scholars have concluded that the medicine man, therefore, is a charlatan, "conning" his patients into the belief that he has magical powers. As Ackerknecht points out, quite the reverse is true. Both patients and medicine man believe that a malefic foreign object somehow has gotten into the patient's body, the spiritual essence in it causes illness, and *by magic* it must be removed. Palming a stone is only symbolic removal, but in the world of magic symbolism is as strong as reality; indeed, it is reality. Symbolic removal of the foreign object, therefore, is just as efficacious as the actual removal of something. In some tribes, the Dakota for example, the same stone is always used for the procedure, and it is impossible for the patient and his family not to know this. In any case, the real source of the illness is a spiritual essence which through magic has been removed.

In many parts of the United States it is still common practice to use poultices of various kinds to "draw the poison" out of the patient's body. The line between the physiological removal of pus or other harmful products, and the removal of a different kind of poison is often hazy, especially when the poultice is not applied to an orifice or an open wound. Certain herbs, mustard and flax seed among others, are noted for their "drawing" qualities, more so when applied by the right hands. If one be honest, the association between certain uses of poultices and the ceremonial removal of disease objects by the medicine man is more than mere chance.

Spirit Intrusion

Possession and all its manifestations constitute the subdivision of spirit intrusion by ghosts, demons, or evil spirits. In some cases, the evil spirits may have been sent by a sorcerer; in other cases, the victim may not have taken proper precautions against the presence of demons who always lurk for the unwary. One can find illustrations in many places for disease produced by spirit intrusion, not the least of which is the New Testament. Some of the most dramatic miracles of Jesus consisted in removing the devils that plagued the bodies of their victims.[10]

Possession by a spirit may cause a person to be struck dumb, or to rave incoherently, to be blind or to have visions, to fall into a coma, or to writhe convulsively. It is a common occurrence all over the world and frequently the cause of disease.

Treatment consists simply in getting the spirit to leave. One method is purely psychological; that is, by incantation, invocation of more powerful demons, or commands to depart, the spirit is removed. In the New Testament Jesus merely commanded the spirit to leave, the implication being that the evil spirit quickly recognized the superior might of the Son of God and fled. Rarely does a healer possess such power; hence, the dramatic effect on the disciples and others who were watching. More frequently the exorcist must call on his array of good spirits to drive out the evil one.[11] Again the proper magic formulas can bring the force of good spirits into play.

Another method of treatment is mechanical. The patient may be bled or forced to vomit by the ingestion of noxious herbal compounds. Evil smelling incense may be burned nearby, or loud and discordant noises made, all of which are calculated to scare the demon away. The custom, which some of us still remember, of shooting off firecrackers goes back to the old Chinese procedure for frightening away demons.

Spirit intrusion as a cause of disease must be understood in the wider context of possession by some form of spirit, for there is beneficial possession as well as evil. In the Judeo-Christian tradition we find frequent reference to possession by God. The ancient prophets were often under compulsion of this kind in giving their messages, and Paul turned from a methodical persecutor of Christians to one of their most ardent leaders because of an infusing of the Holy Spirit. The custom of "laying on of hands" used in the ordination of a priest indicates the passing on of supernatural power, of infusing the Holy Spirit, from the earliest disciples and even Jesus himself. Faith healing among many of the fundamentalistic sects in the Protestant church is really a transfer of spiritual power, or of a spirit, into the one who is ill, ridding him of demons or of disease. In one large city the followers of a prominent evangelist believed that the spiritual power she possessed was transmitted over the radio when she spoke, and they would listen to her with their hands on the cabinet of the receiver. Of the causes of disease which we have discussed thus far, that of spirit intrusion is closest to the spiritual tradition of which most of us are a part, or close to experiences we may have had or witnessed in others.

The "laying on of hands" in modern medical practice often has important ramifications which may be sensed by the astute practitioner. Patients may feel that an examination or treatment is not complete unless the doctor does this in some way. Though perhaps unable to offer a rational explanation, the patient may indicate that he feels better if the doctor does make a definite physical contact. The psychological relationship to magic in this case appears to be remote, but there is every reason to suspect that it operates at an unconscious level.

Soul Loss

An almost universal belief among primitive societies is that loss of the ethereal replica of the body, the soul, can cause a withering sickness and death. Some primitive people believe that dreams are the wanderings of the soul during sleep and are hesitant to wake a person suddenly for fear that the soul will not have a chance to return safely. A person is especially vulnerable to soul loss when he is asleep or when he may be unconscious from fainting or an accident. Not only may the soul leave of its own accord, but at times of sleep or unconsciousness a sorcerer may remove the soul through a magical rite and keep it in his possession until the person dies.

Some believe that the soul can be lost through sneezing, reflected in the carryover in our language of the use of "God bless you" after a person sneezes. At one point in history the phrase was an incantation to prevent the escape of the soul. Others believe that sudden fright will cause the soul to leave; hence, one of the best ways of dealing with an enemy is to frighten him.

Treatment of disease caused by soul loss consists in finding the soul and getting it back into the body again. Divination may at first be necessary to determine where the soul has gone. If the loss is the work of a sorcerer, then entreaty or enlistment of powerful spirits is in order. If the loss be accidental, then the soul must be captured and reintroduced into the body, usually through the fontanel in the head.

Fear of unconsciousness occurs almost everywhere, as most anesthetists and surgeons can testify. Patients may not be able to give explicit reasons for their anxiety about the unconsciousness induced by anesthesia, and indeed the reasons will vary from patient to patient. Carryover of the idea of soul loss in a vague way should not be dismissed as superstition or nonsense on the part of some of these patients. Irrational perhaps, distorted perception of the operation to be sure, but the cultural background of the ages may come through at times in strange ways.

Magic as a Cause or Cure of Disease

Before leaving the topic of primitive medicine, there is profit in examining the question of belief in magic as a cause of disease or as a cure. If a person truly believes that sorcery or breach of taboo is responsible for disease, can a "curse" or spell make him fall ill? Of equal importance, if he truly believes that magical incantations or potions will cure disease, do these have any realistic therapeutic importance? The evidence at hand is not extensive but intriguing.

A few years ago the great physiologist, Walter B. Cannon, gathered together all the reports he could find by anthropologists, missionaries, or physicians concerning death due to magic.[12] Cannon used the term "voodoo death" to cover cases of this kind and found that there were quite a number of them, observed and reported by competent, serious people. When aware of a serious breach of taboo, or of the action of a feared sorcerer, people were known to have died within a matter of hours, or at the most days, and no evidence of the usual kind could be found for the cause of death. A description of the effect upon the unlucky person of "bone-pointing," a form of sorcery, has been given by Dr. Herbert Basedow, as reported by Cannon, and bears repeating here.

> The man who discovers that he is being boned . . . is indeed a pitiable sight. He stands aghast, with his eyes staring at the treacherous pointer, and with his hands lifted as though to ward off the lethal medium, which he imagines is pouring into his body. His cheeks blanch and his eyes become glassy and the expression on his face becomes horribly distorted. . . . He attempts to shriek but usually the sound chokes in his throat and all that one can see is froth at his mouth. His body begins to tremble and the muscles twitch involuntarily. He sways backwards and falls to the ground, and after

a short time appears to be in a swoon; but soon after he writhes as if in mortal agony, and covering his face with his hands, begins to moan. After a while he becomes very composed and crawls to his wurley [hut]. From this time on he sickens and frets, refusing to eat and keeping aloof from the daily affairs of the tribe. Unless help is forthcoming in the shape of counter-charm administered by the hands of the Nangarri, or medicine man, his death is only a matter of a comparatively short time.[13]

Cannon raised the question, "Could these deaths be due to poison?" Many of them are reported from tribes so primitive that the use of poison is unknown or highly unlikely, or in other cases the clinical picture does not fit that of poisoning. His conclusion was that, indeed, the deaths were due to belief in the magical causes of death, specifically from fright occasioned by the act of sorcery. Marshaling the available evidence from his own laboratory and that of others, he indicated that persistent excessive activity of the sympathico-adrenal system can cause death. One symptom of such persistent overactivity is fall in blood pressure to the point seen in fatal wound shock, probably induced by vasoconstriction and pooling of the blood in certain areas. Cannon noted that in most accounts of "voodoo death" the victim refused food and water, a factor that would only accentuate the disruption of body fluids through excessive sympathico-adrenal activity. He therefore found a reasonable basis for death in a person who believes that magic can cause death.

Since Cannon's article there have been other reports of "voodoo death," some by careful clinical observers, as in the case of Drs. Stewart Wolf, Robert Bird, and J. J. Smith.[14]

The patient was observed in the Southwest Pacific on Goodenough Island, d'Entrecasteaux Group, British New Guinea. He was approximately thirty years old, and in the Australian Regimental Hospital under the care of Sgt. Hill of the Australian military service. The patient was admitted with the complaint that "pouri-pouri" has been made "against" him, indicating that a potion had been mixed and incantations recited by a person of recognized competence and power.

The implications were that the victim had broken a taboo and he was made aware of the fact that he had been subjected to "pouri-

pouri." He knew, in short, that he was regarded as dead by his fellow tribesmen. On being ignored, rejected, and excommunicated, and after a period of panic, he had become listless, apathetic, and inert. He expressed at no time a desire to live, and acted as though convinced that his end was near. He had taken to his pallet and refused food and water before being brought to the hospital.

The examination on admission revealed an individual who appeared slightly above his estimated age. He exhibited splenomegaly, skin yaws, and slight arterial hypertension. Although he did not appear severely ill, his state varied between one of frank depression and apathy, without terror, and remaining silent and more or less immobile. His pulse rate was 65, his heart was slightly enlarged, and x-rays of his chest were not contributory. His blood pressure subsequently was within normal range or slightly elevated. His past history revealed that he probably had had malaria, dysentery, and yaws.

He showed no interest in the attention of the physicians. A successful attempt was made to get an antipotion from his tribe, and this was brought to his bedside with assurance that his health would return. For a short time he partook slightly of the mixture presented to him, but then rejected it. The antipotion remained at his side, untouched.

He became increasingly apathetic, seemed detached and resigned, barely moved, and his bed covers remained undisturbed for hours. His skin and mouth were dry. His urine contained a slight amount of albumin and had a high specific gravity. He was seen to pass no excreta after the first few days. He received penicillin, arsenicals, and digitalis. No one came to see him, and he interested himself in no other patients. On the ninth day after admission he was found dead in bed.

Autopsy revealed cirrhosis of the liver, splenomegaly, and widespread arteriosclerosis. Also, amyloidosis of the spleen, kidneys, pancreas, and liver was revealed on histological examination. No immediate cause of death was discovered. The likelihood is that death was due to rejection of fluids, brought about by psychological reactions to tribal rejection.[15]

Both Cannon and Simmons have emphasized that the effect of fright produced by the act of sorcery or breach of taboo is intensified by the behavior of the victim's family and friends, who also believe in the power of magic. First of all, those who are in close kinship relation to the victim change their social support to withdrawal, placing him in a special category, as befitting one under a curse. Kin and friends treat him as a dying man. Often, before death occurs, the social group goes through a second step, that of ritually preparing the victim for death. So strong is the effect of the group action that the sick individual may play his part with apparent resignation and cooperation.

It is important to bear in mind that primitive man is utterly dependent on his fellow tribesmen for survival, and that a closely knit, personal relationship with kinsfolk is central to his life. When this interpersonal connection is broken, one of the basic ingredients for life, as important as water or air or food, is gone.

On the basis of our present knowledge about the intimate relationship between body physiology, emotion, and social pressures, and in view of the evidence cited by Cannon and others, it does seem reasonable that belief in magic as the cause of disease can actually lead to disease and death. The question about recovery from disease or the ability of magic to protect against disease is another matter. Evidence on this point is much more fragmentary, but is as follows:

Cannon quotes Basedow concerning the effects of positive action by the medicine man, or Nangarri, as well as the deleterious effects of bone-pointing.

> The Nangarri, when persuaded to exercise his powers, goes through an elaborate ceremony and finally steps toward the awe-stricken relatives, holding in his fingers a small article—a stick, a bone, a pebble, or a talon—which he avows he has taken from the "boned" man and which was the cause of his affliction. And now, since it is removed, the victim has nothing to fear. The effect, Dr. Basedow declares, is astounding. The victim, until that moment far on the road to death, raises his head and gazes in wonderment at the object held by the Medicine-Man. He even lifts himself into a sitting position and calls for water to drink. The crisis is passed, and the recovery is speedy and complete. . . . The implicit faith which a native cherishes in the magical powers of his tribal magician is said to result in cures which exceed anything recorded by the faith-healing disciples of more cultured communities.[16]

To this we can add the experiences from famous Shrines, of which that at Lourdes is the best known. At Lourdes, in particular, there have been investigations by physicians of some of the cures, with the conclusion that faith in the power of God had been a powerful factor in the return to health. Certainly not all disorders were cured by faith, nor did all of those who came to the waters receive aid, yet there seem to be a few genuine cases.

Although the evidence is scanty, there is a reasonable possibility that belief in the power of magic to cure disease, even as magic has caused disease, is efficacious in some cases. That it does not cure as many cases in our civilized culture as in the primitive cultures could well be due to our divided faith, part allegiance to the natural world, of rational explanation for cause and effect, part allegiance to supernatural forces, the realm of religion. Under circumstances of a divided faith it is difficult to have the all-powerful belief of the primitive toward magic. A shred of doubt remains, no matter how desperately we wish to get well.

FOLK MEDICINE

Tradition plays a key role in folk medicine, that vast body of beliefs held by the nonprofessionals in any society concerning the cause of illness and ways of treating it. Backed by the weight of experience of the older generation, citing empirical evidence from specific cases and from nature, folk medicine has more of an emotional than a scientific flavor. Beliefs are held and remedies accepted not on the basis of experimental evidence but on the authority of respected members of an individual's social group who have had experience. Understanding of the mechanism between cause and effect is much less clear than in scientific medicine, at least for the majority of illnesses. Uncle Ned caught a cold because he got his feet wet, but how wet feet disturbed physiological homeostasis and produced an infection is not understood. However, people always catch cold when they get their feet wet, unless the proper precautions are taken immediately. Being empirical rather than experimental, folk medicine is not well organized. Contradictions often occur, beliefs about one kind of disease bear little relationship to beliefs concerning another kind of disease, but contradiction is minimized by tradition. Folk medicine could be characterized as the "home remedy" variety, incorporating all the emotional connotations that arise with the word "home."

The term "folk medicine" is used here for two reasons. First, its source or roots lie in the practices of folk societies, the peasant groups, close to the soil and to nature. Until quite recent years most of the world's population lived an agricultural life or had a close connection with nature. A considerable proportion, perhaps even the majority, still live that kind of life. Under these circumstances there has been an opportunity to observe curative and preventive processes in nature, what herbs and plants the animals sought when they were sick, what procedures they followed when injured. Operating by instinct to a large extent, animal behavior in sickness was seen as part of the plan of nature in which man could share. Moreover, nature furnished an abundant stock of medicines upon which man could draw and which required only the efforts of collection and preparation. By observation, by trial and error, remedies and procedures developed, thus the empirical nature of folk medicine.

Second, folk medicine involves the group rather than the skills of a few professionals, be they physicians or medicine men. The belief system is shared and practiced by everyone, its ideas freely communicated across generations. Accordingly, there is a tenacity to folk medical beliefs, a resistance to change even in sophisticated societies, because the knowledge is shared by everyone and has the backing of tradition. It can and does exist alongside scientific medicine or primitive medicine without noticeable conflict.

As used here, folk medicine does not include practices that have magic as the essential ingredient. The evil eye and magical soul loss would not be considered part of folk medicine even though some authors have so considered them; for example, Foster[17] and Simmons[18] in their writings on folk medicine in Peru, Chile, and Central America. Our approach to systems of beliefs and attitudes about disease can be sharpened if all beliefs that have magic in them are classified under primitive medicine and folk medicine includes empirical beliefs and practices.

Prevention of disease and treatment of minor injuries and illnesses are the areas where folk medicine has its greatest application, areas where ambiguity and threat to existence are relatively low. Here the tried and true principles can be practiced easily and with full group support. Inasmuch as minor illnesses and injuries are a common experience, there is ample opportunity for the application of folk medicine in all societies, the United States included. Furthermore, there is no doubt that many of the remedies or practices in folk medicine are efficacious, as the modern pharmacopeia can attest. Digitalis came from the tea made with leaves of the foxglove plant, morphine from the juice of the poppy plant, and the antibiotics apparently were at work in the use of moldy materials in poultices, to mention only a few. At the present time a number of serious research projects are examining the remedies of folk medicine in societies the world over, hoping for more additions to the pharmacopeia of scientific medicine.

Folk medicine as a concept applies not only to folk societies and peasant cultures but also to certain beliefs and practices in complex, highly sophisticated societies. Because the form and content of folk medicine varies to a great extent from one group to another, an exposition of the concept will best proceed by illustrations in contrast to the systematic analysis that was used in the previous section on primitive medicine. We shall range beyond the bounds of the United States for some of these illustrations, to India and to certain of the Latin American cultures. This seeming digression is based on the diverse cultural heritage to which patients are heir, particularly in the urban centers of our country. Data from other cultural backgrounds will also give a picture of the variation in folk medical practices. Following these illustrations we shall look more specifically at folk medicine in the United States, noting certain widespread beliefs, but also examining aspects of our culture that facilitate the practice of folk medicine.

The account cannot be exhaustive, granting the limitations of space and time in a book of this nature, yet it is the author's hope that the reader may become sensitized to the concept of folk medicine and look himself for further examples in the day-by-day work with patients and clients.

Hot-Cold Dimensions in Disease

A prevalent idea in many parts of the world is that health is maintained through a proper balance of hot and cold forces and that disease results when a person is overexposed to one or the other. There are many things in nature—foods, liquids, medicine, body states, illnesses, and even inanimate objects—that are inherently hot or cold, or in between, quite apart from their thermal qualities. For example, in India eggs, meat, milk, honey, sugar, and cod-liver oil are classified as hot, or *garam*, to varying degrees, while lemon, orange, rice, water, acid buttermilk, and curd (Indian yoghurt) are known as *tonda*, or cold. Diseases are likewise classified as "hot" or "cold," without reference to the fact of fever or chills. Upper-respiratory tract illnesses, like bronchitis, are "cold" maladies, while diarrhea is a "hot" disease.

Those who are trained in western scientific medicine are often puzzled by the hot-cold belief. It has a long history, however, going back, as Jelliffe[19] suggests, to the humoral pathology of Hippocrates and Galen and before that to Indian philosophy, for the ancient Sanskrit Ayurvedic literature of India describes it. Later the idea must have spread to Greece, and finally was brought to the new world by the Spanish conquistadors, where it is found today among Latin-American peasant groups. Although present in its purest form in India and the Spanish-speaking people of the United States, traces of it are likely in all ethnic groups that were strongly influenced by Greek thought, philosophy, and medical beliefs. For example, one can find occasional references to the idea in beliefs and attitudes toward disease of Italians, especially those who have had the least contact with urban scientific medicine.

An interesting example is cited by Jelliffe of the force of the hot-cold ideology in India and the difficulties it can pose for the practicing physician when treating bronchitis, a "cold" malady.

> Scientifically, in this type of case it may be desirable to advise the mother to give [her child] sulfonamides, together with plenty of water to drink and the lighter portion of the normal diet, including rice preparations. This, however, would not be considered as satisfactory by the mother, as both water and rice are classified as *tonda* (cold) and, therefore, to be avoided in this type of illness.
>
> In this instance persuasion may be possible but often may not be successful against such a deeply ingrained food belief, and in this case, the two attitudes—that of the pediatrician and that of the mother—can be successfully integrated by advising the mother to

give sulfonamides together with water flavored with honey and rice cooked in milk. The mother will accept this advice much more readily, as the honey and milk are thought to neutralize the "cold" in the water and in the rice, and scientifically the same end point has been reached.[20]

Jelliffe has a corresponding example of a hot, or *garam*, disease, diarrhea, and the problems of management by the physician that it poses.

In children recovering from diarrhea, mothers are frequently reluctant to introduce milk, even if diluted, as both the food and the illness are classified as *garam*, so much so that continued feeding with carbohydrate gruels may, in this type of case, act as the starting point for the subsequent development of the protein deficiency syndrome known as kwashiorkor.

Frequently, in this sort of situation it is desirable, from a scientific point of view, that the child should be given a bland, easily absorbable, low residue carbohydrate gruel, a water-absorbing, pectin-containing food, and diluted milk. In a West Bengal rural child welfare clinic, it appears that this is best achieved by adopting three local dietary remedies, which appear to coincide exactly with the scientific viewpoint. By using the carbohydrate *chira mondu* (hand-mashed flat rice) and, as the pectin food, a sherbet made of the Indian wood apple (Aegle marmelos), one is employing traditional dietetic treatment, while in dilute *lassi* (acid buttermilk), one has an acceptable and familiar remedy. The buttermilk, being both acidified and defatted, and a *tonda* food, is particularly suitable from all points of view.[21]

The concept has been elaborated in Latin-American countries, however, to include people, that is, some are naturally "hot," others "cold," and marriages between persons representing the extremes are fraught with danger. Correspondingly, a man who is known to be "hot" should not raise animals that are classified generally as "cold." Returning to the relationships between foods and disease, Redfield describes the folk culture of Yucatan as follows:

Something that is a little too "hot," as beef, may be made safer for consumption by adding a little lime juice, which is "cold." But it is dangerous to bring the greatest extremes together: honey is very "hot," and it should not be followed by water, which is "cold." If a man has a fever, he is hot, and he may be treated with moderate amounts of herbs or foods which are cold. On the other hand, a person who is weak is "cold" and should be given "hot" things to eat and drink.[22]

Most foods are unchanged in their hot or cold attributes through the process of cooking, but water can be changed from one extreme to the other. In its natural state water is cold, but after it has been boiled it becomes hot. However, should water be boiled in the evening and allowed to stand overnight, it goes through a process of "sleeping" and in the morning is dangerously cold; therefore a threat to anyone who might drink it. Wellin[23] has pointed out some of the implications of these changes in the character of water for public health programs that call for water boiling. Where there is a scarcity of fuel and, consequently, where one of the few possible times during the day for boiling water is while the evening meal is being cooked, people reject the idea because of the dangerous qualities the water takes on overnight.

Body Fluids in Folk Medicine

Blood, saliva, urine, and semen are often the center of folk medical beliefs that have little or no substantiation in scientific medicine. The following experience of Carstairs in India is a good opening example.

> In Delwara, as previously in Sujarupa, I was frequently asked by apparently robust men to give them medicine—or better, an injection—to make them strong. At first, I continued to regard them as cases of anemia or malnutrition until my eyes were opened one day to the real condition by the interpolations of a bystander, who was watching me examine one of these patients: "Of course he's weak!" he said. "He was such a libertine when he was a young man that his semen got spoiled, and it's been leaving him ever since."[24]

By careful observation in subsequent patients, Carstairs learned that for every 40 drops of blood formed in the body one drop of semen is laboriously made. The source of a man's strength and his subjective sense of well-being, the semen, is stored in a reservoir in the skull. Cool foods, like dairy products, wheat flour, sugar, and some fruits, are beneficial and lead to an increase in the quantity of semen, while vegetable oil, strong spices, heavier cereals retard its manufacture. Especially to be avoided are meat and eggs and all forms of alcohol.

Semen will, of course, be lost through excessive indulgence in sex, but the loss is greater if the sexual experience is extramarital and will be further intensified if the partner in fornication is of lower caste. Generally all forms of behavior that violate the strict codes of behavior laid down for the orthodox Hindu may cause semen to leak away and have an adverse effect on a man's mental and physical well-being.

Saunders[25] reports that in Mexican folk medicine blood holds an important place in the balance of health and disease. If the blood becomes too thin, a condition that has many causes, among them being eating certain foods to excess, health is endangered. Many folk remedies are supposed to keep the blood at the right consistency or help to purify it. Loss of blood, because of its weakening effect, is also detrimental to health, and a man's sexual vigor may be impaired if he loses a considerable amount of blood. In this connection Saunders suggests that the reluctance of Spanish-Americans in the Southwest to contribute to blood banks may be related to their beliefs about the damaging effects of loss of blood.

Similar beliefs are reported by Adams[26] from a Guatemalan Indian village. To the way of thinking there blood is not regenerated and once lost through a cut or other means it is lost for good. Loss of blood weakens a person and makes him more susceptible to illness. These beliefs came to light because of resistance to a blood-sampling program, sponsored by a governmental nutrition research project, and were especially relevant because the team was eager to obtain many samples from children. The Indians could not understand how any good could come from people who would draw blood from children and weaken them unduly, especially since children are always vulnerable to disease.

There is much folklore in the United States about blood and semen. Blood is supposed to thicken in cold weather and in the spring needs to be thinned out and purified, usually with sulphur and molasses. On the other hand, certain foods can thin the blood dangerously, salt in excessive quantities being one. Condition of of the blood is thought to be related to energy level and susceptibility to disease, counteraction for which can be accomplished through the use of blood tonics. Most Americans are familiar with the advertising emphasis on "tired blood" and the tonic necessary for correction of that condition. Indulgence in sexual intercourse weakens a man; hence, athletes are enjoined from such activities for stated periods before they perform. Sexual vigor can be maintained, however, by resort to regular eating of eggs, or better still, oysters.

Other examples can be found throughout the world, and within the borders of any city in the United States. Many practices and beliefs for prevention of disease or for its treatment center around body fluids, for they are ever present and easily observed, and the beliefs are not necessarily based upon precise knowledge of anatomy and physiology.

Folk Medicine in the United States

The dominant system of belief and practice in matters of health in the United States is scientific medicine. Because of its very dominance many who practice it do not realize that another system also holds sway, to a lesser degree and in a less obvious sense to be sure. Nonetheless, it would be a fair statement to say that folk medicine is rampant in the United States. Its exact dimensions are not known, although its existence is obvious and is felt everywhere.[27] It is an area for research that has been neglected by the behavioral sciences, and a complete account must wait for a substantial research study. However, we can still describe many features of folk medicine in the United States and hope, as in the previous section, to sensitize the reader to look further on his own.

An operational scheme for an analysis of folk medicine has been presented by Saunders and Hewes[28] in terms of the places one can visit, things one can buy, or individuals one can visit. It is a scheme with much utility and is the basis for the following paragraphs.

Persons to Whom One Can Go for Medical Advice and Treatment. The qualified physician with an M.D. degree is the prime source of medical advice and treatment in scientific medicine, but, as Saunders and Hewes point out, there are at least 50 other kinds of persons to whom one can turn for advice in matters of health and disease. Those that come quickly to mind are chiropractor, naturopath, and faith healer. As an illustration, the state of Pennsylvania has carried on a long and costly battle with a cancer clinic in Cambria County, the inspiration of a naturopath from Texas, and under the technical direction of a licensed chiropractor from Pennsylvania. Although food and drug investigators showed that the pills used in the treatment had no value in the treatment of cancer, and perhaps had even a harmful effect in some cases, patients continued to come to the clinic in great numbers, and political pressures to keep it open were strong.

The study of beliefs and practices about health in Regionville[29] showed that many of the families interviewed would use the chiropractor for any illness. Koos had divided his sample into three social classes, and it was in Class III, the lowest socioeconomic group, that the greatest use of the chiropractor was evident, 57.8 reporting that they would use the chiropractor. Similar findings were brought out by Wardwell[30] in his study of the chiropractor in Massachusetts, and like data, although with smaller proportions using the chiropractor, are indicated from the National Opinion Research Center-Health Information Foundation study, of a national probability sample to be described shortly. There is no question that in many communities chiropractors are respected citizens and do a flourishing business.

Other kinds of people also must be noted, the chiropodist, the Christian Science Reader, and midwives. It has been said that in New York City it is still possible to find barbers who will do "cupping." One can go to a hypnotist, or a masseur, to a palm reader, even to grandmother or another relative. Specialists in herbs are to be found even today, and dotting our principal cities are health stores where the latest information on health foods and their uses can be obtained.

Many people turn to the corner druggist. One of the principal dilemmas of the average pharmacist, especially if the store is of the neighborhood variety, lies in the extent to which he shall prescribe for the minor ills about which his customers are continually asking advice. The medicines that can be sold are legion, and the proclivity to buy certain kinds will be considered in one of the succeeding sections. Koos found that the people of Regionville regularly turned to the druggist in matters of minor illness and indisposition.

Places One Can Visit. The reducing salons have become big business in the United States; and taking off excess weight is not only a matter of pride and good looks, it is important for health reasons as well. Turkish baths are the more conventional way to reduce, and steam is thought to have a beneficial purifying effect in addition to its slimming function. Many think that heavy sweating helps to remove "poisons" from the body.

A closely related category of places would include the hot springs and spas, where the water is high in sulphur, iron, and other minerals. Although visits to these spas are not so frequent as in years past, many buy bottled mineral water to drink at home. Also, not to be forgotten are the clinics that give high colonic irrigations. Others to be considered are spiritualist centers, uranium mines, gymnasiums, and the lures of dry Arizona or sunny Florida.

Appliances One Can Purchase. An inventory of the nearest drugstore would be necessary to list all the appliances that one can purchase for use in preventing disease or treating it. Only a representative few will be noted here, such as sun lamps, hot water bottles, enema tubes, trusses, chin straps, vaporizers, atomizers, heating pads, elastic bandages, foot baths, and exercising machines. Of worthy note is the increasing use of vibrators in the form of pads or cushions, chairs, and hand-massage devices. Their use is of a preventive nature, to help the purchaser relax, thereby preventing onset of the "stress diseases," and the aches and pains that go with tension and nervousness. Here is a case where the advances in scientific medicine have been utilized in folk medicine. As noted in Chapter 1, knowledge about psychosomatic disorders has been widely disseminated and accepted among all classes of lay people, and folk medical practices have evolved to meet the new knowledge.

Drugs One Can Buy. Again the numbers are legion! Gone are the days of the medicine man with his herb preparation that would relieve aches and pains, cure snake bite, remove warts, restore "manly vigor," and grow new hair on the head, plus many other wonders too numerous to mention. Other preparations have taken its place. Hadacol, Serutan, Geritol, Lydia Pinkham's Vegetable Compound, and Carter's Pills are some of the more common tonics and medicines today. Before dismissing medicines of this kind too hastily, it is well to look at the findings by Koos of their use in Regionville. He notes that a great many people from Class III buy "kidney" and "liver" pills and various kinds of "stomach medicines." The first two are regarded as "conditioners" and the stomach medicines are used largely for relief of stomach distress occasioned by chronic poor diets. A Class III housewife commented as follows in an interview:

> My husband and I take C——— Liver Pills regular. We get to feeling stuffy if we don't, and keeping your liver flushed out gets rid of the stuffiness. . . . Once in a while I take S——— Kidney Pills, too. It's good to flush out your kidneys once in a while. . . . If I do this, I don't get sick.[31]

The shelves of any drugstore are stocked with various medicines for colds, for indigestion, for headaches and other muscular aches and pains, for going to sleep and for staying awake, for constipation, for hay fever and other allergies, and for calming jittery nerves. Medicine closets at home sometimes are miniature replicas of drugstores and provide the sufferer untold possibilities for his practice of folk medicine.

Again, some comments by the people of Regionville are quite to the point:

> I give my children a dose of cathartic once a week, and they don't have near the sickness other children do.

> I always take S——— Compound every fall. It thickens my blood, and gets me ready for cold weather.
>
> My husband takes aspirin all winter, every morning. He hasn't had a cold in years. It just shows what a little doctoring at home will do for you.[32]

Household Remedies One Can Use. The change in the social structure of the United States, from rural to urban and from the extended family to the small nuclear family, has had an adverse effect on the use of home remedies. Good preparations can now be purchased in the drugstore, many of which are copied from the recipes that grandmother used to have. Although the older remedies are not in frequent use now, they have not completely disappeared from the kitchen. Onions boiled slowly and mixed with sugar or honey, not allowing any of the "goodness" in the juice to escape in the process, are efficacious as a cough syrup. Mention has already been made of sulphur and molasses to thin the blood. The use of whiskey and hot lemonade to break up a cold is still considered good. Salt water gargle relieves a sore throat, and raw beefsteak may take care of a black eye. Lemon juice and hot water on arising is thought by some to be a sure cure for "irregularity," and mustard plasters relieve the congestion of bronchitis. The kitchen remains for some people a compounding shelf, using goods from the store and herbs from the garden to make tried and true medicines.

Procedures One Can Follow. In addition to all the items listed above, a person can carry out certain procedures that he believes will be beneficial for his health and will prevent disease. As well as the cosmetic effects of a good tan, some believe that generous exposures to the sun build up resistance to infection. Others are inclined to view resistance as stemming from a spartan way of life, characterized by cold showers, open windows at night, and vigorous breathing at stated times during the day. In quite a different vein, the road to health can be seen through a vegetarian diet, or at least the use of "natural" foods in distinction to processed foods wherever possible. As noted in a previous section, the growing number of "health food" stores in our cities attests to the importance of notions about diet in American folk medicine.

It is interesting to note the newspaper interviews with people who have reached an advanced age and are asked for the secret of their longevity. Each one is supposed to have some procedure he has followed all his life to which he owes his vigor, for example, eight hours' sleep every night, a shot of whiskey before supper, abstinence from both tobacco and alcohol, regular exercise or lack of it. The following item appeared in the *Boston Globe* on November 7, 1958:

> Man Dead at 100
> Had Unique Recipe
>
> New Gloucester, Me.,
> Nov. 6 (AP)—Centenarian Charles Henry Smith, who attributed his longevity to frequent dosages of baking soda, died here today. He would have been 101 Dec. 12.
> "I think baking soda is what kept me alive," he once told an interviewing reporter. "I used to take a teaspoonful of it after every meal, did it about 50 years. I used to have stomach trouble."

What we have is a reflection of folk beliefs about preventive measures that can be employed against disease or procedures for the maintenance of health.

SURVEYS OF BELIEFS AND ATTITUDES TOWARD DISEASE

Systematic studies in the United States of beliefs, attitudes, and practices in matters of health and disease are only recent occurrences. Those that have been carried out are of value in helping us assess the knowledge about scientific medicine that is held by various groups in the population. We can thus gain a perspective for judging the extent and variation of folk medicine in the United States and see some of the factors that contribute to its presence.

Two surveys are pertinent, both of which have received brief reference earlier. These are the study of Regionville by Koos and the study of a national probability sample of adults by the National Opinion Research Center sponsored by the Health Information Foundation.

The first study, that by Koos, involved a small town and the surrounding community in the hill country of New York, 2,500 households in all, and situated some 60 miles from a large city. The choice of Regionville was dictated by its "averageness," for the town is little different from the small towns that dot the United States, "small-town America in microcosm," as Koos called it.

In Regionville Class I had some of the characteristics of Kahl's upper-middle and some of his lower-middle classes. From it 51 households were selected for interviewing. Class II comprised skilled and unskilled workers, much like Kahl's working class. Here 325 households were interviewed. Class III contained people who were predominantly in the lower class, 128 households being interviewed.

Among the interview questions, each respondent was given a list of readily recognizable symptoms and was asked to indicate for each whether it was significant and should be called to the attention of a doctor. Symptoms were: loss of appetite, persistent backache, continued coughing, persistent joint and muscle pains, blood in stools, blood in urine, excessive vaginal bleeding, swelling of ankles, loss of weight, bleeding gums, chronic fatigue, shortness of breath, persistent headache, fainting spells, pain in chest, lump in breast, and lump in abdomen. Class I respondents were consistent in recognizing the importance of the symptoms. Only two symptoms—loss of appetite and backache—were checked by fewer than 75 per cent of Class I respondents. Class II respondents were less concerned about the importance of the symptoms; although for only two, backache and joint and muscle pain, did the percentage drop below 50. Among those in Class III there was marked indifference, 10 of the symptoms being checked by only 25 per cent or fewer, and only 3 checked by 50 per cent or more. There were obvious differences then among the three social classes in Regionville concerning attitudes toward various symptoms.

Koos remarks that the passage from health to illness for the residents of Regionville is highly variable; in addition to the obvious class differences other factors enter the picture, some of which, of course, are correlated with social class. Some of the residents were afraid of surgery and would tend to ignore the most pressing of symptoms to avoid "going under the knife." Cost was often a deterrent, especially if cost was an unknown factor and the family income meager. A third variable was the relative need for treatment as related to age; some symptoms were given importance if they occurred in a young person but disregarded in the middle-aged or elderly. Recognition of importance of a symptom was tied to the role of the afflicted person in the family, highest priority being given the breadwinner. Of course, the culture content of one's social group also dictated importance. A Class III housewife stated that her friends would hoot her out of town if she consulted a doctor about a backache. Also part of the culture content was the importance of health as compared with other needs and desires of the family, with the need to get things that would help overcome the frustrations of life.

Potential patients in Regionville were far from alike. Psychogenic needs, beliefs and attitudes, social role, class values, and, of course, the obvious physiologic imbalances combined to affect individual perception of a situation or illness.

The other survey provides some of the best information that we have about beliefs and attitudes toward disease as well as health practices and the utilization of medical and other personnel in the treatment of disease. As noted earlier, it was conducted by the National Opinion Research Center and was sponsored by the Health Information Foundation.[33] The data were drawn from a survey conducted during 1955 of a representative cross section of the American public, comprising 2,379 adults. The common sociologic variables of age, sex, region of the country, size of community, occupation, education, income, and family structure were obtained, making it possible to consider various kinds of subgroupings within the total sample. Also, because of the sampling technique, it is feasible to generalize the findings more than in the case of the Koos survey.

Relative to the topic of this chapter, there are data concerning expectations of illness, knowledge about disease, and ways of handling various disease symptoms. These data have been broken down by occupation, income, and education, three variables that are major determinants of social class position in the United States. We can thus draw some general conclusions about differences among social classes in beliefs and attitudes about health and disease.

Under expectations of illness, each respondent was asked whether he agreed or disagreed with certain statements about health. Five of these statements are presented in Table 1 along with the percentage of respondents in each of the occupation, income, and education groups that agreed with each statement. Looking at the first three statements, we see quite striking differences between the upper and lower ranges of the socioeconomic groups. Those with low education and income and those who have "blue-collar" jobs showed the highest agreement that a person has to expect a good deal of illness, that one might as well get used to some aches and pains, and that older people have to expect a lot of aches and pains. For these people illness is much more a part of life than for their fellow citizens in the upper socioeconomic groups. The importance of this finding comes in reference to one of the trends noted in Chapter 1, a growing emphasis on the concept of positive health. To people in the lower socioeconomic groups, positive health may be an idea that has occurred rarely, if at all.

Poor diet and inability because of education or income to utilize adequately the available medical care facilities are factors that go with the low socioeconomic status and probably mean that people in this group actually experience more illness. However, the generally high standard of living in the United States and the growth of health insurance plans make these factors increasingly less important. It seems reasonable that expectations as well as experience of illness are important to the person in the lower socioeconomic groups in his perception of the world.

One caution must also be accepted in drawing inferences from the data in the survey. Feldman and Sheatsley[34] note that there may be an established tendency of less-educated respondents to agree with any extreme statement, regardless of its directionality. Undoubtedly there are class differences in the attitudinal data from the survey but the extent of these is still an open question that will require further research.

TABLE 1. ENDORSEMENT OF ATTITUDINAL STATEMENTS ABOUT HEALTH, BY RESPONDENTS IN OCCUPATION, INCOME, AND EDUCATION GROUPS, NORC-HIF STUDY

STATEMENT	OCCUPATION					INCOME				EDUCATION		
	Professional, business	Clerical, sales	Skilled workers	Other "blue-collar" workers	Farmers	$7,500 or more	$5,000 to $7,499	$2,000 to $4,999	Under $2,000	Attended college	High school only	Eighth grade or less
	Per cent endorsing statement											
No matter how careful a person is, he has to expect a good deal of illness in his lifetime	32	39	50	56	66	31	43	51	68	25	42	70
Some aches and pains you might as well get used to; they're not important	53	51	54	57	67	45	55	57	66	45	53	66
A person understands his own health better than most doctors do	29	34	38	45	55	28	33	42	55	24	33	56
Older people have to expect a lot of aches and pains	56	52	67	68	78	53	60	66	78	47	61	78
Nobody should go to a hospital unless there's just no other way to take care of him properly	35	37	45	45	51	34	37	43	57	30	36	58

Knowledge about disease also varies with socioeconomic grouping, as shown from the data presented in Table 2. Respondents were asked if they could name any of the symptoms of three important and well-known diseases: cancer, diabetes, and poliomyelitis. The number of respondents who could not name any symptoms increased steadily with *decreasing* education and income. In reply to the question: "Do you think it is possible or not possible to catch cancer from someone else?" there are also interesting differences. More than twice as many respondents in the low education and income group as in the high groups thought it possible to catch cancer or said they did not know.

Lack of knowledge about cancer, diabetes, and poliomyelitis may reflect inadequate knowledge of other aspects of scientific medicine, particularly in the matter of contagion, as the cancer data suggest. We can only speculate about the reasons for this, but probably one factor is less exposure to material in the mass media, or presentation of material in a manner that makes it difficult to understand. Our programs of health education are not reaching people in the low education, occupation, and income groups.

Inadequate knowledge does not necessarily mean that an individual cannot or does not utilize scientific medicine, but he may be less inclined to do so, and when he does there may be problems of communication between patient and physician. Those who are unfamiliar with disease as defined by scientific medicine probably depend more on friends and neighbors for information, the very channels through which folk medical beliefs are transmitted. Two of the attitudinal statements in Table 1 also bear on this point. Respondents with the lowest education and income show the highest agreement with the statements that a person understands his own health better than most doctors do, and that nobody should go to a hospital unless there is just no other way to take care of him properly. Although their knowledge about scientific medicine is limited, they are wary of the doctor and the hospital, trusting their own understanding of health. In that medium folk medicine thrives.

The overall results of the NORC-HIF survey indicate that the great majority of respondents think that the chance of having

TABLE 2. KNOWLEDGE OF DISEASE SYMPTOMS, BY RESPONDENTS IN OCCUPATION, INCOME, AND EDUCATION GROUPS, NORC-HIF STUDY

DISEASE	OCCUPATION					INCOME				EDUCATION		
	Professional, business	Clerical, sales	Skilled workers	Other "blue-collar" workers	Farmers	$7,500 or more	$5,000 to $7,499	$2,000 to $4,999	Under $2,000	Attended college	High school only	Eighth grade or less
	Per cent unable to name any symptoms											
Cancer ("correct" symptoms)	18	25	31	39	42	17	23	34	48	12	24	51
Diabetes	40	50	53	56	61	39	42	57	59	36	49	62
Poliomyelitis	18	21	31	37	47	17	21	33	53	12	21	54
	Per cent who don't know, or think it possible											
Do you think it is possible or not possible to catch cancer from someone else?	14	18	24	32	35	15	18	28	34	13	21	36

good health is better today than it was thirty years ago, that they hold the health professions in respect, that they go to proper medical personnel with serious symptoms and they think hospitals are doing a good job. In other words, the survey shows that scientific medicine dominates the United States. At the same time the data indicate that there is room for folk medicine to operate alongside scientific medicine and to be used as an alternative response to illness in certain situations, especially by those from the lower socioeconomic groups. If this is true, there are meanings for health education, for doctor-patient relationships, and for public relations activities of hospitals that cannot be avoided.

IMPLICATIONS OF BELIEFS AND ATTITUDES ABOUT ILLNESS

Scientific medicine, folk medicine, and primitive medicine can be thought of as alternative ways of perceiving illness, or to phrase it more in keeping with Chapter 2, alternative determinants of perception about illness. Although any given society shows one of the three systems to be dominant, we may find all three operating to varying degrees. For example, in describing the Navajo, Adair[35] reports the speech of a medicine man to a group of physicians as follows:

> As I see it, disease among the Navajo people may be divided into three different kinds:
>
> (1) There are those diseases which you physicians can cure better than the medicine man. T.B. is one of those. We have given up trying to treat the disease.
>
> (2) There are those diseases that we both can cure, the medicine man and the doctors. Snake bite is one of these.
>
> (3) And then there are those diseases which we can cure and you cannot. Right in the wards of this hospital there are patients who do not respond to your treatment. Some of them may have lightning sickness caused by being too close to where lightning has struck. We know how to cure that, but you do not.

The medicine man's description fits neatly with the scheme of this chapter. Diseases which the white doctor can cure more effectively come under scientific medicine, those in which both the white doctor and the Navajo have skills are part of empirical folk medicine, while lightning sickness is part of primitive medicine. Most societies in the world that have a predominance of primitive medicine are now being influenced strongly by scientific medicine and more frequently than not we find situations comparable to those existing among the Navajo.

The reverse also has some truth. In urban United States, dominated by scientific medicine, we know that folk medicine is strong, and traces of primitive medicine are still to be found. Even among the highly educated members of our society, the idea occurs occasionally that painful and disabling illness may be some kind of punishment by God for sin. Practices that are essentially magical in nature, prayer, supplication, vows to the Saints or the Deity are carried out. That they are not more successful may be due in no small measure to the fact that our faith is not sufficiently strong, for it is divided between the natural world and the supernatural, a problem that does not exist for the primitive. Among the less-educated groups that seek medical care, other evidences of primitive medicine can be found. Many a public health nurse is able to recount experiences with the evil eye, can describe the use of amulets to ward off colds, copper wire to prevent rheumatism, or "love potions" to attract the unwary male, or tell of finding a butcher knife under the pillow of a postpartum mother to "cut" the afterpains.

Disease and treatment have been defined here as social phenomena, involving a number of people besides the patient. Interpretation of disease events may in some cases depend heavily on the beliefs and practices of kinfolk, on those to whom the patient turns for emotional support. An ever-present possibility is that in so doing he will be "caught in a bind" and experience social pressure to accept an alternative explanation of his condition to the one he might personally prefer. The value of such close emotional support may outweigh in the patient's mind the value of his own interpretation of the illness. Practitioners of scientific medicine may find this value hierarchy difficult to accept, but it may be a crucial factor in good care for the patient.

We might say that there are two variables of importance in bringing into operation one or another of the three disease systems, seriousness and ambiguity. The less serious the disease, the more likely is the patient or his family to refer to the tried and true explanations and remedies of folk medicine. When a person feels logy, mildly depressed, "headachey," feels a cold coming on, wrenches his back, or when he wants to get ready for a new season or keep himself in top shape, he is more likely to have recourse to folk medicine, whether in Boston, Mexico, India, or Egypt. Here both seriousness and ambiguity are low. When seriousness or threat comes high, the person will turn either to scientific medicine or primitive medicine, depending on which is the dominant belief system in his culture, or as in the case of the Navajo, the choice will be determined by the nature of the disease, tuberculosis, or lightning sickness. In both cases, if the ambiguity is of sufficient intensity, the person may employ both scientific and primitive medicine and see both as legitimate approaches, using that which is familiar at first and that which is unfamiliar only as a last resort. In working with people in underdeveloped countries, physicians often remark that patients come to them in extreme conditions, when there is little that can be done to help them, or when they can be saved only by heroic effort. These people have not been neglected, but their condition has been viewed from a different base and other treatments have been tried first. On the other hand, it is not uncommon for families in our culture who have a member with a serious and apparently incurable disease to bring in a Christian Science Healer, or spend their life savings on a trip to a distant shrine, as well as to employ the services of a competent physician. In the latter case the use of primitive medicine, or magic, is perceived as a legitimate approach to disease by the patient and his family. When success of some venture is of great emotional importance to a group, there is uncertainty about the outcome, and where the empirical techniques available to the group are not sufficient for the problem, it is not unusual to find that magic is used to control the situation. In these circumstances magic provides a certainty and confidence that is left unfulfilled by the inadequacies of empirical techniques. Serious illness is a situation of great emotional significance, and often there is uncertainty about its outcome. If the empirical treatments of folk medicine, or the sophisticated procedures of scientific medicine, are inadequate, magic in one form or another may offer the only hope, both physical and emotional.

It is difficult for those in the health professions of the United States to realize that there are other legitimate interpretations of disease than those encompassed by scientific medicine. By legitimate we mean legitimate to the patient, meaningful, useful, important to him. It is easy to ridicule and dismiss folk beliefs or primitive medicine as foolish and "unscientific," as superstitious and beneath the attention of one skilled in scientific medicine. However, ridicule may do less harm to the presence of folk or primitive medicine than it does to the ability of the physician, nurse, sanitary engineer, or medical social worker to provide good medical care or help with medical problems. Anthropologists who have worked in Central and South America consistently report that a good deal of disease goes unattended by practitioners of scientific medicine because it is never brought to them. The farmer or peasant reports that the doctor "doesn't know about these things," such as the evil eye (*mal ojo*) or about *susto*, a disease that is caused by fright or is the effect of bad air. He would not take his son or wife to a doctor for an illness of this kind because the patient would only be treated for something else, or sent away with scorn. Derision of "liver" and "kidney" pills will not bring lower-class Americans flocking into the doctor's office, nor will it help in superior health education. It may serve instead to make their use greater or to increase the practice of that competing specialist, the chiropractor.

To be sure, the answer does not lie in outright acceptance of the tenets of folk medicine or primitive medicine, but rather in the acceptance of the fact that other systems of belief about disease than scientific can be meaningful to the one who is ill. When the giver of medical care knows more about the way in which the patient or his family perceive the situation of illness, then the quality and extent of medical care can increase.

NOTES TO CHAPTER 4

1. Paul, Benjamin D., "The Cultural Context of Health Education," *Symposium Proceedings*. School of Social Work, University of Pittsburgh, 1953, pp. 31–38.

2. Straus, Robert, "The Development of a Social Science Teaching and Research Program in a Medical Center." Paper presented at the Annual Meeting of the American Sociological Society, Washington, D.C., September 1, 1955.

3. Stayt, Hugh A., *The Bavenda*. Published for the International Institute of African Languages and Cultures by Oxford University Press, London, 1931, p. 263.

4. A number of papers by Erwin H. Ackerknecht are particularly pertinent to a discussion of primitive medicine, and I have drawn on them to a considerable extent in this section. The reader is referred to the following articles, in the *Bulletin of the History of Medicine:* "Problems of Primitive Medicine,"vol. 11, May, 1942, pp. 503–521; "Primitive Medicine and Culture Pattern," vol. 12, November, 1942, pp. 545–574; "Psychopathology, Primitive Medicine, and Primitive Culture," vol. 14, June, 1943, pp. 30–67; and "Natural Diseases and Rational Treatment in Primitive Medicine," vol. 19, May, 1946, pp. 467–497. Ackerknecht defines primitive medicine in a somewhat narrower sense than I am using the term, limiting it to the medical beliefs and practices of primitive tribes. However, the essential feature which he ascribes to the system is magic, a quality that I feel is to be found in certain of the beliefs and attitudes toward illness in "civilized" and highly sophisticated societies. It finds clear expression in the primitive societies but is not limited to them. Material about primitive medicine can also be found in Clements, Forrest E., "Primitive Concepts of Disease," *University of California Publications in American Archaeology and Ethnology*, vol. 32, no. 2, 1932, pp. 185–252.

5. Benedict, Ruth, *Patterns of Culture*. New American Library (Mentor Book), New York, 1946, pp. 136–137.

6. *Ibid*., p. 137.

7. For a full description of the condition the reader is referred to Foster, George M., editor, *A Cross-Cultural Anthropological Analysis of a Technical Aid Program*, Smithsonian Institution, Washington, July 25, 1951, mimeographed; or Foster, George M., "Relationships Between Theoretical and Applied Anthropology: A Public Health Program Analysis," *Human Organization*, vol 11, Fall, 1952, pp. 5–16. The evil eye occurs in many parts of the world, for example, "In Mediterranean countries and the Middle East evil flows through the eyes when the individual admires and covets." See Mead, Margaret, editor, *Cultural Patterns and Technical Change*, UNESCO, Paris, 1953, pp. 235–236.

8. Macgregor, Frances Cooke, "Some Psycho-social Problems Associated with Facial Deformities," *American Sociological Review*, vol. 16, October, 1951, pp. 629–638.

9. Hsu, Francis L. K., "A Cholera Epidemic in a Chinese Town" in Paul, Benjamin D., editor, *Health, Culture, and Community*. Russell Sage Foundation, New York, 1955, pp. 135–154.

10. The Gospel according to Mark 9:14–27, *New Testament:* Revised Standard Version. Thomas Nelson and Sons, New York, 1946.

11. A fascinating account of an infestation by devils and the untiring efforts of exorcists, with all of the attendant social consequences, is to be found in Huxley, Aldous L., *The Devils of Loudun*, Harper and Bros., New York, 1952. Mr. Huxley's account is also an unusual example of contagion in the area of psychological disturbance, an event rarely described as well.

12. Cannon, Walter B., "'Voodoo' Death," *American Anthropologist*, vol. 44, April, 1942, pp. 169–181.

13. *Ibid.*, p. 172.

14. Quoted in Simmons, Leo W., and Harold G. Wolff, *Social Science in Medicine* Russell Sage Foundation, New York, 1954, p. 94.

15. *Ibid.*, pp. 94–95. Personal communication.

16. Cannon, Walter B., *op. cit.*, p. 173.

17. See note 7.

18. Simmons, Ozzie G., "Popular and Modern Medicine in Mestizo Communities of Coastal Peru and Chile," *Journal of American Folklore*, vol. 68, January–March, 1955, pp. 57–71.

19. Jelliffe, D. B., "Cultural Variation and the Practical Pediatrician," *Journal of Pediatrics*, vol. 49, December, 1956, pp. 661–671.

20. *Ibid.*, p. 668.

21. *Loc. cit.*

22. Redfield, Robert, *The Folk Culture of Yucatan.* University of Chicago Press, Chicago, 1941, p. 129.

23. Wellin, Edward, "Water Boiling in a Peruvian Town," in Paul, Benjamin D., editor, *Health, Culture, and Community*, pp. 71–103.

24. Carstairs, G. Morris, "Medicine and Faith in Rural Rajasthan," in Paul, Benjamin D., editor, *Health, Culture, and Community*, p. 123.

25. Saunders, Lyle, *Cultural Difference and Medical Care.* Russell Sage Foundation, New York, 1954, pp. 147–148.

26. Adams, Richard N., "A Nutritional Research Program in Guatemala," in Paul, Benjamin D., editor, *Health, Culture, and Community*, pp. 435–458.

27. Two examples can be cited of the interest in folk medicine. Four years ago a Vermont physician wrote a book on folk medicine that quickly went to the top of the best seller list. See Jarvis, DeForest C., *Folk Medicine:* A Vermont Doctor's Guide to Good Health, Henry Holt, New York, 1958. Apple cider vinegar and honey were given strong support for both preventive and therapeutic purposes in many kinds of conditions and a preparation combining these two ingredients built up substantial sales. Dr. Jarvis followed this with a book on rheumatism, and for a time both were best sellers. See Jarvis, DeForest C., *Arthritis and Folk Medicine*, Holt, Rinehart and Winston Co., New York, 1960.

The other example comes from one of the Sunday supplement magazines in an article about folk medicine by the president of the American Medical Association. See Askey, E. Vincent, "The Truth About Folk Medicine," *This Week*, December 18, 1960. Dr. Askey points to some of the remedies in folk medicine that have been used by scientific medicine, but the main weight of his remarks is against the fads, the "worthless" products, the lack of reliance on scientific medicine for many conditions. Here we see a concern on the part of practitioners of scientific medicine in response to the interest in folk medicine which is shown by the general public.

28. Saunders, Lyle, and Gordon W. Hewes, "Folk Medicine and Medical Practice," *Journal of Medical Education*, vol. 28, September, 1953, pp. 43–46.

29. Koos, Earl Lomon, *The Health of Regionville.* Columbia University Press, New York, 1954.

30. Wardwell, Walter I., "A Marginal Professional Role: The Chiropractor," *Social Forces*, vol. 30, March, 1952, pp. 339–348.

31. Koos, Earl Lomon, *op. cit.*, p. 89.

32. Loc. cit.

33. A detailed analysis of the survey results is being prepared for publication by Jacob J. Feldman and Paul B. Sheatsley of NORC. Mr. Sheatsley was kind enough to provide me with a set of the initial tables of data, the "Marginals," and on the basis of these tables I have drawn certain conclusions. These data do not represent a refined analysis, and, therefore, my interpretation of them has been couched in cautious terms. I wish to express my appreciation to NORC for permission to use the data here prior to publication of its own analytic report.

34. Personal communication from Mr. Sheatsley. Also, see Hare, A. Paul, "Interview Responses: Personality or Conformity?" *Public Opinion Quarterly*, vol. 24, Winter, 1960, pp. 679–685.

35. Adair, John, "The Process of Innovation and the Navajo-Cornell Field Health Research Project." Paper presented to the Skytop Conference, Committee on Preventive Medicine and Social Science Research, Social Science Research Council, June, 1958.

Chapter 5

Beliefs and Attitudes About Mental Disease

A DIFFERENT KIND OF PHENOMENON is involved when the average person thinks about mental illness in contrast to other kinds of disease. His knowledge about the onset, the treatment, or the outcome shows a wide gap from that held by psychiatric specialists. At the same time his knowledge is affected by strong attitudes toward the mentally ill, attitudes that are generally negative rather than positive. Laymen regard mental illness in a special way, have a different set, a different perceptual framework from that of diseases primarily physical in nature.

The magnitude of the health problem in the area of mental disease makes the matter of beliefs and attitudes one of considerable importance. Most readers will already be familiar with the statistic that half the hospital beds in the United States are occupied by people who have some form of mental disease. To this must be added the numbers attending outpatient clinics or making regular visits to the office of a psychiatrist or psychologist, and countless others who have not sought professional help but who lead lives filled with fears, frustrations, and unhappiness. Thus, one aspect of the magnitude of the problem is that of *treatment*, taking care of those who come for help, voluntarily or otherwise, and encouraging others to seek the help they need. Physicians in practice, public health officers and nurses, medical social workers are confronted almost every day with cases that need psychiatric attention but resist seeking it. Even more difficult is the question of *prevention*, for any problem of this magnitude calls for prevention as much as it does for treatment. Discovering cases in early stages of the disease process when treatment may be more effective, altering environmental stresses that contribute to tension, facilitating the development of healthy adaptational processes in personality—all these are involved in prevention.

Beliefs and attitudes about mental disease are a central issue in treatment and prevention in two different ways. First, those in the health professions can deal more effectively with patients or their families if they understand how the latter perceive situations involving mental illness. Second, long-range education will be necessary if there is to be conjunction between the approach to mental illness shown by the general public and that shown by scientific medicine. Only through such conjunction can prevention be successful. Fortunately, some excellent studies have been conducted in recent years in which the extent of knowledge about mental illness has been examined, range of attitudes assessed, and data gathered about behavior in the face of a mental health problem.[1] Thus, there are good empirical grounds for drawing conclusions about the present state of beliefs and attitudes toward mental disease and the relation of these to perception and to behavior. The major studies in this field will be examined in the following pages under three different sections: data about knowledge and attitudes, material relative to help-seeking behavior, and changes that are taking place in beliefs and attitudes toward mental disease.

KNOWLEDGE AND ATTITUDES

Colloquial expressions and slang terms often reflect the attitudes that exist in a given area, mental illness being a good case in point. Slang terms abound for describing the patient, those who treat him, or the institution in which he is lodged. People are described as crazy, balmy, loco, or batty, as having slipped a cog, gone screwy, being off his rocker, having bats in his belfry, mad as a March hare, touched in the head, nutty as a fruit cake, having a screw loose, coming unhinged, and addled in the wits. The common term today for psychiatrist is "head shrinker," but he may also be called a "nut doctor," or something similar. Mental hospitals come under a variety of designations, of which the most common are booby hatch and nut house. Although not a slang term, insane asylum is still in frequent use, and Bedlam or House of Bedlam will be remembered by many.

These expressions are all negative in nature, an orientation that is also expressed in the round of jokes and cartoons about psychiatrists. Eccentricity even to the point of being like their patients, and alteration from ordinary appearance or manner in speech or dress, usually provide material for the framework of the joke or the punchline. Only in the most recent years have television dramas begun to portray the psychiatrist as a serious, normal individual who fits in with the best in medical tradition.

Everyday language would suggest that attitudes toward mental illness are primarily negative and contain a great deal of emotional force, but everyday language tells us little about the knowledge that people have of mental illness. As we shall see, knowledge and attitudes must be kept separate in our analysis of the problem. We turn now to studies in which knowledge and attitudes have been assessed, although often not separated, and will have an opportunity to gauge the extent to which slang and colloquialisms reflect basic orientations.

Some studies have been limited in terms of population examined, or in the type of research techniques used, while others have been of the broad survey nature, or have attempted to deal in a definitive sense with certain aspects of knowledge or attitudes. Three studies will be cited that fall into the first group and three that can be placed in the latter.

During the two academic years 1949–1950 and 1950–1951, the George Warren Brown School of Social Work conducted a study about mental illness among a sample of St. Louis residents.[2] Among the techniques used to gather information was the presentation of three brief case histories representing different kinds of mental disturbance, "aggressive psychotic," "withdrawn psychotic," and "neurotic." About three-quarters of the sample defined the first of these as mental illness, but a smaller proportion, 56 per cent, called the second mental illness, and only 15 per cent felt that the last was mental illness. Subsequent studies have reported the same kind of results.

When questioned about the causes of mental disease, respondents often named naturalistic causes that were external to the individual, like a blow on the head or undue pressure from a job situation. Hereditary and supernatural causes received scant support, but so did early childhood relationships. Another category of causation contained factors that were internal, but not the same as found in theories of dynamic psychology. Bad habits, lack of will power, nervousness, worry, and drinking were listed, implying that the individual was somehow himself responsible for his condition.

Data about attitudes were gathered from a series of questions about projected relationships with mental patients. Approximately 90 per cent indicated they would be willing to talk with a former mental patient, even to have him in the same organization or club, or work on a job with him, but only 22 per cent would be willing to have him marry someone in the family. As in the case of minority group prejudice, there was a social distance factor involved relative to people who have or have had a mental illness.

Employees in a mental hospital, ward attendants, laundry workers, cooks, dining-room assistants, and other workers were studied by Middleton[3] for their opinions about mental illness. About 40 per cent believed mental illness to be hereditary and a like number that masturbation is one of its principal causes. Fifty per cent agreed with the statement that people who lead immoral lives often go insane. Middleton's subjects thus emphasized different reasons from those given by respondents in the St. Louis survey, but once again the knowledge was not in line with dynamic psychological theory. Parenthetically, it might be noted that the people studied by Middleton probably represented a lower socioeconomic group than found in the St. Louis survey and were a unique group in that they worked in a mental hospital. Also the emphasis on "moral" factors in causation might help to explain the punishing type of behavior sometimes shown toward mental patients by employees of a hospital.

A group representative of a higher educational level in the state of Utah was studied by Branch,[4] who administered a questionnaire by mail. The individuals questioned were physicians, public health nurses, judges, lawyers, members of the Women's Legislative Council, and law enforcement officers. Unfortunately, as in most questionnaire surveys conducted by mail, there is the problem of bias introduced by incomplete returns, but notwithstanding that, the results are similar to the two studies just cited. One question concerned the cause of mental illness and allowed multiple choice answers. Of those replying, 15 per cent checked sinful living, 37 per cent venereal disease, 26 per cent overwork, 21 per cent injury to the head, 54 per cent hereditary, 44 per cent home environment, and 74 per cent family and other troubles. These reasons can easily be grouped into moral factors, hereditary factors, and variables external to the individual.

All three of the studies cited have data concerning knowledge of mental illness, while one of the studies has, in addition, data about attitudes. Although the populations in the three studies differed, there was a common emphasis on moral factors or those external to the individual in terms of heredity or events in the environment. There was little attention paid to early developmental variables and the susceptibility to stress occasioned by disturbed interpersonal relationships in childhood. At the same time the St. Louis study indicated an unwillingness to accept former mental patients in a close interpersonal relationship.

One of the most complete investigations, both in terms of subjects and of data, was carried out by the National Opinion Research Center with a national probability sample of just over 3,500 adults. Data were gathered through an intensive interview of about an hour and a half with each respondent in the sample. It is impossible to summarize all the findings here, but the points pertinent to the discussion are as follows.[5]

How do people define mental illness? How does it differ from other forms of human behavior? How can one recognize it when it occurs? Here are questions that relate to fundamental beliefs of people and data from the survey throw light on them.

About half the respondents equated mental illness with psychosis, where unpredictability, impulsiveness, loss of control, extreme irrationality, and legal incompetence were the distinguishing characteristics. Through explicit questioning, two-thirds of the sample would include "nervous conditions" under the term "mental illness," distinguishing these from psychosis; yet it appeared that this was an intellectual acceptance rather than an emotional one. When these same people were encouraged to talk about mental illness, without having to define it explicitly, they would use the frame of reference whereby mental illness was equated with psychosis.

In addition to direct questioning, the study used the technique of the case history or description of behavior. Six descriptions were developed: paranoia, simple schizophrenia, anxiety neurosis, alcoholism, compulsive-phobic personality, and a childhood behavior disorder. To each description the respondent was asked to indicate whether anything was wrong; if so, what was wrong, what could have caused it, and whether or not the person should be regarded as mentally ill. The percentages of the sample diagnosing each case as one of mental disease were as follows:

Description of Behavior	*Respondents*
Paranoia	75 per cent
Simple schizophrenia	34
Alcoholism	29
Anxiety neurosis	18
Childhood behavior disorder	14
Compulsive-phobic personality	7

Thus, there was a striking inclination to recognize mental illness only in the form of marked psychosis, and even that by only 75 per cent of the respondents. Shirley Star, director of the study, concluded that although most people generally began by saying that there are all kinds and degrees of mental illness, they were not willing in the last analysis to recognize anything less than the most extreme form.

From the overall data, Star is of the opinion that there are three interrelated principles on which people base their decisions about mental illness. The first of these is *irrationality*. When reason is lost and intellectual functioning breaks down, then the mind can be affected. Second, *a loss of self-control*, usually to the point of violence, and certainly to the point of irresponsibility, must be present. Finally, *departure from normalcy*, or behavior that is not reasonable or expected under the circumstances, is a mark of mental disease. Most people look for understandable causes of deviant behavior before they are willing to assign it to the category of mental illness; therefore, when disease is recognized, it is of severe form. The three principles really reflect a consistent view of human behavior that is rooted in the cultural heritage of western Europe, emphasizing rationality and the ability to exercise self-control.

Mental illness, hence, is a rather terrifying thing, posing a threat to the basic view of man and human conduct, knocking the supports from under rationality and free will. The farther one can keep from mental illness, the safer he is, a fact that supports the feeling that psychotics should be locked up.

In contrast, the view of human nature and of mental disease that is espoused by modern dynamic psychology regards emotional illness as evidenced by behavior inappropriate to the reality situation of the individual in question. When such inappropriate behavior is frequent and rigid, some form of mental illness is present. Dynamic psychology operates on the premise that characteristic emotional patterns are related to early interpersonal experiences and that unconscious motivations play a prominent role in behavior. For example, when we discussed psychogenic needs in Chapter 2, it was noted that these could be both conscious and unconscious, and, indeed, were often the latter. Emotional patterns consequently are not always rational and in attempts to modify them emphasis must be placed on some form of emotional insight more than on modification of the external environment. Mental illness, as such, does not pose the threat of violence and fear, but is regarded as a process that is essentially understandable if one can get sufficient facts at hand.

Thus, we see two differing sets of beliefs about human behavior and mental illness, one based on the rational normative view of man, and the other based on the view of man as a developing being who is often motivated by unconscious forces that grow out of interpersonal experiences in his early life. About three-quarters of the subjects in the sample fell into the first category while the rest tended toward the second, and this latter group was heavily loaded with urban intellectuals who have had extensive education and are members of one of the professions.

A second major source of data concerning beliefs and attitudes toward mental illness comes from a series of studies at the Institute of Communications Research of the University of Illinois by Nunnally and Osgood.[6] Material about knowledge and beliefs was obtained principally from a special questionnaire, while attitude studies were carried out with versions of the Semantic Differential, an instrument that requires the respondent to rate a concept in respect to sets of bipolar adjectives, like weak-strong, ugly-handsome, and strange-familiar. There are seven intervals between each pair of adjectives, and a number of pairs are listed on a page. At the top is a concept, such as psychiatrist or some other term, and the respondent is asked to rate the concept somewhere along the seven-point scale between each set of adjectives. This measuring device has received wide acceptance among psychologists and presently is being utilized in a great variety of research situations.[7] In addition, an analysis was made of the handling of mental illness in the mass media.

For measuring what the public knows about mental health issues the research group started with several thousand statements collected from a variety of sources, both professional and nonprofessional. After sorting and "boiling down" the list, a factor analysis was made, producing ten factors, of which some examples were: look and act differently, avoidance of morbid thoughts, and immediate environment versus emphasis on personality dynamics. The ten factors were represented in a 50-item questionnaire, which was then administered to representative samples of the population in Nashville, Tennessee, and Eugene, Oregon.

In terms of knowledge the investigators concluded that information about mental illness is not highly structured, not to the extent that would be shown by political beliefs. Correlations among the items were rather small, and respondents often agreed with statements that were logically inconsistent. The investigators suggest that material about mental health is not sufficiently discussed in schools, the mass media, or other areas for a stable structure of opinions to develop.

Generally speaking, results of the questionnaire showed that the average man rejects the superstitions and obvious misconceptions, as seen in the statement: "Most people who 'go crazy' try to kill themselves," or "If a child is jealous of a younger brother it is best not to let him show it in any way." Also there was rejection of the ideas that a change in diet will help a nervous breakdown and an excess of sexual intercourse leads to insanity. Where there was misinformation it occurred most frequently in respondents with less than a high school education or who were over fifty years of age.

There were certain areas where the average respondent and the expert showed disagreement, particularly in terms of the techniques required to maintain personal adjustment and to restore it once disequilibrium occurs. The public tended to support the idea that books on "peace of mind" prevent many people from having nervous breakdowns, that concentration on happy thoughts or memories will keep an individual from being bothered by unpleasant things, or that one can get rid of unpleasant memories by trying hard to forget them.

Knowledge about mental illness had not been aided by plays, movies, radio dramas, comic strips, short stories, and the like as late as 1954, the year in which the Institute of Communications Research made a study. Often the presentation of mental illness was distorted, emphasizing the bizarre symptoms, irrationality and lack of control. These symptoms, of course, reflect the basic fears about mental illness that Star postulated in the National Opinion Research Center study. Furthermore, the occurrence of mental disorder was explained most often by pressures in the external environment, and when the pressures were alleviated the emotional disturbance improved. An alternate explanation of cause could be seen in organic factors, blows to the head, or some sort of physical deprivation at one period or another in life. Although a useful device for presenting drama, the approach taken by much of the communications media has been to impede rather than improve the knowledge of the average man about mental disorder. However, it should be noted in the past ten years newspapers and magazines have given considerable space to serious and generally accurate coverage of research and treatment in mental illness by qualified reporters of science and medicine.

Knowledge or belief is one thing, attitudes toward mental disorder is another. Most studies indicate that the intellectual acceptance of facts or verifiable statements about mental illness often works at cross purposes with attitudes toward the mentally ill. Public attitudes, as measured by the Semantic Differential, were generally negative toward persons with mental disorders, showing fear, distrust, and dislike. The two scales that showed the greatest difference between the normal and the mentally ill were predictable-unpredictable, and tense-relaxed. Within the group of mental disorders psychotic conditions drew more negative attitudes than did neurotic, psychosis being seen as more disruptive and more frightening. Psychotics were held in lower esteem than neurotics, and the latter were rated as weaker and more delicate. By far the most important variable was unpredictableness, again showing the congruence between this study and that done by Star.

Differences between educational and age-groups relative to information were not so marked when attitudes were considered. Although differences between educational groups were still statistically significant, they were much smaller.

Language is the vehicle through which beliefs and attitudes are expressed but the content of a given language can also help shape beliefs and attitudes. To this end the Institute of Communications Research has studied the terms that are available in our language for the discussion of mental health problems. The supply of these is limited, and the available terms are mainly in the slang category, the kinds of expressions that were mentioned at the beginning of this section. Terms and concepts that are used by the experts are not understood by the general public and have no counterpart in everyday language, a situation that is much more acute than in physical disease. The investigators concluded that limitations in language make it difficult for health education in the area of mental disorders to be effective. Also because of the negative affect associated with so many of the available terms, a new set of verbal symbols will have to be utilized. A set of terms that is sufficiently diverse to handle the variations in phenomena, yet unbiased and neutral in affect, is sorely needed and is one of the major tasks facing mental health educators and other specialists in the field.

The third survey was carried out for the Joint Commission on Mental Illness and Health by Gurin, Veroff, and Feld at the Survey Research Center, The University of Michigan.[8] The study was designed to find out how a representative sample of 2,460 respondents in the United States view their troubles. How well adjusted do they consider themselves to be, how happy, how anxious, how worried? What do they do about their troubles, and when they seek outside help where and to whom do they turn? Although focused more on feelings of psychological distress and the perceived reasons for the distress than on explicit knowledge of mental illness and concurrent attitudes, there are nevertheless important implications in the data for the topic of this chapter.

Generally speaking, people tended to externalize their problems, to locate them in tangible events in the environment, pressures of a job or like factors, seeing the problem as a reaction to these outside pressures rather than as problems in personal or interpersonal malfunctioning. Thus, worries and tensions were more often expressed in nonpsychological terms. There was variation, of course, among demographic groups in this regard. Younger people and those with more formal education were more likely to manifest psychological than bodily symptoms in distress and to locate the causes in psychological factors than in pressures from environmental events. Also in reporting the experience of problems in the past they more often phrased them in psychological terms. The investigators reported further that youth and education seemed to be associated with greater goals and strivings in life, greater satisfactions, but also no less tension and worry.

An illustration of beliefs and attitudes about mental disease in action comes from the efforts of a research team to educate the residents of a community in a western Canadian province about mental health.[9] In a sense it was a project of preventive psychiatry, the hope being that with more awareness in the community of the early signs of mental illness patients could be treated sooner and perhaps without hospitalization. Also there was the hope that with improved understanding of mental disorders discharged patients would have an easier time of rehabilitation in the community.

Prairie Town, so named by the team, was an old and stable community of 1,350 inhabitants, conservative in outlook and highly individualistic. Social interaction was epitomized by the large numbers of clubs and organizations, giving residents an opportunity to be busy in social activities as much as they might wish.

Members of the research team postulated that in general those who have mental illness are rejected because of fear, ignorance, and guilt. They knew that community education around a topic involving such strong emotions would be both difficult and delicate, and they set about their task slowly by winning friends and carefully explaining their program. Specifically, the education program had three objectives: to show that there is a wide range of behavior that can be called "normal," that behavior is understandable in terms of cause and effect, and that the borderline between the normal and abnormal is vague and arbitrary. As it turned out, the people of Prairie Town agreed with the research team on the first two aims but showed strong disagreement on the third. As in the National Opinion Research Center survey and the St. Louis study, mental illness was equated with severe psychosis, of which hospitalization was a sure sign, and once having been committed to a hospital a person could never be quite the same again.

Combining research with education, the team first interviewed a sample of the community for beliefs and attitudes about mental illness, then followed the survey by an intensive educational campaign of six months. At the end of the period the interviewers returned for new interviews on the same topic. At first generous support appeared to be forthcoming in the educational efforts, evidenced by invitations to put on programs for various organizations, cooperation by the local newspaper, and interest in discussion groups. Gradually "apathy" developed toward the work of the team. Attendance fell off drastically at meetings, organizations canceled remaining programs in planned series, and some people expressed open hostility. In a sense the climax occurred when one young woman, an avid supporter of the educational effort, succumbed to the tensions arising out of the conflict between team and community and had to be hospitalized for an acute anxiety attack.

When the interviewers returned at the end of the educational program the resentment of the townspeople had become serious. In many cases there were indignant refusals to requests for an interview. Everywhere there was coldness and ill-concealed resentment. To add discouragement, results of the second survey showed that attitudes toward mental illness and mental patients had changed not at all in spite of the strenuous efforts.

From a retrospective point of view the Cummings summarized the reasons for the difficulties as follows: "It was evident that we had been trying to change ideas that were very deeply and firmly held and that the more energetically we tried to dislodge them, the more tightly people held onto them, and the angrier they became at us for trying to take them away."[10]

Analysis of the beliefs and attitudes of the people in Prairie Town shows them to be identical with a large proportion of the respondents in the other studies which we have examined. Mental illness represented unpredictability and irrationality, was a fearsome thing, and the community protected itself against this threat by confining mental illness to severe psychosis and decreeing that people so labeled should be locked up. Taking away or blurring the distinction between normal and abnormal was too big a threat. Attempts to change the state of affairs posed a serious threat to social stability and were met with strong resistance.

Reflections on the Studies of Beliefs and Attitudes

From the data obtained in the studies we have cited, a number of conclusions can be drawn about knowledge or opinions relative to mental illness. First, the general public knows many of the facts about mental disease and tends to reject many of the blatant misconceptions. With the growth of mass communications in our society there is every reason to believe that the general public will become increasingly knowledgeable as to cause and behavior in mental illness. Second, in spite of the fact that the public is not grossly misinformed there are marked differences in knowledge among subgroups in the population. Those who are younger and who have a higher level of formal education are likely to define mental illness in psychological terms, while those who are older and have less schooling are likely to perceive emotional problems as caused by concrete factors in the environment, or perhaps as punishment for sins. The greatest amount of misinformation occurs in this second group. Third, there is still a considerable divergence between the opinions of experts in psychology and psychiatry and the general public. The average man is unwilling to extend the range of mental illness much beyond psychosis, while the experts would include the severe and most of the milder neuroses.

Perception of any situation is limited by the knowledge which the perceiver can apply to the situation. In the case of mental illness, the inadequate knowledge possessed by sizable numbers in our population means they will perceive those who are mentally ill in much narrower and more distorted terms than scientific experts or many others of their fellow citizens. Inadequacies in the terms which the general public has available for talking about and discussing mental illness places a further limitation on the knowledge variable.

Of equal or greater importance as a limiting factor in perception is the set of attitudes possessed by the perceiver, a crucial factor in the area of mental illness. Acquisition of new knowledge or the application of knowledge presently held can be thwarted by the presence of negative attitudes. The negative semantic meanings that most respondents attach to "mental patient" give some indication of the reluctance these people would have to learning and applying new facts. Three of the studies to which we referred, the St. Louis survey, the National Opinion Research

Center survey, and investigations by the Institute of Communications Research, show very clearly that attitudes toward mental illness are generally negative and are very strong, indicated by the colloquial expressions to which we referred at the beginning of the chapter. As such they provide a formidable deterrent to congruence of perception with the experts in scientific medicine. At the same time they impede the acceptance and psychological support that are vitally needed by those who have a mental illness or have just recovered from one.

The source of many of the beliefs and attitudes about mental illness undoubtedly lies in folk and primitive medicine. Only in recent years have we escaped from the demonology that dominated thinking about mental disease all through the Middle Ages and into the modern era.[11] Traces still remain, reflected in the opinions that psychosis is a punishment for sinful living, or that agitation and irrationality can be cured by the laying on of hands. In this case the tenacity of beliefs that come from primitive medicine can be understood in terms of the ambiguity and threat principle discussed in the previous chapter. Apart from beliefs that rest on magic, many are drawn from folk tradition, based on tradition rather than fact, passed down from one generation to another through informal channels. Here we have the emphasis on external factors like a blow to the head or some kind of physical deprivation in the environment, or some kind of pressure which the individual cannot control. In keeping with our definition of folk medicine there is a vagueness as to cause-and-effect relationships, at least in understanding the pathway between stated cause and effect in mental disease. At the same time there is adherence to enduring cultural values rather than to scientific objectivity, and a tenacity and resistance to change.

Association of beliefs and attitudes toward mental disease with the long-standing tradition of viewing man as a rational, self-controlled being, maker of his own destiny, is not the only reason for their cohesiveness and toughness. Only in very recent years has scientific research provided any reasonable clues to the understanding of etiology of schizophrenia, depression, phobias, and other serious mental disorders. Even now the unknown is vastly greater than the known. Tracing of the workings of the unconscious and emphasis on the importance of early interpersonal relationships gave new indications about the etiology of neurosis and insight into certain aspects of psychotic disorders, but these findings proved inadequate for complete explanation. Biochemical research may well constitute the next major breakthrough, but the apparent complexity of the problem is still baffling. The very inadequacies of scientific knowledge in the case of mental illness, therefore, have made it difficult for people to abandon a tried and true explanation for a very frightening event, real or only potential.

HELP-SEEKING BEHAVIOR

The ability to seek effective help in time of distress involves both the knowledge of available resources and a favorable orientation toward those resources. As to the first of these factors, the available studies show consistent results. First, most people know that there are professional specialists who treat mental disorders; they know the meaning of the word "psychiatrist." For example, in studying lower-class patients in a western hospital, Saunders found that psychiatrist was just behind surgeon in the extent to which people could identify the term correctly.[12] They knew what psychiatrist meant more often than they knew what many other medical specialties meant. Second, most people do not differentiate clearly, if at all, between psychiatrist, psychologist, and psychoanalyst. Differences in training and degree, in the use of specialized techniques, or in the use of a certain kind of therapeutic approach are often not recognized. Educational differences among respondents are, of course, important, and those with college training can usually differentiate psychologists from the others but often do not know the variations in meaning between psychiatrist and psychoanalyst. Third, most people are not clear about what the psychiatrist does in treatment. In the studies by the Institute of Communications Research the majority of respondents agreed with the statement that the main job of the psychiatrist is to explain to the patient the origin of his troubles, in contrast to the view held by experts in the field. Even well-educated people often do not know how a psychiatrist works or what he tries to do in therapy other than to prescribe drugs.

An illustration of some of these points comes from the NORC data where it was clear that the majority of the public knew that psychiatry exists, but it was remote and unfamiliar to most people. Only 23 per cent of the sample reported even a slight acquaintance with anyone who had been treated by a psychiatrist outside a mental hospital. Furthermore, only few people thought of psychiatry as a branch of medicine that had any relevance for themselves or the kind of people they knew. For example, three-fifths of the respondents had never known anyone who had been helped by seeing a psychiatrist, *and* could think of no one in his acquaintance who would benefit from a visit to one, *and* had no interest in seeing a psychiatrist himself. The overall reaction could be summarized by saying that anyone who needs psychiatric treatment should see a psychiatrist, but practically no one ever needs psychiatric treatment. Thus, although there is public knowledge about psychiatry and acceptance of it, most people do not see it as relevant for them or their friends. The reason behind this position, as we have already seen, is the constriction of "psychiatric treatment" to severe psychosis. Other forms of interpersonal problems were handled by traditional techniques, reference to family or close friends, talking with the minister or priest, or consultation with the family doctor.

Attitudes toward the professionals in mental health were found to be favorable by the Institute of Communications Research. In the Semantic Differential studies psychologist, psychiatrist, and psychoanalyst were regarded as moderately intelligent, valuable, honest, and sincere, none of the roles being more highly regarded than others. In part this evaluation seems to be due to the generally favorable evaluation of all professional people. Those who treat physical problems received a higher rating, however; were evaluated as more understandable, effective, valuable, safe, and as much more predictable. Some of the negative orientation toward the mentally ill was generalized to those who are responsible for their treatment. Again we find that in the determinants of perception there are the rudiments for effective action but also the cause for hesitation and resistance.

Further data come from studies of what people have actually done or would do when they were faced with a mental health problem. In the first of the St. Louis surveys respondents were asked what types of people could be called on for help in the "cases" presented and were given four professionals—minister, doctor, social worker, and lawyer. The minister was heavily favored, and even in the case of the "aggressive psychotic" was placed nearly on a par with the doctor. During the second survey doctors were differentiated into psychiatrists and ordinary physicians, with the result that the psychiatrist was considered to be a helpful person for mental illness by 79 per cent of the respondents. The minister, medical doctor, and social worker were seen as helpful by fewer respondents, and for the social worker the respondents thought primarily of financial or other forms of environmental aid.

The study carried out for the Joint Commission on Mental Illness and Health by the Survey Research Center asked respondents what they had done when faced with an emotional problem. The person selected for help far more frequently than any other was the clergyman, 42 per cent, followed by the doctor, 29 per cent. Those who did visit a psychiatrist reported they were less satisfied with the help they received than were those who saw clergymen or physicians. Furthermore, most people described the ways they were helped in terms of comfort, reassurance, and advice rather than in terms of insight or change within themselves. The investigators also found that in the great majority of the cases clergymen and physicians did not refer these people to psychiatric specialists but handled the problem themselves, particularly so in the case of the clergy.

The crux of the problem in seeking help is the willingness of the individual concerned to utilize help and the availability of that help for him. Gurin, Veroff, and Feld characterized the help-seeking process as having three stages. First comes the definition of a problem as being a mental health problem; second, the translation of that definition into a decision to seek help; and finally, the selection of a particular therapeutic resource. Psychological orientation to the self and one's problems was found to have an effect at all three stages but to have greatest impact at the first stage, the initial perception of a problem as one of mental health. Facilitating factors in the environment were relevant to the second and third stages, and particularly to the selection of a particular therapeutic resource. Definition of a problem in mental health terms was associated with "introspection, with a structuring of distress in personal and interpersonal rather than external terms, with a self-questioning more than a dissatisfied or unhappy reaction toward life roles, with psychological rather than physical symptoms."[13] Women, younger people, and especially those with more education were the groups most likely to have this psychological orientation and thus were more ready for self-referral. Decision to seek help and selection of a source for that help differed among urban and rural groups, religious, income, and regional groups, showing the effect of facilitating factors. Here the investigators had in mind the availability of resources in the community, the extent of information about these resources, and social customs and group support for help-seeking behavior. For rural groups the professional facilities available are less numerous; lower-income groups cannot afford the fees of private psychiatrists; and conservative religious groups give more social support to the use of the clergy than psychological specialists.

Beliefs and attitudes about mental illness are important determinants of the perception of a problem in mental health terms, and to this point the material in the previous section is directly relevant. They help to shape the kind of psychological orientation that an individual has toward life. Beliefs and attitudes toward mental illness also concern facilities for helping those who are in emotional distress, and here the material in this section has been pertinent. Decision to seek help and the source selected will depend in part on knowledge about resources and favorable orientation toward the effect that professional help may have. A wide gap still exists between subgroups in the population in terms of beliefs and attitudes toward mental illness and between experts in the field and the general public. That the gap appears to be narrowing is our concern in the next section.

CHANGES IN BELIEFS AND ATTITUDES

Not all the respondents in the various studies have expressed the beliefs and attitudes toward mental disease which we outlined in the first section. Evidence is also available to indicate that the size of this minority is increasing, that certain forces are at work which slowly are bringing changes in perceptions of mental disease.

Age and education are two variables associated with change in attitudes, the younger and better educated individuals being more likely to show a humanitarian and scientific attitude toward the mentally ill.[14] In the NORC study the proportion of each educational group showing high scores on an index of psychological orientation was as follows: college educated—50 per cent, high school educated—30 per cent, and grade school educated—14 per cent.[15] However, finer analysis of the data shows that behind education are more important variables of *interest* and *experience.* When the group with a college education was divided into those who had both self-reports of high exposure to information about mental illness and acquaintance with someone who had been treated by a psychiatrist outside a hospital versus those who did not have these characteristics, the proportions on the index of psychological orientation were 74 and 41 per cent. Although education was important, it became much more so when variables of interest and experience were also present. It may well be that a college education provides a fertile ground for implanting new ideas, if this process is conducted in the right way. It is encouraging to know that the urban intellectual class has a rather strong psychological orientation, because in many aspects of American life here is where leadership for new ideas arises. Other members of the population with considerable education are a susceptible group to leadership by the urban intellectuals, and it is in this area that change is likely to first occur.

Elements of interest and experience are being fostered by a number of trends, not the least of which is the *growing use of community volunteers in mental hospitals.* Within the past fifteen years more and more hospitals, especially state institutions, have organized volunteer groups to visit with patients, work with them in recreational activities, and even take patients to their homes.[16] Many volunteers express surprise at the lack of violence in mental hospitals and at the eagerness with which patients respond to these advances from the world outside. In the process of working with patients and members of hospital staffs, there is an opportunity to learn more of the "facts" of mental illness and psychological theory. Only a small proportion of the population to be sure has been touched by volunteer work, but the programs in general have been successful.

A different trend, still in its infancy, can be found in the *organization of people who have been patients in mental hospitals.* Although one of the aims of such groups is the mutual support needed for rehabilitation in the community, other aims include the education of the public to new ideas about mental illness, to show that patients can "come back." Evaluation of the effects of these organizations is difficult at the present time, but a comparable situation can be found in the influence of Alcoholics Anonymous in changing attitudes toward alcoholism from moral degeneracy to the category of a disease. The fearlessness with which former alcoholics have spoken up to the public and explained their predicament has undoubtedly influenced attitudes. Similar results may occur through the actions of former mental patients.

Closely allied with these two trends is the *growing public and legislative concern about conditions in mental hospitals,* aided by the press and by magazines as well as community action groups. Inadequate staffing and depressive surroundings have made difficult the recovery of patients who possessed potential for return to normal life, thus confirming the stereotype that there is no return from mental illness. Indeed, those who handle patients in our large public hospitals have too often been imbued with the "Legend of Chronicity,"[17] lacking both the insight and motivation to start patients on the road to recovery. Starting in key hospitals in England and in the United States, new approaches and techniques in the treatment of psychotic patients have been coupled with increased financial resources from legislative bodies to produce higher discharge rates and more humanitarian treatment for patients who must remain. Mental patients and mental hospitals are thus presented in a different light, one of the important first steps in the rearrangement of the psychological field that leads to changes in beliefs and attitudes.

Accelerated research, especially in the development of new drugs, is still another important trend that will likely contribute to change of attitudes. The tranquilizers have made it possible for many patients to be treated in the physician's office rather than in the mental hospital. Often they can recover without the social stigma of being committed to the hospital. Many of those who are hospitalized can recover faster, can utilize psychotherapy better, and reenter the community more successfully. All of this helps to foster the idea that mental illness can be cured like other kinds of disease. Certain of the fear-inducing aspects of mental illness are thereby reduced, making stereotypes more amenable to change.

Research is contributing in another way, by making mental diseases scientifically more understandable. Neurophysiological and biochemical investigations in conjunction with psychological and sociological approaches are beginning to piece together the psychobiologic unity of the organism. As this picture becomes more complete, there is less ground for holding to the moral-rational view of normal and abnormal human behavior, and more reason for putting it on an objective cause-and-effect basis. Results and implications of these investigations are disseminated but slowly to the bulk of the population; yet we must not discount the great interest of the public in newspaper and magazine articles on matters of health and disease and the growing sophistication in such matters. Communication barriers are much lower than was the case even twenty years ago. Again the psychological field for many people is being rearranged.

Finally, *changes in medical education* are contributing to changes in attitudes of younger physicians toward mental disease and toward psychiatry. Medical students today find that a greater proportion of their time is devoted to psychiatry, both in lectures and in contacts with patients. In many schools this study begins during the preclinical years, emphasizing modern psychological theory and the roots of abnormal behavior. By the time a student deals with patients, both diagnostically and therapeutically, he has a background of theory not true of medical students twenty-five years ago. In diagnosis more emphasis is placed on understanding the psychodynamics in the case than in attaching a diagnostic label, and many students have an opportunity to follow through on their analysis of personality factors through the process of psychotherapy. Not only is psychiatry as a medical specialty drawing more able candidates, but students who will enter other specialties or general practice are learning how to use the psychiatrist more constructively. The long-range effect of the reorientation in medical education will be to bring about changes in attitude on the part of the physician's patients. The high regard with which the doctor is invested means that the attitude he expresses toward mental disease will not be taken lightly by his patients. At the "grass roots level" the younger physicians may thus contribute to a rearrangement of the psychological field of many people *vis-à-vis* mental disease.

IMPLICATIONS AND CONCLUSIONS

Cultural lag is the key term in the implications of the material we have discussed in this chapter, lag between the leaders of scientific medicine, both professionals and laymen, and large sections of the public. There are discrepancies in beliefs and attitudes about mental illness that markedly affect perceptions of deviant behavior. Varying perceptions mean alternate behaviors in securing advice, planning for treatment, rehabilitating patients, and reacting to community programs of education and prevention. The sophisticated physician, social worker, nurse, or public health specialist will not always perceive mental disease in the same manner as those he or she seeks to treat or influence.

To be more specific, consideration must be given to the beliefs and attitudes of the public toward mental disease in mental health programs. The project in Prairie Town indicated that the educational team and the public were operating on two different sets of premises, a situation that led to rigidity rather than change. Star has phrased it by saying that we are in a transition period where the modern *definition* of mental illness has been widely disseminated without anything like an equal acceptance of the point of view about the nature of mental illness and about the factors in human personality that support the term. As yet, most people are not able to work with this new definition within the context of their traditional beliefs about human behavior, or within the context of the belief about "medical" diseases of the type caused by bacteria, viruses, or other specific entities. Star suggests that the better part of valor may be to place less emphasis on educating people about mental disease and more emphasis on talking about normal behavior, about how people develop and the reasons for everyday behavior. Concurrently, the suggestions of Nunnally and Osgood are relevant, that effort should be expended on the development of a new set of terms for talking about mental disease and for continued research on the context in which mental health information should be incorporated. These tasks will not be easy, but in line with some of the trends noted earlier, a reorientation may occur that will lead eventually to acceptance of new beliefs and attitudes about mental disease.

Those who deal with patients and their families rather than community programs can find implications here for their everyday work. Resistance to a physician's exploration of emotional factors in a disease, to committing a family member to a mental hospital, or to following through on advice for psychiatric consultation cannot be chalked up to stupidity or superstition. Behind the resistance are real attitudes that are consistent and tenacious, and recognition of their reality will be the first step in devising treatment programs around them.

Perhaps the most important implication applies to health professionals themselves. It is our contention that in beliefs and attitudes toward mental disease there is much pressure from the folk medical approach rather than from scientific medicine, and that the effect extends to some members of the health professions as well as to the laity. A curious and difficult contradiction then occurs in the perceptions of those who are unwittingly influenced by folk medical beliefs. The scientific and folk medical approaches to disease, and to mental disease in particular, are incompatible and where a practitioner attempts to utilize both, side by side, the best medical care cannot be rendered the patient.

NOTES TO CHAPTER 5

1. The material presented in this chapter is limited to one society, that of the United States. Cross cultural variation in the definitions of mental illness and in attitudes and reactions toward it constitutes an extensive field of investigation. People in other societies may regard certain forms of behavior such as trances or hallucinations as being signs of unusual or magical powers rather than as pathological states. To a certain extent, the "normal" is a relative matter. There are problems in conceptualizing this cross cultural variability relative to mental illness that the author felt were not germane to the main theme of this chapter, thus a decision was made not to include cross cultural material here. The reader is referred, however, to several sources: Opler, Marvin K., editor, *Culture and Mental Health*, Macmillan Co., New York, 1959; Opler, Marvin K., *Culture, Psychiatry and Human Values*, Charles C Thomas, Springfield, Ill., 1956; Linton, Ralph, *Culture and Mental Disorders*, Charles C Thomas, Springfield, Ill., 1956; and Klineberg, Otto, *Social Psychology*, rev. ed., Henry Holt and Co., New York, 1954.

2. George Warren Brown School of Social Work, *Summary of Thesis Research, 1949–1950*, Washington University, St. Louis, Mo., 1951; *Ibid.*, *Summary of Thesis Research, 1950–1951*, Washington University, 1952.

3. Middleton, John, "Prejudices and Opinions of Mental Hospital Employees Regarding Mental Illness," *American Journal of Psychiatry*, vol. 110, August, 1953, pp. 133–138.

4. Branch, C. H. Hardin, "Utah's Experience with the National Draft Act for Hospitalization of the Mentally Ill," *American Journal of Psychiatry*, vol. 109, November, 1952, pp. 336–343.

5. A complete analysis of the findings of the study will be published shortly in book form by Shirley A. Star of the National Opinion Research Center staff. In the meantime, the reader is referred to two papers by Dr. Star: "The Public's Idea About Mental Illness," presented to the Annual Meeting of the National Association for Mental Health, Indianapolis, Indiana, November 5, 1955, and "The Place of Psychiatry in Popular Thinking," presented to the Annual Meeting of the American Association for Public Opinion Research, Washington, May 9, 1957.

6 Institute of Communications Research, "The Development and Change of Popular Conceptions About Mental Health," Summary Report, University of Illinois, Urbana, Ill., April, 1958. Co-directors of the project were Dr. J. C. Nunnally and Dr. C. E. Osgood. An overall report of the study is to be found in Nunnally, Jum C., Jr., *Popular Conceptions of Mental Health*, Holt, Rinehart and Winston, New York, 1961.

7. For further discussion of the Semantic Differential, see Osgood, Charles E., George J. Suci, and Percy H. Tannenbaum, *The Measurement of Meaning*, University of Illinois Press, Urbana, Ill., 1957. Also reference to *Psychological Abstracts* or current psychological journals will provide results by other investigators and further studies by the Institute for Communications Research.

8. Gurin, Gerald, Joseph Veroff, and Sheila Feld, *Americans View Their Mental Health.* Basic Books, New York, 1960.

9. Cumming, John, and Elaine Cumming, "Mental Health Education in a Canadian Community" in Paul, Benjamin D., editor, *Health, Culture, and Community.* Russell Sage Foundation, New York, 1955, pp. 43–69.

10. *Ibid.*, pp. 55–56.

11. See Huxley, Aldous L., *The Devils of Loudun*, Harper and Bros., New York, 1952. Also, if the reader is interested in the handling of mental illness in primitive tribes, he is referred to Ackerknecht, Erwin H., "Psychopathology, Primitive Medicine, and Primitive Culture," *Bulletin of the History of Medicine*, vol. 14, June, 1943, pp. 30–67.

12. Saunders, Lyle, personal communication.

13. Gurin, Gerald, Joseph Veroff, and Sheila Feld, *op. cit.*, p. 298.

14. Woodward, Julian L., "Changing Ideas on Mental Illness and Its Treatment," *American Sociological Review*, vol. 16, August, 1951, pp. 443–454; Whatley, Charles D., "Social Attitudes Toward Discharged Mental Patients," *Social Problems*, vol. 6, Spring, 1959, pp. 313–320; Freeman, Howard E., and Gene G., Kassebaum, "The Relationship of Education and Knowledge to Opinions about Mental Illness," *Mental Hygiene*, vol. 44, January, 1960, pp. 42–47; Freeman, Howard E., "Attitudes Toward Mental Illness Among Relatives of Former Patients," *American Sociological Review*, vol. 26, February, 1961, pp. 59–66.

15. Star, Shirley, personal communication.

16. von Mering, Otto, and Stanley H. King, *Remotivating the Mental Patient*. Russell Sage Foundation, New York, 1957. The reader is referred specifically to Chapter 8, Social Self-Renewal and Community Volunteers. Another analysis of volunteer activity will be found in Greenblatt, Milton, Otto von Mering, J. Lawrence Dohan, and David Kantor, "The Use of Volunteers and Other Community Resources," in Greenblatt, Milton, and Richard Williams, editors, *The Patient and the Mental Hospital*, The Free Press, Glencoe, Ill., 1957.

17. von Mering, Otto, and Stanley H King, *op. cit.*

PART THREE

THE PEOPLE THAT TREAT DISEASE

Chapter 6

The Physician

How varied is the healing art and how different are those who practice it? A medicine man from one of the primitive tribes of Central Africa, arrayed in feather anklets and wristlets, wearing a brightly painted, grotesque mask, leaps and shouts over his patient. A *curandera* from the hill country of Mexico, a woman wise in the lore of herbs and of magic, lays the split, fresh carcass of a pigeon over the painful belly of her patient while water is being boiled to brew a special herbal tea. A senior resident in a large Boston hospital, attired in crisp white coat, with pen and flashlight clipped in his breast pocket and a stethoscope dangling from his neck, intently percusses the chest and back of his patient. Each is carrying out in characteristic manner the prescriptions of a specialized role within his society.

Nearly all societies have specific roles for the diagnosis and care of the sick. In simple societies one or two roles may fill the need, while in more complex structures a great number of interacting roles may be needed. Contrast the medicine man, unique in his society, with the resident who in the course of his work will deal with special subcategories within his general role as a physician, with surgeons, radiologists, allergists, anesthetists, psychiatrists, to mention only a few. But he also works in an intimate way with nurses and orderlies, laboratory technicians, pharmacists, and hospital administrators. Even beyond this he competes for patients with the chiropractor, and sometimes even with the faith healer.

Most societies define clearly the rights and duties of those roles concerned with the treatment of disease, for disease and illness pose a direct threat to life and to the future of the society. To entrust responsibility to certain individuals for treatment of disease is a move that must be guarded by careful definition of what society expects of them, what they can do and cannot do, the privileges they are allowed, and the responsibilities they must bear. Role analysis of the people who treat disease, and of those who work with them or for them is therefore crucial to an understanding of factors that bear upon perception of illness and the kind of behavior anticipated at such times. We will expect to find generalized role patterns in any society for those who treat disease, but we will also expect to find some variations in the way the general role is perceived by different groups within the society. Inconsistencies or incongruities in role perception will have importance for misunderstandings and difficulties in the relationship between the healer and his patient.

The main feature of the chapters in Part Three will be an analysis of the rights and duties, the demands and expectations of various roles in our society that bear upon the treatment of disease. In turn, we will discuss the physician, the nurse, and medical social worker. After looking at the generalized social role expectations for each, we will discuss features of the role that may produce distortions of perception, either by the individual that fills the role or by the patient, or perhaps by both. At the same time we will look at the relationships between various roles, the doctor and nurse, or nurse and social worker, for example; and analyze the conflicts that may occur, indicating the implications for patient care.

Although the emphasis will be upon role definition, other determinants of perception will be important in understanding variations within roles. Psychogenic needs and ego-adaptive mechanisms, social class and ethnic groups, and values all bear upon the material in this section.

GENERALIZED FEATURES OF THE PHYSICIAN'S ROLE

A major professional role in American society, that of the physician is ranked high in terms of prestige and power. Studies of the relative prestige attached to various professions and occupations, such as those of physician, judge, clergyman, schoolteacher, scientist, nurse, engineer, and many others, show quite consistently that the physician appears near or at the top of the list. In general, feelings toward the physician contain a mixture of affection, respect, awe, and reverence, but often also include some hostility. The latter may not be clearly expressed, or always conscious; however, inasmuch as it occurs, the question of ambivalence toward the physician must also be considered. We will return to this topic after analyzing the demands and expectations of the generalized role of the physician.

Among social scientists Talcott Parsons has dealt most specifically with the theoretical aspects of the physician's role, defining it in terms of *high technical competence, emotional neutrality, and collectivity orientation.*[1] Becoming a doctor is an achieved role, requiring the special ability of superior intelligence, probably even a certain kind of intelligence that has more of the skills found in mathematics and the natural sciences. The amount of formal education necessary for the degree of Doctor of Medicine is as great as for any profession, but beyond graduation from medical school training as an intern and often as a resident is necessary before the physician has the necessary technical competence expected of his role. Furthermore, a person cannot achieve the role of physician merely because he is wealthy, or comes from the right family, or is a member of a certain ethnic group. He is not automatically admitted to medicine because his father happens to be a doctor. To be sure, coming from the right social group or family and having a father in medicine will help a person toward medical school, but achievement of the role comes only if he has the special abilities required.

The practice of scientific medicine has become highly complex, requiring knowledge of procedures and drugs, requiring techniques that are beyond the experience of the layman, even considering the significant increase in knowledge about disease and about medicine in the general population. The physician, therefore, has access to a body of knowledge and skills unavailable to others. The implications of high technical competence for the perception of the physician by the patient and his family are quite direct. Illness is frightening, especially when it is unexpected and severe, and in a culture that is not dominated by fatalism. Having someone with the ability to handle the threat of illness is most reassuring to the patient's family. Almost any person can recount the feeling of relief, the lifting of a load, when the doctor comes. The symptoms of the patient may be unchanged, even grow worse, but no longer pose the stress they did before the physician's arrival.

Emotional neutrality is expected behavior for an applied scientist, a term most applicable to the physician. As an applied scientist he must look at a given set of facts as objectively as possible. He must not let emotional factors interfere in his diagnosis and plans for treatment. One of the implications of emotional neutrality is that the physician is not supposed to refuse a patient because he does not like him or does not agree with him on some matter. Also, he is not supposed to judge the patient on moral grounds. Another implication is that the physician should not treat members of his own family, at least in cases that are serious or complicated. The shift from role as father or husband, where emotional involvement is part of the pattern of expectations, to role as physician where emotional neutrality is the expectation, cannot be made easily and often is impossible. To be sure, the physician often must treat members of his family when other doctors are not available or time is of the essence, but it is a stress that is generally avoided. To the same extent many patients prefer a doctor with whom they have little social contact, although here the problem of emotional neutrality is not the only reason, as we shall see shortly.

In addition to scientific objectivity the physician must be aware that the patient is a person with feelings, someone important in his own right. An element of concern, therefore, is important in the role expectation along with the control of emotion. This has led Fox[2] to suggest that the term "detached concern" may be applicable to the physician's role under many circumstances. Both emotional neutrality and detached concern are applicable to the physician and each will be used in the following pages as seems more pertinent.

In common with certain other professional roles, that of the physician can be characterized as collectivity-oriented, or other-oriented, rather than self-oriented. Our particular society can be described broadly as one that fosters self-orientation. Competitive capitalism emphasizes the acquisition of individual gain through dealings with other members of society. In the business world each party to the situation is expected to be oriented to the rational pursuit of his own self-interests. As an example, we might cite the activities of the potential buyer of a new car who shops from one dealer to another looking for the best buy. The various salesmen will try to set a price that assures as much profit as possible and still enables them to make a sale.

Contrasting with the self-orientation of the market place, the health professions must put the welfare of the patient first, before self-interest. Thus, we speak of the physician as being in a service or helping profession. In large part the other-orientation of the physician is due to the vulnerability of the patient to exploitation, vulnerable because he may be physically helpless, incompetent to treat himself, and too emotionally concerned to make rational decisions. Society expects that the physician will not exploit that vulnerability but will give priority in his actions to the interests of the patient.

Emphasis on other-orientation does not deny to the physician the possibility of comfortable, even large income, but if the wealth is expressed in an ostentatious manner, or if the doctor overemphasizes money by charging high fees, most people will feel that the ideal of other-orientation has in some way become tarnished. Conflicts between other and self-orientation usually center on money in one form or another and may be illustrated by a case that occurred a few years ago when a young boy was trapped when a well caved in. Rescue efforts took several days and involved the labors of a number of people and the use of expensive equipment. Regular bulletins on television and in the newspapers kept the country informed of progress. During all the rescue operation and for some time afterward a local physician was in almost constant attendance. Later, after a sizable fund had been raised by neighbors and interested citizens to help the family meet the expenses incurred, the doctor sent a large bill. However, a storm of protest, some of which came from within the medical profession, forced a withdrawal of the physician's bill. In a situation which society defined as calling for other-orientation in the extreme, it was not considered legitimate for anyone to send a bill, even when it meant considerable financial sacrifice on the part of those who participated in the rescue. Although the physician might justifiably feel that the hundred hours or more of his time deserved recompense, he did not realize that the ordinary other-oriented expectations of his role coincided with a social situation that required such behavior to a high degree of all participants.

The sanctions against advertising, sanctions imposed by physicians themselves rather than other members of society, grow out of the emphasis on orientation toward others rather than primarily toward the self. Only in recent years have the names of participating physicians been given in news releases of unusual operations or dramatic cases.

Emphasis on other-orientation is an aspect of the role of the physician that is subject to much pressure and strain. Both physicians and their patients are often ambivalent about the business as compared with the service aspects of medical practice, and with increasing separation of many physicians from close daily contact with their patients it is easy to neglect service considerations. In addition, the physician is caught up in the general trend that emphasizes higher wages, consumer goods, better housing, and activities to fill leisure time, all things that go with the high standard of living in the United States today. Having sacrificed money and time for his education, the physician feels that he is due an adequate return in money. Not only is there a potential conflict with society's expectations of other-oriented behavior, but there are potential psychological conflicts in the doctor-patient relationship, as we shall see later.

Two additional factors are of considerable psychological importance in understanding the demands and expectations of the physician's role. The first is the *necessity for access to the body of the patient and to intimate details of his life.* In order to make a diagnosis on a scientifically justifiable basis, the physician assumes the right to examine by various means any aspect of his patient's anatomy. He also assumes the right to ask the patient any question that might bear on an understanding of the case. These are fearsome privileges, not given lightly by any society, and ours is no exception. In fact, these "privileges" of the role run counter to our rather strong emphasis on modesty and inviolacy of the individual. Protection is needed, therefore, against the potential threats created by allowance of access to body and intimate details of life. One protection is already built into the role, that of emotional neutrality. The physician is first and foremost an objective scientist; he regards the patient's body and personal life as a case to be studied and weighed on the evidence of the facts he can obtain. Therefore, emotional involvement with the patient, or moral judgment about his activities, are ruled out.

A further protection is provided through the emphasis on professional confidence, legally a privileged communication, which assures the patient that whatever he reveals to his physician will not be repeated in public. It may be transmitted to other doctors, but such action is within the circle of professional confidence. The physician who is inclined to betray this trust, perhaps through inadvertently discussing his cases with a wife who likes to gossip, finds that the sanctions of society and of organized medicine are often harsh and unbending.

The need for access to the patient and the protective devices which are erected to contain its threat can lead to strains in the doctor-patient relationship. In some ways it is easier for the physician to fill his role if he perceives the patient more as a case than as a person; yet the impersonal approach often runs counter to the emphasis on disease as affecting the whole person and on treating the psyche as well as the soma, and counter to deep psychological needs for love and affection on the part of both the doctor and patient. This theoretical dilemma has not yet been satisfactorily solved in medical practice and will occur in other contexts throughout this book.

The second factor of psychological importance is that the physician is almost continuously in contact with pain, suffering, and death, not only of his patients but also in the reactions of members of the patients' families. There are few roles in our society so constituted. That of the nurse is one; yet there is a crucial difference, for the nurse does not assume ultimate *responsibility* for diagnosis and treatment of the patient. The patient's life is not in her hands to the extent that it is entrusted to the physician. Moreover, she experiences a sharp break between contact with patients and the rest of her life, a break dictated largely by the clock. When she goes "off duty" she steps into a different world. Except for certain kinds of specialists, the dermatologist for example, the doctor is able to separate little of his life from that of his patients.

Other roles that deal with suffering and death are those of the mortician and clergyman. The former, however, deals with death after it has happened, and then with a business approach that enables him to separate emotions from his job to a large extent. The clergyman, on the other hand, approaches death with the message of immortality and life beyond the grave, something that the physician's role, with its emphasis on scientific objectivity, prevents him from doing. To the physician each death means a limitation of medical knowledge in general or a failure of his skill.

Continuous contact with suffering and death is likely to conflict with strong psychogenic needs for inviolacy and harm-avoidance and to arouse anxiety. The physician first deals with the problem in medical school, when as a student he may find in himself the symptoms of each new disease he studies. The experience is so common that it is regarded as one of the normal "rites of passage" in becoming a doctor. In the ordinary course of events, the physician has many more successes than failures, and the emotional return of good will and affection from his patients offsets the burden of responsibility and of anxiety. Most physicians, therefore, come to handle very ably the threats imposed by the constant association with suffering and death. For the insecure individual, however, the threats may be too severe and lead to ego mechanisms that find their expression in gruffness, marked impersonality toward patients, and callousness toward pain in himself as well as others. When this occurs we see the relationship between the social aspects of a role, the exposure of the physician to suffering and death, and personal needs like inviolacy and harmavoidance.

Prestige: Asset and Liability

Returning again to one of the thoughts expressed at the beginning of this chapter, the prestige granted to members of the medical profession is compounded of affection, awe, respect, and reverence. These feelings grow out of the aspects of the physician's role which we have just discussed: superior knowledge, almost to the point of the physician's being viewed as a wonder worker, interest in people and their troubles, and a willingness to assume responsibility for matters of potentially great threat to the individual, literally matters of life and death.

There is reason to suggest that the doctor has a good deal of what Weber has called "charismatic authority." Weber[3] thought of charisma as an extraordinary quality possessed by persons or objects that is thought to give these persons or objects a unique, magical power. An individual possessing charisma is set apart from ordinary men and treated as endowed with supernatural, superhuman, or at least specifically exceptional powers or qualities. These are not available to the ordinary person, and the individual concerned is treated as a leader. Weber speaks of charisma as inhering in individuals because of their personalities and powers, but he also defines it as an attribute that can be "depersonalized" and can inhere in an office or institution regardless of the person involved. A priest of the Roman Catholic Church possesses charisma as an attribute of his office, and the power is not affected by the personal qualities of the priest himself. In other words, this power is part of the role.

As an attribute of the role itself, the physician carries charismatic power, having qualities that are extraordinary and apart from ordinary men. Indeed, there is more than a bit of magical feeling about the role. In Weber's terms the charisma has become depersonalized and is an attribute of the role or office itself rather than the personality of a particular individual.

As Lee has pointed out,[4] the great prestige afforded the physician has both assets and liabilities. One of the chief assets lies in the willingness of patients to follow the doctor's advice rather than to trust to their own devices, "doctor's orders" it is called. The physician has a social support that grants him considerable freedom of effort in dealing with disease. He can devote his full energies to fighting disease rather than draining off part of his energy in vying with other kinds of people for the right to treat patients or trying to get the patient to accept his advice.

Another asset lies in the very power ascribed to the physician. Many doctors are of the opinion that for a great number of their patients the task is a mobilization of natural forces in the body toward health. Although they can aid this process by drugs, surgery, or manipulation of the body in various ways, they also contribute by the kind of motivation they give the patient by helping him feel that once he is in the hands of a doctor he will get well. The wise physician well knows that the practice of medicine involves much more than a knowledge of anatomy, disease symptoms, and drugs.

A final asset of the prestige afforded is the return it provides to the physician for the difficulties of his job, for the heavy responsibilities he is willing to undertake, and for the almost continuous contact with suffering and death. As we have pointed out, one of the components of prestige is affection. In his study conducted for the California Medical Association of the doctor-patient relationship, Dichter[5] called attention to the fact that the physician has strong needs for feelings of affection and gratitude by his patients, to be loved and admired, and when these are not expressed, he is severely disturbed. By and large, doctors receive expressions of affection and gratitude to the extent granted to few other roles. In the structuring of roles, society must build in rewards for the strains that go with the performance of certain roles. For the physician prestige is one of the most valuable rewards he receives.

The liabilities associated with high prestige are not so obvious to members of the medical profession and are often a source of frustration to the unsuspecting physician. High prestige means high expectations and ideals, and deviation from the ideals results in stronger blame or censure than for those who are not placed on quite so high a pedestal. Scandals about fee splitting, convictions for malpractice, and political lobbying that runs counter to changing public attitudes toward medical care are viewed with alarm that is proportionate to the prestige granted. The gruffness of a doctor who is tired from a long day's work, unwillingness to tell the patient details of his illness or treatment, high fees for what the patient feels are minor procedures, reluctance to make night calls, long waits in a doctor's office even when the doctor is on an appointment schedule—all are bits of behavior that seem normal and justified to the physician, yet call forth bitter criticism from his patients. For the giving of high prestige the patient expects ideal behavior in return, and is quite disturbed when it is not forthcoming.

A second liability lies in the uneasiness people experience in granting so much power and prestige to any one group. This point can perhaps best be discussed by putting it under the heading of *ambivalence*, the mixture of strong positive and negative emotions toward the same object. One wag has defined ambivalence as watching your mother-in-law drive over a cliff in your brand new Cadillac convertible. Though crudely put, it reflects the intensity with which emotions can be held when a person is ambivalent. When a great deal of power and prestige is granted to someone else, there are usually unconscious feelings of jealousy that accompany it, of a wish to share some of the power that is granted, and of a fear of the consequences of the power should it be misused. Thus, although most people admire and look up to the physician, they often feel hostile toward him, often for only slight cause. Furthermore, if the admiration and affection which is given to the physician is not returned in the form of a personal interest in the patient, a symbolic expression of returned affection, the feelings of hostility can be heightened.

The prototype situation for the ambivalent reaction toward the doctor is the parent-child relationship, especially with the father. One of the lasting insights of psychoanalysis has been the delineation of both love and hate toward the father as one of the aspects of normal personality development. Usually the feelings of love are sufficiently strong so that the hostile reactions can be controlled and later sublimated in activities directed toward achieving independence from the family. The psychoanalysts have pointed to the power which the child sees his father possess, to the wish to share some of that power, and to the fears which the child has that the power might be used against him as indeed it sometimes is for disciplinary purposes.

No one will be surprised by the statement that the physician often fills a fatherlike role for the patient and for the public at large. He has in certain situations the responsibility for life and death, for giving or withholding favors, for making decisions that are crucial to the future of the patient. Weston La Barre,[6] the anthropologist, describes the situation as one where even grown men with power and responsibility in the outside world are required to submit without question, like a child, to the authority and decisions of the doctor. Although there is an increasing emphasis in medical care upon requesting the patient's cooperation and upon allowing him to question treatment plans, the emotional reaction involving submission also operates. If the patient does not follow "doctor's orders" the physician is justifiably disturbed, and other members of society feel that the patient through his disobedience does not deserve their sympathy. Further, the physician's role is defined as one that puts the welfare of others above his own interests. It is no surprise then that people should react emotionally to the physician, much as they have reacted toward their fathers, and in the course of this reaction show a good deal of ambivalence.

Not only is the role of the physician in the United States characterized by high technical competence, emotional neutrality or detached concern, other-orientedness, need for access to the body of the patient, almost continuous contact with suffering and death, and built-in features of ambivalence, but it also has what we might call *rugged individualism.* In his study of physicians for the California Medical Association, Dichter[7] noted that in interview after interview the doctor said he had chosen the profession of medicine in order to be free, and this usually meant free from interference. The difficulties of medical school and the time required to complete a medical training only served to enhance the feeling of the right to be independent. The firm and often militant resistance of American physicians toward what they perceive as control of medical practice by governmental agencies or private corporations can be explained in large measures by this aspect of the role. That present-day patients are more often challenging the right of the doctor to be fiercely independent is at least one reason for some of the slow changes that are occurring in the structure of medical practice.

The particular pattern of relationship among the variables which we have discussed will differ from one physician to another. They cannot be used to predict the behavior of any one individual in a definitive way, but they do help to set the framework within which general perception and behavior of the physician occurs.

AUXILIARY CHARACTERISTICS IN THE PHYSICIAN'S ROLE

Age, sex, ethnic background, race, religion, dress, mode of living, and numerous other variables of this sort come to be associated with professional roles in our society, especially with those holding high prestige. Everett C. Hughes of Brandeis University has referred to these factors as a complex of *auxiliary characteristics* that grow up around a particular role and affect the perception of its incumbents.[8] At the least they provide a kind of ideal picture that people carry in their minds, and in the choice of a physician they may bear more weight than the doctor's technical competence, which is largely unknown to the patient. Hughes notes that the Protestant physician of Old American stock is acceptable on principle to a greater variety of patients than is the doctor who departs from this pattern in some notable characteristic.

The complex of auxiliary characteristics becomes embedded in stereotypes that find their expression in ordinary talk, in cartoons, the movies, fiction, and television. Looking back to the past century, one of the important auxiliary characteristics was the wearing of a beard, a symbol of wisdom growing out of experience. Woe to the young physician whose capacity for beard growing was below par. The surgeon of today as seen in movies is handsome, socially poised, young of face but graying about the temples. Except in problem dramas, one does not see Negro physicians, or women, or those who have so-called Jewish features; or when these do participate, the setting is usually that of the research laboratory rather than the examining room.

Although the public has a certain perception of the doctor based on the complex of auxiliary characteristics, it is the colleague group, the fraternity of physicians, that works out the picture most intricately.[9] Specifically, the set of auxiliary characteristics is used in establishing membership in the "inner fraternity," the group that exercises so much control over the admission of new candidates to the role and the professional advancement of those who have already been accepted. Colleagues in medicine are competitors, and the appearance of competitors who do not follow the expected type is likely to arouse greater anxiety and hostility than those who are like oneself in essential characteristics. Measures to control those who deviate from the expected type result in a certain amount of social segregation, to the laboratory, or selected specialties, or to chosen hospitals and clinics, measures that serve among other things to perpetuate for both physician and patient the stereotype of expected characteristics.

Hughes describes the clash between the expected auxiliary characteristics and characteristics that deviate from the norm as *contradictions* or *dilemmas of status*. The most extreme dilemma arises in the case of the Negro physician. The white physician does not know whether to treat his Negro colleague as a professional equal or as a Negro. In the latter case there are numerous unwritten rules of behavior and expectations that conflict with the sharing of confidences part of the brotherhood of doctors. The dilemma is usually solved by keeping the relationship formal and specific to medical situations, and to shun other contacts with his Negro colleague. If the white physician has sufficient experience and prestige, he may act as a consultant to Negro colleagues in Negro hospitals or clinics, but the reverse is seldom observed.

Dilemmas occur in relation to other auxiliary characteristics like sex, ethnic group, and religion. By and large they have been solved until recently by the use of quota systems in medical schools, by confining women to specialties such as pediatrics or psychiatry, and by the growth of strictly Jewish and Catholic hospitals and clinics. The social segregation is maintained through the selection of interns and residents for house staffs and through the referral system with patients.

The inequities which one can observe as a result of auxiliary characteristics may not always be due to conscious discrimination. Members of minority groups go through a process of social conditioning in which their expectations for achievement may be affected and reduced initiative may result. The process is complex but the end result, from whatever means, can be seen in the network of relationships among health professionals.

Research data in the area of auxiliary characteristics are not extensive, but some studies are available as support for the points made above. The problem of the woman physician, for example, has been investigated by Josephine J. Williams,[10] who used a sample of 100 middle-class women and one class in a medical school. Middle-class women were selected because Williams concluded that it was by this group that a woman would have to be accepted in order to build up a good practice. In her sample the first choice of a physician by the average patient was an experienced, recommended man of the same faith as the patient. The respondents were agreed that it would be ridiculous for patients of either sex to object to a male physician. Only 13 of the subjects in the study gave a woman physician as first choice.

Data from the medical students showed that half the men in the class thought women were less stable emotionally than men, and most of them were of the opinion that men were better surgeons. These findings pointed to the fact that some physicians feel women are at a biological disadvantage in medicine, especially where one of the generalized features of the role of the physician is emotional neutrality.

Further data came from a survey of graduates of medical schools in the United States between 1925 and 1940, made by

Dykman and Stalnaker.[11] To summarize some of their findings, most women physicians practiced on a full or part-time basis but did not equal men in the volume of work. Men had relatively higher incomes, a greater number of hospital appointments, published writings, and memberships in professional societies, all marks of prestige in the profession. Women physicians were more likely than men to be on salaried employment. As might be expected, a significantly greater proportion of the women had been inactive professionally for periods of time since receiving the medical degree, a turn of events often caused by pregnancy or family problems. Finally, it is interesting to note that 64 per cent of the women physicians would recommend medicine as a career for a daughter, as compared to 35 per cent of the men. In spite of some deficiencies in social rewards, a large proportion appeared to be satisfied to the point of recommending it to one of the closest members of the family.

The reactions of a woman medical student at Harvard Medical School of the Class of 1955 highlight the dilemma faced by members of her sex. Bear in mind that only in recent years did Harvard admit women to the medical school, and then it was the climax of a long history of pressures and controversy.[12] The student, June Pryor, writes in the *Harvard Medical Alumni Bulletin* as follows:

> At the present time there is much individual variation in the feelings of fellow students and Faculty toward women in medicine. Many still reflect the conservative attitudes of the past decades. It is gratifying, however, to find that many others do not consider our presence a gross indelicacy, a regrettable break with tradition or an indication of sad psychological failure. We are sure that many of our classmates are all for us; however, somehow we get the general impression that others are not. Some were afraid that we would use our femininity to obtain special favors, prize patients, and the like. One recently voiced argument was that the presence of females inhibited the instructors to the regrettable point that dirty jokes were eliminated from the curriculum, thus abolishing what they assumed to be a most valuable mnemonic device. (To my way of thinking there is little evidence that this disaster has befallen us.)[13]

The career conflict undoubtedly contributes a great deal to the continuation of discrimination against women in medicine, for it is difficult to fill the role of physician and the roles of mother and wife and to meet all the expectations of each role. Regarding the woman physician who marries and devotes a good deal of energy to her roles as wife and mother, other doctors may feel that the time and expense involved in medical education has been largely wasted. They are inclined to argue that the limited facilities of medical education should be reserved for those who will utilize their training to the fullest.

The career dilemma for the woman physician can be resolved by a decision not to marry, and indeed Dykman and Stalnaker found that about 40 per cent of the women physicians were not married at the time of the study as compared to 5 per cent of the men. Partial resolution can be made by a decision not to engage in full-time practice. The latter, of course, strengthens the feelings of some physicians that it is a waste of time to give women a medical education. When women do enter medicine, anticipation of the career conflict and the expectation of marriage may lead them to seek salaried appointments rather than private practice, a hypothesis again borne out by the Dykman and Stalnaker data. The risks of private practice are not to be entered into lightly until one is sure that marriage is out of the question, a certainty that most women do not reach until it may be too late for the establishment of a successful private practice.

Salaried appointments often involve research tasks or institutional appointments where the doctor does not come in contact with the public as much as in private practice. The dilemma of the career conflict therefore contributes to a continuation of the expected set of auxiliary characteristics of the physician, part of which is that the role be filled by a man.

The role of women in medicine differs as one moves from one society to another, and the foregoing remarks should be regarded only as generally applicable to the United States. In Mark Field's interesting study of the sociology of medicine in Soviet Russia,[14] he notes that 75 per cent of the physicians in 1955 were women, as against 10 per cent forty years earlier. Behind this change lie a number of factors. For one thing, the Soviet regime has fostered equality of opportunity for women and men throughout society, encouraging women to do heavy manual labor, to fight in wartime, and to be educated in the various professions. At the same time, the role of physician has received much lower prestige than engineering, science, and industrial management. Manual workers often command higher rates of pay than the average doctor, while scientists and engineers have, in addition to higher pay, many of the "extras" in the Soviet system, such as better housing, a car, and vacations in special areas. Medicine as a career has therefore not been as attractive to men as other professions, and owing to the long-standing shortage of medical personnel, women have been welcomed with open arms.

The sample of emigrés who constituted the source of much of Field's data were questioned about their feelings concerning the competence of men and women doctors in Russia, and half indicated that the illness and the physician were the controlling factors. One-fifth had no opinion on the subject, but among the rest the vote was seven to one in favor of men. Apparently the woman physician finds a growing acceptance of equal competence with her male colleagues.

At the same time, women are much less likely than men to hold high positions in the medical hierarchy of the Soviet medical system. Among physicians holding high rank, four out of five were men. When Field visited Soviet Russia in 1956, it was his impression that most high administrative and clinical posts were held by men. The career conflict undoubtedly plays a part here, but we also must not discount the long-standing stereotype of the physician as a man and the reluctance of men to place women above them in administrative structures. Therefore, even in one society where women dominate medicine numerically, they still face problems of discrimination, and sex as an auxiliary characteristic is still a determinant of perception.

A further study of the importance of auxiliary characteristics in moving through the medical career comes from a report by Oswald Hall,[15] based on a set of interviews with representatives of the medical profession in an eastern American city.

From the autobiographical material Hall obtained, it was apparent that an "inner fraternity" of doctors existed, based on religious and ethnic characteristics. The bonds among the men and the functions of the inner group appeared quite extraneous to the practice of medicine but exercised a profound influence on the careers of young men entering the profession, and the places and ways in which their practice would be carried out.

Four main ethnic and religious groups comprised the bulk of the physicians—Yankee, Jewish, Italian, and Irish. By and large, Protestant, Catholic, and Jewish doctors were attached to hospitals of their own religious persuasion. Doctors' offices were concentrated in certain residential sections of the city, with most of them in the highest rent areas, and usually in buildings with two to eight offices. From a spatial point of view there were opportunities, therefore, to weld sets of close working relationships.

Staff membership at the main hospital provided the pivotal positions of power, carried out through the dispensing of internships, externships, and staff appointments. Unless a doctor has the privilege of taking his patients to the hospital and treating them there, he is severely limited in his ability to practice. In the main hospital in the city, the controlling group consisted of Yankee specialists. "They are spatially homogeneous. They belong to the democracy of first names. They can practice integrated specialties, and thereby share clienteles. They can designate the appointees to position on the hospital system. By continually recruiting young men to their offices, they maintain the stability of their group through time."[16]

The inner fraternity was further maintained through the referral system. Lucrative specialized fields of medicine were covered by members of the group who referred their patients from one to the other as symptoms warranted, yet were under obligation not to tamper with the loyalty of the patient to his general practitioner. The inner fraternity always referred patients to its own members, never to outsiders, although outsiders were sometimes obliged to refer patients to the inner fraternity because of the standing of the specialists within that group.

If a young physician, fresh from medical school, had the correct auxiliary characteristics of ethnic group, race, and religion, and desirable personality characteristics, he was in a favorable position for an appointment to an internship in the main hospital. The next step of extern meant a testing of his seriousness for the profession of medicine, inasmuch as he would spend long hours with clinic and charity cases. If he demonstrated this further auxiliary characteristic, he was then likely to be drawn into the network of office practice and staff appointment at the main hospital and to participate in the intricate referral system, which could mean high prestige and comfortable income.

Focus on ethnic group membership constituted another study of auxiliary characteristics of the physician's role, a study carried out by Stanley Lieberson[17] in Chicago. He drew samples of Anglo-Saxon, Irish, Italian, Jewish, and Polish physicians, assuming first that doctors of a given ethnic group tend to locate their offices in the residential areas of their own ethnic group. Because of the auxiliary characteristic of ethnic group membership, physicians would find it difficult to build successful practices among outgroup members. To put it another way, the patient is highly concerned with his choice of physician but is likely to make that choice as much on the basis of ethnic similarity as on technical competence. As one might expect, Lieberson's expectations were borne out by the data. A different kind of situation arose, however, with ethnic groups where there was a disproportionately large number of physicians. Jews comprised about 7 per cent of the population of the city but made up around 30 per cent of the physicians. As a consequence, there were not enough members of the ethnic group to provide patients for all the Jewish doctors, a situation that forced some of them to seek patients from other ethnic groups. In order to compete successfully with physicians from other ethnic groups, additional features or characteristics were needed to strengthen their medical role. Lieberson made the hypothesis that specialization and location of an office in the high status central business district, the Loop, would provide the necessary support. Nearly 50 per cent of the Jewish doctors were engaged in specialties, a figure considerably in excess of the rates for Irish, Italian, and Polish physicians, and only slightly in excess of the rate for Anglo-Saxons. Furthermore, Jewish physicians were most likely to practice in the Loop, whether general practitioners or specialists, followed closely by Anglo-Saxons, and trailed by the other three ethnic groups. Lieberson concluded that the group under most pressure to compete for outgroup patients is likely to need and does use the devices of specialization and location of office as reinforcing characteristics of the medical role.

SPECIALIZATION—A VARIATION IN PROFESSIONAL ROLE

Not until 1869 did the American Medical Association recognize that specialties were legitimate and proper fields of medical practice, although continental Europe and Great Britain had accepted the idea much earlier. Opposition to the division of medical practice into specialties was based in a complex of social and psychological factors. As George Rosen[18] has pointed out, the suspicion and hostility of medical practitioners toward their colleagues who wished to confine themselves to diseases of certain organs had an economic and philosophic basis, as well as a distrust of quacks. Often specialization, as in ophthalmology, pertained to a field where people without medical training had long held sway. Distrust of the quack easily generalized to the physician who entered the same field. Furthermore, medicine was regarded as a unique and an indivisible art to which division by specialization could only do damage. The general practitioner was opposed because he felt that he would be degraded in prestige and thereby injured financially.

Yet it was precisely the financial factor that gave much strength to the move toward specialization. Practitioners realized that people were willing to pay for specific and particular knowledge about the diseases of certain organ systems, and that in addition their work would be less arduous. At the same time medical knowledge was becoming increasingly complex. One person could no longer hope to comprehend all or even a large part of the known medical facts and techniques of treatment.

Therefore, better medical care could be provided by having some physicians leave general practice and enter specialties.

Today specialization in medical practice is everywhere accepted and still increasing. It deserves some discussion here because it constitutes a variation in professional role leading to subtle differences in behavior, values, and expectations of various specialists and probably reflecting different personality constellations. It is not really an auxiliary characteristic but rather a role variation. Auxiliary characteristics do affect specialization, however, as we have already seen. Women rarely enter surgery, for their male colleagues think they would make poor surgeons and discourage them from surgical training. Women do enter pediatrics and psychiatry in large proportions. Jews tend to enter specialties more frequently than other ethnic groups, especially psychiatry. Specialization has a definite effect on perception, especially among colleagues in the health field. Within the general expectations of the physician's role fellow doctors, or nurses, or medical social workers are set to act differently toward a surgeon from the way they act toward a dermatologist or a psychiatrist. Although the effect is less evident among the medical laity, relationships among health professionals do have secondary effects on patients and their families.

Relative Prestige of Medical Specialties

Those who are connected in any way with the field of medicine know that some specialties have much higher prestige than others. For a long time surgery has led the list, being regarded as the most glamorous, dramatic, and lucrative. Today it fights for first place with internal medicine. Public health and psychiatry have tended to come at the other end of the scale, and have often been regarded as the domain of people who do not want to be or cannot be "real doctors." Studies of prestige ranking among the specialties, therefore, are confirmatory rather than novel.

Among the data gathered in preconference testing for the Fifth Teaching Institute of the Association of American Medical Colleges (AAMC) there was an item about 12 different specialty fields.[19] The sample included the entire student body of 15 medical schools, geographically scattered throughout the United States, divided equally into tax-supported and private, and into schools with MCAT (Medical College Admission Test) scores above the national average and below the national average. Students were asked: "In your judgment, what is the average prestige that members of the medical profession at large assign to each of the following types of doctors?" Comparable ratings by members of the faculty in each school were also made. The results are tabulated below by specialties. It will be noted that surgery, internal medicine, and neurology head the list, while psychiatry and dermatology are at the bottom. The value of student rankings is further enhanced by the rank-order correlation with faculty ratings, an unexpectedly high .91.

TABLE 3. STUDENT AND FACULTY RATINGS OF PRESTIGE OF SPECIALTIES [AAMC STUDY][20]

(Special student and faculty groups)

Specialty	Opinion of importance M.D.'s attach to specialties	
	Ranking by students	Ranking by faculty[a]
Surgery	1	1
Internal medicine	2	2
Neurology	3	3
Pathology	4	5
Pediatrics	5	7
Obstetrics	6	4
Radiology	7	7
Ophthalmology	8	7
General practice	9	10
Otolaryngology	10	9
Psychiatry	11	11
Dermatology	12	12

[a] Fields were assigned the same rank when they were tied.

Prestige has numerous effects in an occupational setting, not the least of which are variations in financial reward, power in professional affairs, and emotional satisfactions in job performance. The clear consensus among physicians and medical students about the hierarchy of prestige therefore affects the way that doctors in various specialties will perceive themselves and their colleagues. Adjustment to these perceptions by the individual physician will be necessary, else there is real possibility for strain in colleague relationships and possibility of a lessening of good medical care.

Personality and Specialization

Casual conversation with doctors over a period of time reveals a stereotyped picture of personality characteristics of certain specialists, of which the surgeon is perhaps the clearest but the psychiatrist is a close second. Surgeons are perceived as rather cold, hostile individuals, and stories are told of instrument throwing and knuckle rapping in the operating room, and of indifferent concern for the feelings of patients. Aggression seems to be the key word in the stereotype.

Moving from stereotypes to empirical studies, we do find some support for the notion that physicians who choose different specialties have different personality characteristics. We are speaking here in broad generality, for there are many individual physicians who do not fit the "type" but perhaps they "prove the rule." Research on this topic is not extensive but certainly is suggestive.

Psychogenic needs form the basis of a psychological test instrument known as the Activities Index, which was used by Stern and Scanlon in testing medical students, medical school teachers, and practitioners at the State University of New York College of Medicine at Syracuse.[21] Students were grouped according to their first choice of internal medicine, surgery, psychiatry, pediatrics, and obstetrics-gynecology, and compared with teachers and practitioners in these fields. The teachers seemed to be largely undifferentiable by specialty, in contrast to the students and especially the practitioners. Largest differences were found between obstetrics-gynecology and pediatrics. The latter group were characterized by more socially aggressive, assertive and demonstrative needs, while the former were more restrained, self-conscious, and diffident than any of the other groups. These results may be colored by idiosyncratic influences at Syracuse, but they do suggest that differences exist and would appear in studies at other places.

A similar test, the Edwards Personal Preference Scale, was used by Back and others[22] in comparing a group of 32 students who did not intend to go into public health with 7 physicians who were students in a school of public health. The medical students had significantly higher scores for aggression and achievement, while the students in public health were higher on needs for deference, abasement, and nurturance. Both groups were also compared on the Allport-Vernon-Lindzey Study of Values, with the medical students higher on theoretical and esthetic values, and the public health students higher on social and religious values. In general, the medical students showed needs and values relating to individual achievement and enjoyment, in contrast to needs and values relating to identification with or subordination to a larger whole which characterized the public health students.

Although not designed to study differences in personality characteristics, a project by Coser on medical and surgical wards provides inferential data.[23] She noted that the behavior characterizing nurses, house staff, and attending physicians was different on the two wards. Joking, swearing, laughing, grumbling, banter between doctors and nurses, and discussion between doctor and nurse of individual patients, all could be found on the surgical ward. Informal talk between doctors and nurses on the medical ward was rare. The atmosphere was more restrained and polite. It was Coser's conclusion that the different behavior could be traced to differing social structures on the two wards, and this, in turn, was traceable to differences in task orientation and self-images of surgeons and internists. In surgery, tasks must be performed in the minimum amount of time, and there can be no doubt about who makes decisions. Furthermore, decisions must be made quickly and implemented without hesitation. In medicine, the problems are more of differential diagnosis and selection of an avenue of treatment. Decisions are often tentative, and various courses of action may be tried with appropriate modifications along the route. Consultation and teamwork accomplish this end better than the unquestioned authority of a single person. On the medical ward the house officers are taught to think and reflect, while on the surgical ward they are taught action and punctual performance. When Coser interviewed doctors on both wards, the internists said they liked the intellectual challenge of medicine, whereas the surgeons indicated they liked to work with their hands, especially at something that permitted them to be reasonably decisive.

Perception of physicians in various specialties is a function not only of relative prestige but also of the personality characteristics that have come to be associated with that specialty, in stereotype and often in actuality. Individual physicians are guided into subdivisions of their profession by the emotional satisfactions they feel will accrue, satisfactions that are in harmony with their own need structures. The complex of interactions among doctors of various specialties can only be understood by taking this fact into consideration.

Marginal Roles in Medicine

Sociologists refer to an individual who has a foot in two cultures at the same time as a marginal man, not completely belonging to either culture. For some roles there are variations in the rights and duties that make the incumbent marginal to the role, fulfilling it in large measure, but not completely. Two of the specialties in medicine fit the definition of the marginal role—psychiatry and public health; and we now turn our attention to the features of each that produce this "partly in, partly out" feature.

The physician in public health rarely handles patients on an individual basis, unless it is in connection with duty at a marine hospital. His time is spent rather in administration, community relations work, or the kind of sleuthing involved in handling epidemics. To put it another way, he does not do "doctoring" as other physicians do.

In public health the physician does not have the unquestioned authority of his colleagues in hospitals or private offices, nor is the relationship with his patients—the public—calculated to induce awe and strong affection as is the case when matters of great emotional significance are involved, like pain and suffering. The respect he receives is due more to his being a physician, and what kind of person he may be, rather than the kind of service he performs.

Another factor is that public health physicians are salaried, are frequently under civil service with its bureaucratic structure, or are political appointees. Although nowadays doctors frequently receive a salary rather than fees for service in hospitals, industrial organizations, and even in some medical plans, the idea still runs counter to the emphasis on independence and individual initiative that is so closely associated with American medical practice. In the Dichter study conducted for the California Medical Association, referred to earlier, most of the physicians interviewed said they liked medicine because it gave them an opportunity to be independent of outside pressures. The public health physician is at variance, therefore, with the main stream of medicine in this regard.

The marginal role of public health in medicine raises a problem for the recruitment of new personnel to meet a whole series of expanding health needs. The problem is intensified by the experience of the student in medical school. Not only do some medical schools provide no systematic training in public health, but in most of the schools that do the instruction time is minimal and the student has little opportunity to see anything challenging about public health. He can readily get the impression that public health is peripheral to medicine and relatively uninteresting. Actually, few students enter public health directly from medical school. Most of them enter the field after some years of private practice, when they find that medicine is not giving them the kind of satisfaction they expected.

An illustration of the marginal role of psychiatry can be found in the opening words of a recent newspaper article: "Doctors and psychiatrists find that . . ." with a clear distinction being made between psychiatrists and other physicians. Also, many of the laity confuse the terms "psychiatrist," "psychologist," and "psychoanalyst." Psychologists do not have a medical training.

Psychoanalysts usually do, but some of the most prominent psychoanalysts do not have an M.D. degree. The psychiatrist, therefore, is often confused by the laity with professional people who work closely with medicine but are not physicians.

Another reason for the marginality of psychiatry to medicine lies in the fact that many of the technical skills peculiar to the field are shared by disciplines outside of medicine. In recent years psychiatry has moved out of its base in neurology and has become more concerned about psychodynamics, with concomitant shift of therapeutic interest to psychotherapy. The science basic to the practice of psychiatry has become less and less that of neurophysiology and more and more that of dynamic psychology, and even of sociology and anthropology. Neurophysiology has long been considered one of the basic *medical* sciences, while psychology has been a basic *academic* science.

The techniques of psychotherapy have often been developed outside the field of medicine and are shared by people in non-medical occupations, such as clinical psychology, psychiatric social work, counseling psychology, and occasionally by the clergy. Although Sigmund Freud, who was a physician, had much impact on psychotherapy, the same is true of Carl Rogers, a practicing psychologist. The main skills around which psychiatry is built are therefore shared by other disciplines.

Furthermore, psychotherapy is "conceptual medicine," as Harvey Smith[24] puts it, in which the stethoscope and ophthalmoscope are not used, and in which findings from the x-ray and laboratory enter but peripherally, if at all. The rest of medicine keeps one hand firmly on the body and sometimes feels that psychiatry has both hands up in the clouds. Closely allied here is the mistrust in medicine of subjective data, with reliance on the results of physical examination in preference to reports by the patient. In contrast, much of the data with which psychiatry deals are of a subjective nature.

Looking back to Chapter 5, we find yet another reason for suspicion of psychiatry as a legitimate medical specialty. The strong fears that people have about mental disease, the unwillingness to call a person mentally ill until he has reached frank psychosis, the emphasis on rational, normative behavior, carry over into the profession of medicine. Many physicians have the same feelings, perhaps not expressed as clearly or with as much emphasis, but they are present nonetheless. One course of evidence in support of this point of view can be found in the difficulties psychiatrists often have concerning referrals from other doctors, especially the general practitioner. Not only are other physicians often reluctant to send their patients to a psychiatrist, they frequently do so only after trying desperately to find a physical basis for the disorder in question. Smith indicates that general practitioners will sometimes check up on the psychiatrist through the patient by asking him what the psychiatrist is doing and how he is working.

In spite of the marginal role of both public health and psychiatry in medicine, there are strong forces that keep both specialties tied to their brethren. The experience of medical school, discussed in the section "Student Culture" on page 200, binds strongly together all holders of the degree of Doctor of Medicine. Public health physicians and psychiatrists have in common with general practitioners, internists, surgeons, and others a fund of knowledge not held by other professionals, and a certain esprit de corps just by virtue of being doctors.

Furthermore, the rest of organized medicine fights fiercely for its own members even when they are in marginal positions. In the difficulties between psychiatry and clinical psychology, the American Medical Association has stood squarely behind psychiatry in defining psychotherapy as medical practice, and thereby limiting it to those who hold an M.D. degree. Salary differentials and positions on research teams often attest to the strength of common membership in the fraternity of medicine.

Parenthetically, it should be noted that some interesting changes are taking place within medicine, in that greater numbers of students are selecting psychiatry for a specialty. Furthermore, in some medical schools those who choose psychiatry come from the upper half of the class in terms of academic standing. An effect of this change eventually will be to reduce the marginal character of the psychiatric specialty.

One of the dangers of marginal role positions is the potentiality of role conflict, to which both the public health physician and the psychiatrist are subjected. That the conflict is not more severe for more members of these specialties is due to their identification with other physicians and the support granted them by their colleagues in the rest of medicine.

INTERNALIZATION OF PROFESSIONAL ROLE

We now turn our attention to that process by which the physician learns the necessary skills, the proper attitudes and values, and the expectations of his professional role. Looked at from the point of view of the individual, the process can be called *internalization*, making explicit in one's own life and action the teachings of society. From the standpoint of social organization, the process can be called *socialization*, training the individual to fill the special demands of society that go with the professional role. Either term is pertinent to the process under discussion, depending on the position from which the reader views it.

Robert Merton and his colleagues have called this process the emergence of the professional self. Social scientists have expressed great interest in recent years in the development of professional self-images, especially in the field of medicine. In fact, it is in this area that some of the best social science research has been done, and some of the most pertinent findings for the health professions emerged. As a way of introduction to the material to follow in this section, we refer to the paper by Merton, Bloom, and Rogoff[25] for a statement about the interests of social scientists in medical education.

> It is our most general objective to find out, in some detail, how this happens: how these aspirants, with their abilities, anticipations, fears and hopes emerge as institutionally certified physicians, outfitted with a characteristic definition of their role (i.e., what it means to be a doctor), with attitudes toward that role (i.e., a disposition to regard some parts of the role as indispensable and others as secondary), with a self-image (an appraisal of how they measure up to the requirements of the role), and with a set of professional values (relating their role as physicians to others in the community).

To be sure, the picture we have of the internalization of professional role is far from complete, for it is a new area of research. Our account here cannot be considered definitive, but hopefully it is enlightening and suggestive.

The two main sources of research data are the Bureau of Applied Social Research at Columbia University, which has concentrated on the medical school at Cornell University, with supplementary data from the University of Pennsylvania and Western Reserve University, and the Community Studies, Inc., of Kansas City, Missouri, which has conducted a project at the University of Kansas Medical Center.[26]

The second study has utilized the techniques of *participant observation* and *interviewing* as the main avenue for gathering information. Members of the research team presented themselves to medical students as interested observers who had no connection with making faculty judgments about students. Very quickly they were accepted on these grounds and became a normal part of the students' social world. Team members went with the students to classes and clinics, sat in on "bull sessions," ate meals with them, and talked with them at all hours about their experiences and reactions. They watched and talked while things were happening, looked at immediate behavior as well as getting retrospective accounts. Some idea of their acceptance by the students can be seen by the following incident. When students were learning physical diagnosis and were taking turns listening for a heart murmur, they suggested that the observer have a try at it, for he might as well learn first hand what they were up against. In due time the students had no hesitation in talking in front of the observer about their attitudes toward various faculty members or patients, or the ways they handled or evaded problems they faced and tasks they were asked to perform.

Emphasis in the studies at the Bureau of Applied Social Research has been more on the use of *questionnaires* and *attitude* and *value scales*, but not neglecting participant observation, interviewing, and a skillful use of *daily diaries*. Furthermore, the research instruments have been used in what social scientists refer to as a *panel design*, whereby members of a particular class are tested periodically throughout their medical school training. Periodic retesting of the same individuals allows study of change that is more valid than can be obtained from testing all four classes in a school at once.

Thus, by direct and indirect methods, by observing and by testing, by following the same students through their medical school training, we have some insights into the forces that shape the professional self-image.

Growth Through Zones of Discontinuity

The medical student faces a series of new demands, different from those made on him earlier in his education, leading him in effect to shift to a new set of attitudes and behaviors.[27] In the process of shifting, of learning the new role, the student is often in conflict, or in a situation of *discontinuity*, to use a sociological term. Here is the leading edge of growth in the development of a professional self-image and the *zones of discontinuity* are areas where we do well to concentrate research attention. We shall describe a series of these, realizing that they are not mutually exclusive but overlapping; nor are the ones presented here necessarily all that the student faces.

All the Facts Versus a Judicious Selection. The time has long since passed, if truly it ever existed, when a physician could know all the facts about medicine. Yet the freshman student in medical school expects that he is going to learn the "facts of medicine," which he is inclined to believe are clear-cut and available. These are the technical tools he must acquire in order to be a doctor. Very soon he discovers that there are more things to be learned than it is humanly possible for him to learn. He could spend all his time studying gross anatomy in the dissecting room and from his books, yet not know everything; and this is only one course that he must master to the satisfaction of the faculty. Clearly some decision must be made about priorities of facts—what are important, and what can be disregarded or left until later.

In the study at the University of Kansas Medical Center, Becker and Geer report that the two major variables enter the decision process about facts: which ones are important for examinations, and which ones have relevance for the everyday practice of medicine.[28] For example, in gross anatomy the students are instructed to peel back carefully the skin of the cadaver and dissect the peripheral nerves, a painstaking and time-consuming task. Through discussions among themselves, and with students in other classes, they decide that this particular knowledge has little relevance for later practice; and they learn that they probably will not be questioned about it on examinations. Therefore, they decide not to perform that task.

Knowing what the faculty may ask on examinations is crucial because the student can never become a doctor unless he graduates from medical school. The important facts, then, become what the faculty thinks are important.

Lectures that contain material bearing on the everyday practice of medicine receive rapt attention. Those that deal with more esoteric subjects do not command the same strict attention and may sometimes even be avoided. Students can become quite annoyed with a teacher who is interested in research rather than treatment, or who deals with a topic that may rarely concern the practitioner. For this reason, the introduction of behavioral science material into the medical curriculum faces real difficulties, inasmuch as students may not find a close relationship between course content and the practice of medicine. Also, courses in preventive medicine and public health are often regarded by students as a waste of time.

The student thus learns that there are some things he must know well, but there will be limits on his grasp of medicine which he must accept. This is one of the first and most important parts of his self-image.

Self-Limitation Versus Limitation of Medicine. Training for uncertainty is the way Renée Fox characterizes the discontinuity of limitation of knowledge among students at Cornell.[29] Once students have realized that they cannot learn all the facts of medicine and must make a judicious choice among the things presented to them, they face a new conflict. When they cannot detect certain signs or put together results of various tests and examinations, when they cannot make an accurate diagnosis, they begin to wonder how limited they are in ability. The tendency at first is to blame themselves, but it does not take long to find out that residents, attending staff, and senior professors sometimes do not agree on diagnostic findings and conclusions. Disagreements arise over the interpretation of x-rays; diagnoses are proved wrong by the pathologist; and respected members of the faculty straightforwardly admit they do not know the answers to some questions. The limitations of medical knowledge thus become a reality, and the student becomes more adept at assessing his own shortcomings in relation to those of his profession. He finds that medicine is often an uncertain business, but he also notices that senior colleagues are not unduly dismayed by that fact; and he, too, begins to take on an air of assurance that is so much a part of the picture of the ideal physician.

Idealism Versus the Demands of Clinical Work. Much concern has been expressed over the fate of idealism in medical school. The entering student is pictured as an individual full of high purpose; eager to aid mankind, to be a healer, to serve his fellows with little thought for himself. When he leaves, he is viewed as more interested in bodies than people, as aloof and often indifferent to suffering, and concerned with making money rather than serving mankind. Both pictures are extreme, and neither does justice to medical education or to those who enter the profession. They do point, however, to a significant discontinuity that appears in medical school, the clash between idealism and the demands of clinical work, demands that involve a great deal of time and involve a certain kind of approach to the patient. They also point to changes in professional self-image that occur during medical school.

Becker and Geer have described this discontinuity as it occurred at Kansas, indicating that the early idealistic preoccupations are sidetracked by the day-to-day activities at school. Cynicism appears among the students, but it is specific to the educational situation and is kept separate from their belief that medicine is a wonderful thing and that they will make good doctors. Also, it is fashionable, part of the student role, to be cynical. In the clinical years the student has the problem of coping with the steady stream of patients and still finding time to do a heavy load of laboratory work, to study special features that interest him, and to find some relaxation in the midst of it all. Technical aspects of cases become important because the members of the teaching staff are constantly quizzing him on details. Again the thoughts about idealism are obscured. As the end of school draws near, the thoughts about idealism are resumed, partly in the form of discussions about ethical problems which the young doctor will encounter in practice. Now, however, idealism is couched in more realistic terms, for students are aware of the human failures to which doctors are heir, like all others of their fellows, and they are also aware of their own limitations.

Becker and Geer suggest that some of the early idealism of the students is a reaction against the notion that physicians are "money-hungry cynics." The pressures of the school situation push this idealism aside for the time, but by graduation it returns in their desire to be good doctors and find careers that can bring their ideals to fullest realization.

Information of a different kind but related to the topic of idealism comes from a study by Eron[30] on cynicism among students in law, medicine, and nursing. The instrument used was a cynicism scale, the variable being defined as "a contemptuous disbelief in man's sincerity of motives or rectitude of conduct, characterized by the conviction that human conduct is suggested or directed by self-interest or self-indulgence." Subjects rated their agreement along a seven-point continuum, with a series of statements describing cynicism. Freshman law students had higher scores than freshman medical students, but the scores of senior law students declined while those of senior medical students increased. Something occurred during the intervening four years to lead medical students to a greater verbal expression of cynical attitudes.

Eron's study does not refute that of Becker and Geer. Although it has the advantage of using a quantitative technique, it compares two different classes at the same point in time. Also, it does not provide information about the reasons behind the shift, or information as to whether the cynicism is related to the educational experience or will be generalized to professional life. It is clear that further research is needed in more medical schools with the use of scales and interviewing.

Fear and Anxiety Versus Assurance. Early in the chapter we noted that one of the generalized features of the physician's role was the almost continuous contact with suffering and death and its anxiety-generating properties. At that point we also noted that medical students often exhibit difficulties in handling the problem by imagining they have symptoms like those of patients they examine, especially when the symptoms are connected with serious diseases. Here we have a major discontinuity for the medical student, conflict between the anxiety induced by contact with suffering and death, and the calm assurance that is expected of the physician by his colleagues and patients.

A number of features gradually work to reduce this particular discontinuity. One we have already mentioned, the necessarily heavy concern with technical aspects of cases being studied. In many of these cases the student must be familiar with a wealth of detail on a patient, previous medical history, presenting symptoms, laboratory findings, reactions in the hospital; in addition, he must be ready to discuss the implications of various kinds of treatment in view of his knowledge of biochemistry and physiology. The time involved in keeping himself prepared for faculty questioning leaves precious little to be invested in fear and anxiety. To put it another way, the student has little time to think a great deal about the patient as a person or about himself. By the time his clinical load eases up in his fourth year, other variables have come in to help him handle the potential anxiety.

One of these additional features is brought out by Fox in her study of "Training for Uncertainty," and is characterized as the development of certitude. During the clinical years the student has a chance to see his medical knowledge taking root in the treatment of patients, yet without the full responsibility of care. Also, most of his cases will be straightforward, not the diagnostic and therapeutic uncertainties that will confront him later. At the same time, he has a chance to develop a close working relationship with the clinical faculty, to watch them in action, listen to them think out loud. He begins to feel and act like a doctor. It is made clear in these contacts that a display of uncertainty on his part is not condoned by the faculty and distresses his patients. The result is a kind of enforced assurance, of learning to be sure by acting as if he were sure.

Doctor Versus Student. The title of the book that grew out of the studies at the Bureau of Applied Social Research, *The Student Physician*, is an apt one in epitomizing the last of the discontinuities about which we will talk here. In reality, the medical student rarely thinks of himself as a student physician, but as a student in some situations and with certain kinds of people, and as a doctor at other times. Huntington[31] has shown that in three medical schools about 30 per cent of first-year students thought of themselves as doctors in their dealings with patients, but the student who so viewed himself in his contacts with other students or faculty was rare indeed. Only 2 per cent had this self-image.

In the situation with patients, certain expectations operate on the medical student that make him feel more like a doctor. H. Jack Geiger, while a student at Western Reserve, described some of the feelings the freshman has as a result of intimate contact with one family where the wife is pregnant.[32] Many times the relationship between "doctor in training" and patient develops to the extent that she insists on his presence at time of delivery. The obstetrician, anesthetist, and several nurses may be kept waiting while someone routs the student out of class, yet she wants her "own doctor" with her. Contact with patients does much to help the student see himself as a doctor and act like one.

Pressures from the faculty and his senior colleagues pull him back to the student status. Gradual increase in responsibility for patients is given during his four years, but the slowness with which it comes is often irksome. Becker and Geer refer to the derisive remarks made in "bull sessions" when students ask each other what they would do in different kinds of situations. The expression "I'd call a doctor" is often heard. Even though they might be quite confident of their ability to handle the situation, it would be necessary to defer to higher authority. There is no question that they are students and not doctors.

The student versus doctor discontinuity does provide the opportunity for students to try out the role of doctor in limited situations and get used to it gradually before they assume it in full status. At first they don't feel like a doctor, and later they don't feel like a student, but the demands of the social situation of medical school keep both sides of the conflict in hand until the student receives his degree and is "really a doctor."

Facilitating Mechanisms

Not only does the social milieu of medical school pose certain discontinuities, it also provides facilitating mechanisms for the successful working through of the conflict in the discontinuity. Each of these has been referred to more or less explicitly in the preceding section, yet there is value in singling them out here for discussion.

Student Culture. The "body of understandings and agreements among students about matters related to their roles as students" is the definition Becker and Geer give to the term "student culture." The understandings and agreements relate to issues that arise within the school situation, how one behaves, what things are important, how to keep out of trouble, and things of like nature.

A medical school class very quickly becomes a cohesive unit. All students are studying the same thing, often in intimate groups, as when they gather around a dissecting table. Everyone faces the task of amassing more information than he is capable of handling, of having a tremendous body of facts "thrown at him" in a short time. Harassment and tension produce group unity and soon techniques appear for solving problems, techniques that provide the individual with group support. Successful solution of problems further strengthens group unity and solidifies student culture.

The value of student culture for the student lies in the framework it provides him for interpreting events and issues that are unfamiliar and do not fit into categories he has learned earlier. At the same time, it provides social support in reinterpreting the demands of faculty so that the student can to a certain extent bend his medical education to his own interests. Through it the student has a mechanism for coming to terms with heavy and often conflicting demands upon his time and interests, and with disturbing issues that involve fundamental values.

Identification with Faculty. Learning a role involves watching and working with others who are skilled in that role. Part of the training of the physician comes from learning the requisite facts and skills of medicine, and part of it from seeing these facts and skills utilized by members of the profession. Each is incomplete without the other. During the clinical years, when the student comes to have close relationships with the faculty, he finds a sense of colleagueship. He meets with small groups of residents and senior staff for discussion of patients and gets a chance to see how doctors think and organize material. He goes with them to the bedsides of patients and sees how they handle patients; he also has an opportunity to try out his incipient skills under the residents' guidance. He meets physicians from the community who provide a bridge between the patient in the hospital and his world outside. Constant questions come from the faculty, mistakes are met with strong censure; yet the student finds himself more and more accepted as a member of the medical fraternity, as "one of us." On this he can build an image of himself as a physician and work through the discontinuities.

Responsibility and Clinical Experience. Two of the most important aspects of the social system of the teaching hospital for the medical student are responsibility and clinical experience. Each rank in the social hierarchy is entitled to greater responsibility and is assumed to have greater clinical experience. When responsibility is given or withheld, it can be a reflection of judgment by the faculty of the student's knowledge and ability. Here, then, are mechanisms for gradually bringing the student to an awareness of the expectations of his role as a physician in dealing with patients.

Not only in formal teaching but also through informal conversation about cases, the student learns that the physician holds ultimate responsibility for the patient's welfare. The clinical faculty often ask him to project himself into situations where he might exercise responsibiltiy, using situations in which the student is highly involved emotionally—his own cases. Thus, he grapples in his mind with problems that he soon must face in actuality, assessing them in terms of his limited clinical experience. He hears discussions about the way doctors "get into trouble" with patients and references to the death of patients at the hands of a physician.

These two variables thus reinforce the main values associated with the practice of medicine and by being given to the student in gradual amounts help him grapple with the conflicts about knowledge, idealism competence, and assurance.

Anticipatory Learning

Professional image is not complete when the student graduates from medical school. Internship, and perhaps a residency, will do much to shape the picture of practicing physician, of what kind of physician the young doctor really wants to be. We have described in an earlier section the variations in professional role that go under the name of specialization, today an important aspect of one's self-image as a physician. Medical school provides a situation for anticipatory learning about specialization on which later firm decisions can be made.

Most students enter Cornell with intentions not to specialize, so report Kendall and Selvin,[33] but modify these intentions gradually during the course of their training. They are not willing to commit themselves to any field of medicine, suspending judgment until the clinical experiences of the third and fourth years. Gradually the interest in specialization grows out of the realization of the complexities of modern medicine and awareness of the inability to master it all. Students are increasingly uneasy about the prospects of general practice, and many look toward a specialized internship in preference to a rotating one.

By the time of graduation some students have a clear idea of the specialty they wish to enter and are successful in obtaining the right internship to further their plans. Others may have delay forced on them because their academic achievements do not warrant assignment to a specialized internship, or they prefer a rotating experience while they mull over the problem. Some, of course, are still set for general practice. For all students there has been an opportunity in medical school for anticipatory learning through contacts with senior faculty in each of the specialties, through conversations with residents, and through many informal discussions among themselves. They know their professional self-picture is not yet complete but have in hand some of the requisites for bringing it to completion.

CONCLUSIONS AND IMPLICATIONS

In this chapter we have taken up the role of the physician in broad outline, delineating those features that bear directly or indirectly on the demands and expectations of the role as viewed by the physician himself, by his colleagues, and by people outside the medical profession, especially the patient and his family. The first approach was to generalized features of the role, technical competence, emotional neutrality, other-orientation, contact with suffering and death, and necessity for access to the patient's body and intimate details of his life. Within these social expectations the physician has his professional life and in them is the background out of which more specific perceptions are determined. The auxiliary characteristics of the role help to sharpen expectations and perceptions, factors such as sex, ethnic group, age, race, religion, and even the way a person looks and dresses. Another feature that leads to varying expectations is that of specialization within the profession, where varying prestige is attached to different medical specialties and affects the physician's picture of himself and that held by his colleagues. Some variations in the professional role are marginal to the rest of medicine, public health and psychiatry in particular. Public health physicians and psychiatrists both use techniques and approaches to disease that are somewhat different from those used in the rest of medicine and, in fact, at times may be more like the skills of disciplines outside the field of medicine. The marginal role imposes stresses upon its incumbents, yet the strong feelings of membership in the fraternity of physicians prevent these stresses from inducing disruptive strains.

Finally, we have looked at the professional role of the physician as it slowly emerges through the experience of medical school.

Here the crucial variable is growth through zones of discontinuity, working through of conflicts and behavior, ideals, attitudes, and values, and leading to a stable identity of self as a physician.

Some cautions must be introduced concerning the material that has been presented. Broad outlines cannot predict the behavior of specific individuals, who have their own idiosyncratic hierarchy of needs and adaptive mechanisms. Nor can we predict variations in role expectations as between the northeastern urban areas and the rural South. Regional differences and personal uniqueness are constrained, however, by the broad outlines of professional role as sketched out here.

Again, the data on which many of the points in this chapter are based have been gathered from small samples, specific medical schools, and certain sections of the country. A potential bias is always present until research has been of sufficient extent to bring in more dimensions of the problem. Let the reader take the material with prudence but with an urge to stimulate further investigation.

A final caution lies in the static nature of the material. Medicine is a living, dynamic profession that is always changing, even though slowly and conservatively. Those in the forefront of academic medicine, in the *avant-garde* of medical care, see new roles for the physician that eventually will have an effect on the ordinary practitioner. Already we are seeing changes in the structure of medical practice, in the training of physicians, in the utilization of new disciplines like the behavioral sciences. Relationship of doctor and patient is being scrutinized ever more closely, and the help of related professions like medical social work and nursing being reappraised. The changes that are occurring, however, do fall within the broad outlines of the role as presented in this chapter. There is always peril in holding something still for didactic presentation, but it is a necessary risk.

In summary, we have some of the guidelines about the rights and duties of a professional role that influence the way its incumbents perceive the world, the expectations physicians have of each other, and expectations of the patient and his family concerning medicine.

NOTES TO CHAPTER 6

1. Parsons, Talcott, *The Social System*. Free Press, Glencoe, Ill., 1951. The reader is referred specifically to Chapter 10, Social Structure and Dynamic Process: The Case of Modern Medical Practice.

2. Fox, Renée C., *Experiment Perilous*. The Free Press, Glencoe, Ill., 1959.

3. The reader is referred to Bendix, Reinhard, *Max Weber*, Doubleday and Co., Garden City, N. Y., 1960, for a discussion of Weber's theory of charismatic power. Ideas from several of Weber's writings, some untranslated, are brought together by Bendix in a short and clear presentation.

4. Lee, Alfred McClung, "The Social Dynamics of the Physician's Status," *Psychiatry*, vol. 7, November, 1944, pp. 371–377.

5. Dichter, Ernest, *A Psychological Study of the Doctor-Patient Relationship*. California Medical Association, Alameda County, May, 1950.

6. La Barre, Weston, "The Patient and His Families," *Casework Papers 1958*, Family Service Association of America, New York, 1958, pp. 61–71.

7. Dichter, Ernest, *op. cit.*

8. Hughes, Everett C., "Dilemmas and Contradictions of Status," *American Journal of Sociology*, vol. 50, March, 1945, pp. 353–359.

9. A study of the colleague relationships among physicians can be found in Hall, Oswald, "The Informal Organization of the Medical Profession," *Canadian Journal of Economics and Political Science*, vol. 12, February, 1946, pp. 30–44. Also the reader is referred to Reitzes, Dietrich C., *Negroes and Medicine;* published for the Commonwealth Fund by Harvard University Press, Cambridge, Mass., 1958.

10. Williams, Josephine J., "Patients and Prejudice: Lay Attitudes Toward Women Physicians," *American Journal of Sociology*, vol. 51, January, 1946, pp. 283–287; and "The Woman Physician's Dilemma," *Journal of Social Issues*, vol. 6, no. 3, 1950, pp. 38–44.

11. Dykman, Roscoe A., and John M. Stalnaker, "Survey of Women Physicians Graduating from Medical School 1925–1940," *Journal of Medical Education*, vol. 32, March, 1957, part 2, pp. 3–38.

12. Fitz, Reginald, "Votes for Women," *Harvard Medical Alumni Bulletin*, vol. 17, January, 1943, pp. 30–32.

13. Pryor, June, "Women at Harvard Medical School," *Harvard Medical Alumni Bulletin*, vol. 28, April, 1954, p. 23.

14. Field, Mark G., *Doctor and Patient in Soviet Russia*. Harvard University Press, Cambridge, Mass., 1957.

15. Hall, Oswald, "The Informal Organization of the Medical Profession," *Canadian Journal of Economics and Political Science*, vol. 12, February, 1946, pp. 30–44.

16. *Ibid.*, pp. 42–43.

17. Lieberson, Stanley, "Ethnic Groups and the Practice of Medicine," *American Sociological Review*, vol. 23, October, 1958, pp. 542–549.

18. Rosen, George, "Changing Attitudes of the Medical Profession to Specialization," *Bulletin of the History of Medicine*, vol. 12, July, 1942, pp. 343–354.

19. Reader, George G., "Development of Professional Attitudes and Capacities," *Journal of Medical Education*, vol. 33, October, 1958, part 2, pp. 164–185.

20. *Ibid.*, p. 177. This tabulation appears as Table 8.15 in Dr. Reader's article.

21. Stern, George G., and John C. Scanlon, "Pediatric Lions and Gynecological Lambs," *Journal of Medical Education*, vol. 33, October, 1958, part 2, pp. 12–18.

22. Back, Kurt W., and others, "Public Health as a Career of Medicine: Secondary Choice Within a Profession," *American Sociological Review*, vol. 23, October, 1958, pp. 533–541.

23. Coser, Rose Laub, "Authority and Decision-Making in a Hospital: A Comparative Analysis," *American Sociological Review*, vol. 23, February, 1958, pp. 56–63.

24. For a discussion of the marginal role of psychiatry in medicine, the reader is referred to Smith, Harvey L., "Psychiatry in Medicine—Intra or Interprofessional Relationships?" *American Journal of Sociology*, vol. 63, November, 1957, pp. 285–289.

25. Merton, Robert K., Samuel Bloom, and Natalie Rogoff, "Studies in the Sociology of Medical Education," *Journal of Medical Education*, vol. 31, August, 1956, p. 554.

26. A third study also throws light on the process of medical education and development of professional self-image, one dealing with the teaching of comprehensive medical care during the clinical years. The project was conducted at the University of Colorado and is reported in Hammond, Kenneth R., and Fred Kern, Jr., *Teaching Comprehensive Medical Care*, published for the Commonwealth Fund by Harvard University Press, Cambridge, Mass., 1957. Students were divided into an experimental and a control group, the former to have experience in comprehensive medical care, the latter to continue the traditional senior clerkships. The effect of the two programs on acquisition of knowledge, skills, and attitudes in various areas was then assessed, as perceived by the student, by members of the faculty, and as measured by tests and questionnaires. Although the study at Colorado did not have the same approach to an understanding of medical education as those carried out at the Bureau of Applied Social Research and the University of Kansas, there are data in the Colorado study that will have direct bearing on much of the material in this last section of Chapter 6.

Results of the Kansas study are to be found in Becker, Howard S., Blanche Geer, Everett C. Hughes, and Anselm L. Strauss, *Boys in White*, University of Chicago Press, Chicago, 1961. Also, there are two papers by Becker and Geer: "The Fate of Idealism in Medical School," *American Sociological Review*, vol. 23, February, 1958, pp. 50–56; and "Student Culture in Medical School," *Harvard Educational Review*, vol. 28, Winter, 1958, pp. 70–80. The major publication of the studies from Columbia is Merton, Robert K., George G. Reader, and Patricia L. Kendall, *The Student Physician*, Harvard University Press, Cambridge, Mass., 1957.

27. The reader will find the following article helpful in approaching the question of role transition: Cottrell, Leonard S., Jr., "The Adjustment of the Individual to His Age and Sex Roles," *American Sociological Review*, vol. 7, October, 1942, pp. 370–382.

28. Acquiring facts is a perennial problem in medical school, not only in the freshman year. In the study at Colorado students who participated in the Comprehensive Care Program were afraid that they were not learning as many facts as their colleagues in the traditional clerkships, because they did not see as great a variety of patients or as many cases that showed clear-cut disease syndromes. Later testing indicated no difference between the two groups in level of medical knowledge, but the significant point is that senior students felt great pressure to learn as much as they could in order to have an adequate preparation for practice.

29. Fox, Renée C., "Training for Uncertainty" in Merton, Robert K., George G. Reader, and Patricia L. Kendall, *op. cit.*, pp. 207–241.

30. Eron, Leonard D., "The Effect of Medical Education on Attitudes: A Follow-Up Study," *Journal of Medical Education*, vol. 33, October, 1958, part 2, pp. 25–33.

31. Huntington, Mary Jean, "The Development of a Professional Self-Image," in Robert K. Merton, George G. Reader, and Patricia L. Kendall, *op. cit.*, pp. 179–187.

32. Geiger, H. Jack, "The Patient as a Human Being," *The New York Times Magazine*, December 2, 1956, pp. 64–72.

33. Kendall, Patricia L., and Hanan C. Selvin, "Tendencies Toward Specialization in Medical Training" in Merton, Robert K., George G. Reader, and Patricia L. Kendall, *op. cit.*, pp. 153–174.

Chapter 7

Doctor-Patient Relationships

UNTIL THE PHYSICIAN DEALS WITH A PATIENT, his role is devoid of meaning and life, an abstract concept but hardly a reality. The essence of being a doctor lies in treating people who are sick; to this end medical education and clinical experience are directed. This chapter is, therefore, a necessary counterpart to the one that precedes, giving meaning and perspective to the structural factors of the physician's role.[1]

A patient is not a passive object that the physician manipulates, not an inert host in which micro-organisms grow, not a machine whose parts wear out or malfunction. Rather, the patient is an active being, through whom the physician must work in dealing with disease. Intertwined with biological dysfunction are emotional reactions of the patient to his disease or injury, overlaid with all manner of social norms, values, and expectations. Treatment of disease and injury, except when the patient is unconscious, is a process of social interaction, essentially communication between two unique people, an art as well as a science.

Physician and patient both bring certain things to the treatment situation. The physician has a set of expectations about his role, already presented in Chapter 6; he has his own personal needs, the effects of his physiological state at the time, and the carryover of things that have happened to him that day. The patient has a set of expectations about his own role, for all societies have a patient role involving defined rights and duties. He, too, has his psychogenic needs, sentiments, and values. Both physician and patient have auxiliary characteristics in addition to their specific roles in the treatment situation, variables of age, sex, ethnic group, social class, manners, dress, and speech. They perceive each other and interact accordingly on the basis of their reciprocal role expectations and the coloring effect of the auxiliary characteristics and personal needs.

A physician, as well as an astute social scientist, L. J. Henderson, referred to the doctor-patient relationship as a social system.[2] Both participants in the system are moved by sentiments and interests as well as the formal aspects of their social roles, and the interaction of sentiments is likely to be the most important phenomenon in any social system.

There is no doubt that social interaction between doctor and patient is highly charged with emotion. Alice Joseph[3] has stated that with the possible exception of the relationship between the sexes, it is not approached in emotional content anywhere else in our society. What occurs can contradict or interfere with the "technical" aspects of medical treatment, or it can bear on future relationships which the patient has with doctors.

Analysis of the psychosocial setting in which medical treatment occurs is the substance of this chapter. We shall approach it first by presenting the generalized expectations of the sick role as a social role, then consider the things that the patient brings with him, psychological and social concomitants of illness and of his place in society. Finally, we shall draw some implications for doctor-patient relationships by using a "contrast" situation, that of the use of nonmedical personnel for treating illness, particularly the chiropractor. The process of communication between the doctor and patient can then be viewed in full perspective, the physician's role seen in its dynamic aspects, and implications drawn for members of the health professions.

THE SICK ROLE

The social role attendant on illness has been considered in its structural aspects by Parsons[4] much as he considered the role of the physician. Like other social roles, it is a constellation of expectations that involve both rights and duties; in this case, two of each.

First, concerning the rights of the patient or sick role, the individual concerned is exempted from his normal social role responsibilities. Important business or social obligations can be broken without fear of censure by other members of society when a person is sick. Other excuses, no matter how pressing, do not have the same power to release us from ordinary social responsibilities. That this right can be and is abused, does not detract from its overall importance for perceptual expectations. Lying behind the right is the prestige of the physician, neatly phrased in the term, "doctor's orders." What employer will protest if one of his key personnel is "ordered" to bed, or to take a vacation, or to stop working overtime? Should he raise objections, social censure is often strong. Society, as it were, frees the sick person from his ordinary duties and obligations in order that he may concentrate on the process of getting well.[5]

Another right involves the realization that the sick person cannot get well by an act of decision or will. It is not "his fault" that he is ill; therefore, he has the right "to be taken care of." Other members of society are obligated to him. The primary obligation falls on members of the patient's family, but lacking these, or in the face of family indifference, other social institutions assume the obligation—police, hospitals, Red Cross, social work agencies. In some societies, like the Soviet Union, the state assumes considerable responsibility for taking care of its sick.

At the same time society regards illness as an undesirable state, even one of deviance, as Parsons has suggested in another of his papers.[6] The patient is therefore expected to "want to get well," and to seek technical competent help toward that end. Here we see the two duties in the role, the desire to get well and the obligation to obtain help. The person who "enjoys" being sick or who refuses to seek competent help for his condition is not favorably regarded by his fellows. Under these circumstances he may be denied the rights of the sick role, and expected to fulfill his normal functions in society. By not seeking professional help he is regarded as a drag on society. The patient is entitled to competent help; hence, physicians and hospitals take "charity" cases, physicians are on call twenty-four hours a day, and police departments provide ambulance service. Society stands ready to provide help when the patient seeks it, but he, if able, must initiate the action.

The generalized features of the sick role are thus determinants of perception in situations of illness. When sickness occurs, the patient adopts a new set of perceptual expectations relative to his own behavior, his obligations toward others, and the kind of behavior they owe him. At the same time, family members, physicians, nurses, and sometimes other people in the social structure are helped to see their function toward the sick person, their duties toward him. Both the sick and well perceive a set of reciprocal obligations.

Within this broad framework other variables influence the process of perception, producing variations in the pattern of expectations on the part of the sick person and bearing on the interaction between doctor and patient. To these we now turn our attention.

WHAT THE PATIENT BRINGS WITH HIM

Physiological Effects of the Illness

Many patients come to the doctor in pain, perhaps with a sore throat, stomach cramps, a stiff back, throbbing head, or other assorted stabbing, dull, itching, burning sensations, tender-to-touch spots in various parts of their bodies. They may have fever, nausea, shortness of breath, spots in front of their eyes, or a general feeling of malaise. They may have broken bones and may be bleeding, nearly fainting from the pain, or just be vaguely uncomfortable. Whatever it be in the way of discomfort, the altered physiological state is undoubtedly a determinant of perception, narrowing the range of attention to stimuli, lowering thresholds for emotional reactivity, changing customary personality manifestations. The astute physician knows full well that a person with disturbed physiologic equilibrium is not himself and is likely to have altered perceptions of the world from the effects of his physiologic state alone.

Psychological Reactions to Illness

Illness poses a threat to the organism, sometimes of death, at least of reduced function which will be temporary or perhaps permanent. A change in customary relationships and routines, temporary or permanent, also threatens, so that social as well as biological homeostasis is disturbed. There is a decrease in the ability to be autonomous, a realization that the individual is not a whole person, not complete and strong. The threat is not one to be ignored and, except in the case of minor illnesses, it arouses strong psychogenic needs and calls forth ego-adaptive mechanisms, occasionally even of a pathologic nature. Psychologic reactions to illness, therefore, are important determinants of perception that enter into the patient's relationships with others, especially the physician.

Needs for attention and sympathetic help often increase in response to illness.[7] The patient is concerned about *his* illness, not about pain in the abstract, but about *his* pain. The sharp, stabbing sensation in the lower-right quadrant of the abdomen is a very personal thing to him, not to be regarded impersonally. At the moment it is the center of his world. Most people who are ill not only want attention paid to their trouble, but also wish to be cared for and to have a strong influx of positive emotional expression by others, affection, and love. The prescription of TLC, "tender, loving care," comes out of the strong psychogenic needs of the patient himself.

A number of writers have likened the patient situation to that of childhood, where the social expectations of the sick role and the psychogenic needs of the sick person combine to facilitate an emotional regression. Lederer,[8] for example, has characterized the main features of the regression as *egocentricity, constriction of interests, emotional dependency, and hypochondriasis.* In our society this is a normal part of being sick and the behavior does not lead to the kind of disapproving judgment that would result from the same behavior in a healthy person.

Egocentricity can be seen in an exaggerated concern with trifling matters that relate to the self, expecting people to attend to his wants immediately, to provide services, or do errands that would ordinarily be of little concern to the patient. In extreme, we have the sickroom despot, dominant, intolerant, infuriating to doctor, nurse, and family. In caricature, we have the husband, home in bed with a cold, running his wife in circles with demands for service and whims of every sort. In most cases we have a person who is more subjective than usual as he perceives the situation around him.

Constriction of interests may be due in part to the physiologic effects of the illness, a narrowing of perceptual range associated with fever, altered blood composition, or other factors. In part, the exemption from normal role obligations causes constriction of interests, as do the demands for attention and accompanying narcissism. An avid baseball fan may be quite unconcerned over the fact that his team is languishing in the cellar, a manufacturer undismayed by a threatened strike at his plant, a professor oblivious to the fact that there is no one to take his classes. Clearly this is not a time to ask someone to make decisions or to expect much cooperation concerning events outside the sickroom.

Emotional dependence comes also from the coalescence of physiologic, social, and psychologic factors. For adequate care to proceed, the sick person must accept the decisions of others, the "orders" of his doctor, the routine of the hospital, the intervention of family and friends. Again, the situation is like that of the child who is subject to his parents.

Not all patients may be happy with emotional dependence. To some it has the proportions of a threat as great as the illness itself. More often than not it leads to a situation of ambivalence, uncritical and full love combined with criticism and resentment. The sick person wants to be cared for and loved, yet resists the pressures for dependence that are an outgrowth of his illness. Hence, the patient may shift in his perceptions of those who care for him, at one point seeing them as angels of mercy, at another point as thoughtless and heartless. In those where ambivalence is most marked, difficulties can be expected to occur in communication with the physician.

The fourth feature, hypochondriasis, is usually evidenced in much interest in the results of medical procedures or tests that relate to the sick person and sensitivity to aches and pains that otherwise would pass unnoticed. Through constriction of interests there is a heightened perceptivity of bodily functioning, a process that is potentiated by the natural anxiety about the course of his illness. Again, distortions of perception can occur, comments of the physician may be misinterpreted, medical procedures viewed as threatening beyond reason and logic.

Another author, Ernest Dichter,[9] has written about the feelings of anxiety and insecurity that are manifested in patients who go to the hospital. His material is most pertinent to Part Four of this book, but some of the points have a bearing here. From interviews with patients, Dichter and his associates found that a common theme was fear and need for assurance; fear of death, of mutilation, of being incapacitated, of being helpless and dependent. Response to the anxiety and insecurity took the form of emotional regression to a more childlike state. Dichter noted the same egocentricity, constriction of interests, and emotional dependence as described by Lederer, but indicated that one adaptive mechanism adopted by patients was to project into those around them feelings associated with earlier family experiences. The physician easily became the father, all wise and all powerful, the holder of ultimate responsibility and decisions. Patients sometimes invested the doctor with power beyond that which he possessed and were as jealous of their relationships with him as are siblings in a family.

There is every reason to believe that the projection of feelings which Dichter described in the hospital can occur in doctor-patient relationships outside the hospital. Thus, partly from the social role assigned the physician and partly from the needs of the patient, the doctor can be perceived as having characteristics like a father. In most patients these feelings are not likely to be conscious; nevertheless, they will influence the process of perception. The pattern of behavior which characterized the father-child relationship of the patient will tend to show up in relationship to the physician, whether it be overly dependent, submissive attitudes, rebellion and pressures for autonomy, or other patterns. Thus, the physician does not have a passive individual, presenting certain symptoms to be diagnosed and treated, but an active individual who brings more than his symptoms to the doctor. Growing out of his psychological reaction to illness, the patient brings certain sets toward the doctor that influence the way he interprets the doctor's behavior, understands his directions, feeds back further information, and carries out his orders.

Psychological Reaction in Severe Illness

When pain and suffering are intense and the threat of death is very real, the psychological components of the patient's world become of considerable importance. Perhaps the most graphic examples come from situations of incurable cancer, a disease that seems in our culture to have become the repository or focus for much of human anxiety about life and death. In cases of cancer and other disease states of comparable severity, we can see rather vividly the psychological reactions that accompany a physiologic disorder and that may alter the patient's perception of the physician and disrupt good communication between the two.

Data that are available to help in the discussion here come from three sources; surveys of patients who delayed and those who did not delay in seeking medical treatment for conditions that proved to be cancerous, observations from clinical experience of the psychogenic needs and adaptive mechanisms of the cancer patient and of the physician who treats him, and, finally, the subjective reports of cancer patients about reactions to their illness.

Turning first to studies of delay, we may find here evidence of factors that influence perception of disease and of the physician who might treat it. Aitken-Swan and Paterson[10] report a study from England involving 2,700 patients with cancer of the breast, cervix, skin, and mouth, 45 per cent of whom delayed consulting their doctor three months or more after onset of symptoms, and 17 per cent of whom delayed a year or more. Of those who delayed, 75 men and 239 women were interviewed. Some of these patients had suspected that they had cancer and the authors concluded that about half of them "adjusted" to the threat of cancer by denial or suppression of thoughts about cancer, or by a kind of fatalistic acceptance of their illness. Commenting on this study and others by his group in England, Paterson[11] states that fear is important in causing delay in England, also that among other things shame is still linked with cancer, to his mind evidence of the horror with which cancer is still regarded. Paterson also makes the interesting observation that only one-third of the women in their survey believed that cancer could be cured in contrast to the two-thirds reported in American surveys.

Another study comes from the M. D. Anderson Hospital in Houston where Cobb and her associates[12] found that patients who were "prompt" in coming to the doctor were aware of the significance of their cancer, while "delayers" somehow suppressed or never had an awareness of the meaning. The investigators report that among the prompt patients fear operated to mobilize resources and overcome inertia, and that these patients expressed their dependency needs through intelligent cooperation with the physician. For those who delayed, fear appeared to have a paralyzing effect, and dependency needs were expressed in a childlike groping for security or rebellion against those on whom they had to depend.

Titchener and his associates[13] studied 200 randomly selected surgical patients in a municipal general hospital, some of whom had cancer. About 36 per cent of all the patients delayed coming for treatment after the onset of symptoms, but the figure rose to 71 per cent among the cancer patients.[14] Findings of the study, which applied to both cancer and noncancer patients, indicated that one reason for delay was a fear of punishment growing out of a high need for aggression, for which the patient expected retribution from people in the environment. In some patients this took the form of a fear of death. Another reason was characterized as a reaction formation against deep-seated dependency needs. Surgical treatment necessitates a dependent situation for the patient, but some patients could not accept being dependent and reacted by continuing to believe they were in good health. Finally, there was evidence in some patients of shame, a fear of the "examining eye" of the physician, especially when the disease involved the sexual organs, and there was history of guilt about sexual misdemeanors.

Titchener and his colleagues believe that most people have some knowledge about the meaning of symptoms and the treatability of surgical illnesses, but that other factors can interfere with, or distort, the utilization of this knowledge, or to put it in the framework used here, distort the patient's perception of the physician and hospital as a place for help in meeting a threat to the body. The authors conclude: "If the physician can be sensitive to the underlying psychological determinants of the delay in his patients, there is a greater chance that plans for therapy will include attention to the factors producing resistance to treatment."[15]

Even more pertinent to the doctor-patient relationship are the comments of physicians who have studied the reactions of the cancer patient to his illness. Branch[16] states that suffering and loneliness are the two major concerns of cancer patients, and that the cancer patient always is in need of strong emotional support. Many patients are desperately afraid of being alone and of not finding the resources to meet a situation that may well mean death. Unwittingly, the physician may contribute to the patient's fear through his reactions to his own helplessness in curing the disease. If the patient has become important to the doctor, the doctor may not know what to do or say after the diagnosis has become established. Some doctors, says Murphey,[17] may react by becoming more reserved and silent and evading the issue with the patient. One physician has been quoted as saying of a patient: "I know he has cancer, and he knows he has cancer, and I know he knows, and he knows that I know he knows—but the word itself has never passed between us."[18] Thus, the patient through his strong needs for help may perceive the doctor as his greatest source of help, yet if the doctor evades him, the patient perceives the doctor as rejecting him and his feelings of loneliness are only compounded. Murphey also states that some patients react with aggression and hostility because their strong dependency needs are not met or are unacceptable to them. Complaining, turning to another doctor, feeling that family and friends are against him are ways that aggression may be expressed by a patient in addition to the direct outbursts of anger against doctor or nurse. Other patients may be overwhelmed with guilt in the face of the threat posed by the disease, and, as indicated in the study by Titchener, perceive the physician as one who will lay bare the indiscretions of their past lives.

Before turning to the implications of these reports, it is worth referring to the subjective account of a cancer patient, in this case ably expressed by Richard L. Neuberger, the late Senator from Oregon.[19] Although his disease was diagnosed early and responded successfully to treatment, he describes the numbness and fear, the cold chills that accompanied his awareness of the diagnosis and later the altered perception of life, of his friends and associates, that grew out of the realization that death was never far away. As one reads his words, the sense of the fullness of the psychologic reactions to illness comes clear, an understanding that the astute physician or good nurse must already have. A human organism with a malignant neoplasm is more than a body with disease. It is also a reacting individual who has feelings about his illness, and these feelings influence the way he perceives his physician and utilizes his advice and care.

Summary and Implications. All patients do not react to illness in the same way, whether it be an upper respiratory infection or incurable cancer. Each patient has his own constellation of psychogenic needs and characteristic ways of dealing with crises, and has a pattern of relationships with other people in his past life. Also, each has been conditioned by his cultural or subcultural associations to perceive illness in a certain light. Thus, there is a certain uniqueness to the perception of illness by each patient. However, the range of psychologic reactions is limited, so that variations in patient reaction fall into clusters. Some will accept the dependency involved in illness and cooperate with family and physician to hasten recovery; others will utilize the dependency to control wives, mothers, friends, and doctor; still others will fight against the dependency by denying illness or being openly hostile. Some patients will be ashamed and guilty, some stoical, some frightened, some cheerful through their suffering. Whatever the psychologic reaction to the illness, it will affect the perception by the patient of his physician and of the treatment program which is prescribed. Furthermore, the reaction of the physician to his patient will have a *feedback effect*, sometimes causing a further distortion in the patient's perception, sometimes correcting it. The doctor who evades facing the issue with a cancer patient intensifies the feelings of loneliness and anxiety and may contribute to heightened hostility or depression. The doctor who increases his emotional support to the same patient may build up the resources and strengths of his patient so that threat of dependency is reduced and threat of death met calmly. The wise physician also comes to recognize these patterns in his regular patients and will remember them in assessing and treating *any* particular illness.

Effects of Social Class Position

A quite different set of variables is also of importance in understanding the patient role and doctor-patient relationships. This set of variables relates to the patient's membership in certain kinds of social groups rather than to his particular psychologic reaction to his illness. Specifically, social class and ethnic group membership provide a framework of customs, values, attitudes, and beliefs that influence the patient's perception of the physician and affect the doctor-patient relationship. It is within such a framework that the more idiosyncratic psychologic reactions occur.

Social class position has an effect on interaction of physician and patient, on perception of each by the other. Because of the prestige afforded the physician, the education necessary for the achievement of his role, the income accruing to him, and the power that he is able to exercise both in the therapeutic relationship and in community activities, he occupies relatively high social status. Speaking generally, the physician is usually found in the upper-middle class and top-ranking specialists are likely to be in the upper class. Many physicians come from physician's families, or at least from white-collar families, and thus have always occupied at least middle-class status positions. Those whose origin is in a lower-class family find that medicine provides an excellent vehicle for social mobility. In the process of mobility the patterns of life, values, and attitudes that were associated with the original status position tend to disappear and to be replaced by those of the new social class position into which the person moves. Not infrequently lower-class values are rejected more emphatically by the individual who moves up the class scale than by one who has always occupied an upper-middle position.

Many patients who come to the doctor are of working-class or lower-class position. In addition to the difference in outlook which the lower-class patient brings to the situation, the discrepancy between doctor and patient may be further intensified if the meeting takes place in a charity clinic. The doctor will receive little if any fee and may regard such clinic work as necessary but not highly desirable from a personal point of view. However, discrepancy in class position can be important in private office practice as well as charity clinic.

Ozzie Simmons[20] has discussed this point in some detail in a publication of the Social Science Research Council, noting that the physician's part in the therapeutic relation is based on his technical competence, his impartial interest in the health needs of the patient, and his obligation to give priority to the patient's well-being over his own personal interests. If the physician carries out his role fully, he will inspire trust, respect, and confidence in his patient and ensure cooperation. This is an ideal not always achieved and one that can be disrupted by class considerations. The greater the social distance between doctor and patient, the more difficult it is to establish mutual trust, respect, and cooperation, and the more likely it is that the two people will not perceive each other in terms of the ideal roles of doctor and patient, but in terms of their social class status in the larger society.

Illustrations can be cited from the study of Regionville by Koos, the NORC-HIF survey to which we referred in Chapter 4, and studies of psychiatric treatment. In Regionville,[21] Class III, or lower-class families, frequently were not happy with the relationship they had with local doctors. When all respondents in the survey were asked how satisfied they had been with treatment they had received from Regionville physicians, over 50 per cent of the Class III respondents reported they were moderately or very dissatisfied, or else gave no opinion. This was in contrast to 30 per cent in Class II, and only 24 per cent in Class I. When questioned about the reasons behind the dissatisfaction, some thought that the doctor had prescribed drugs that were too expensive, or that he made too many home visits or required too many office visits. Some indicated that they believed the doctor's treatment was not effective, while others thought that he did not seem interested in the case or was not interested in "caring for us." Economic considerations played a part, but so also did differing ideas about treatment and feelings about being important to the doctor. One cannot tell whether the perception by these patients was due realistically to a rejection by the physician, or whether it represented some feeling of inferiority from lower-class position; as Koos suggests, this is a good topic for future research. At any rate, the psychological reality of the situation was that many Class III patients did not feel comfortable with the doctor. Koos sums it up as follows:

> The total impression gained from the questioning was that much of the dissatisfaction resulted from a lack of communication between the physician and his patient. Part of this lack was due, no doubt, to the fact that the physician and patient too often represent differing subcultures, and "speak different languages."[22]

Differences in attitude toward the doctor that are associated with social status position can also be seen from responses to questions in the NORC-HIF survey, which are listed in Table 4.[23] In interpreting these data the same caution must be observed as was pointed out in Chapter 4, namely, that lower-class respondents have a tendency to agree to any extreme statement in a questionnaire. With some of the statements differences among occupational, income and educational groups are very slight, while in other cases they are rather marked. Respondents who had less education and income and were in "blue-collar" or manual occupations were more inclined to agree that doctors "give you medicine even if you don't need it," that "they don't give you a chance to tell them what your trouble is," that "they don't tell you

…TION, INCOME, AND EDUCATION GROUPS, NORC-HIF STUDY

STATEMENT	OCCUPATION					INCOME				EDUCATION		
	Professional, business	Clerical, sales	Skilled workers	Other "blue-collar" workers	Farmers	$7,500 or more	$5,000 to $7,499	$2,000 to $4,999	Under $2,000	Attended college	High school only	Eighth grade or less
	Per cent saying, "true of most doctors"											
They [doctors] don't take enough personal interest in you.	31	31	36	33	29	29	32	31	39	31	31	35
Doctors make you wait entirely too long when you try to see them in their offices.	41	41	47	48	44	45	46	43	50	43	41	51
Doctors like to give you medicine even if you don't need it.	24	20	27	29	39	22	25	27	41	19	24	37
They don't give you a chance to tell them exactly what your trouble is.	18	25	32	29	28	18	26	26	34	19	24	32
Doctors will tell you frankly when they don't know what your trouble is.	42	45	42	45	48	45	44	43	46	42	45	44
They don't tell you enough about your condition; they don't explain just what the trouble is.	42	47	54	53	51	43	46	51	56	45	47	55
They tell you there's nothing much wrong with you when you know there is.	14	15	20	28	33	11	16	24	37	10	19	34
Doctors give quite a bit of their time free to people who need it.	63	57	56	53	50	60	56	54	54	63	56	51
Doctors don't like to get other doctors' opinions about a condition.	17	24	24	26	35	16	20	25	36	16	21	32
Doctors give better care to their regular patients than to people they don't know so well.	37	30	38	40	49	36	36	38	52	39	35	45
	Per cent saying, "great deal of trouble"											
How much trouble would you have getting a doctor to come to your home at night or on a Sunday?	19	16	24	29	26	18	21	24	35	17	23	30

enough about your condition," that "they don't like to get other doctors' opinions about a condition," that "they tell you there's nothing much wrong with you when you know there is," and that "they give better care to their regular patients than to people they don't know so well." Answers to these attitudinal statements indicate poorer communication with lower-class patients, suspicion of the doctor and his control, and differing ideas about symptoms and disease. The expectation of difficulty in getting a doctor for a home visit at night or on Sunday is further reflection of social distance between doctor and patient in the lower socioeconomic groups. As in the case of the Regionville data, one cannot tell how much these attitudes were due to actual experiences with physicians or merely to expectations arising out of social status position. Whichever explanation is correct, attitudinal differences in social status position mean that the physician faces varying perceptions from patients in different social status groups and these perceptions will affect the relationship he has with the patient.

Another aspect of the perceptual distortion in doctor-patient relationships concerns the reaction of the physician. When the lower-class person is quiet and submissive, most cooperative in the treatment situation, the doctor may perceive this as recognition by the patient of the doctor's skill and knowledge and as the proper respect for such technical competence. Simmons[24] found in a health center in Chile that this was not the case, the deference being based on feeling of social distance. Patients did not necessarily view the doctor as a man of great technical skill and knowledge, for they had some fairly firm medical beliefs of their own, but were deferential to him because his social class standing was high. There is every reason to believe that the same situation exists in certain doctor-patient relationships in the United States. In such cases the deference shown does not always indicate the mutual trust and cooperation that the physician thinks is present.

A number of studies have shown that in treatment for psychiatric disorders, patients from the upper classes are more likely to receive psychotherapy, while patients from the lower classes are more likely to receive "organic" treatment or merely custodial care. Perhaps the best example is the report by Robinson, Redlich, and Meyers[25] from the Yale study of social stratification and psychiatric disorders. Their data showed consistently that treatment did not depend on psychological and medical determinants alone but on the status position of the patient as well, and that psychotherapy usually takes place in a setting where the social and cultural background of the patient is similar to that of the therapist.

A study from Boston[26] came to the same conclusions for patients in a number of mental hospitals and amplified the relationships further by measuring the patient's attitudes toward mental illness and "psychological mindedness" or introspection. By and large, patients in the upper classes received psychotherapy no matter what their attitudes were toward mental illness. Among patients in the lower classes, a much smaller percentage received psychotherapy, but of those who did, all had favorable attitudes toward mental illness, a humanitarian attitude, as the authors phrased it. The data seem to indicate that when the psychotherapist is of the same social class as the patient, he will judge that psychotherapy might be beneficial. When patient and therapist are of different social class positions, psychotherapy is judged worthwhile only if some other common features can be established, such as attitudes toward mental disease.

The illustration from psychiatric treatment concerns the doctor-patient relationship primarily from the doctor's point of view, while the Regionville and NORC material focus on the patient's point of view. Although this chapter has emphasized those things which the patient brings with him to the doctor-patient relationship, it is important to indicate that the doctor's perception of the patient affects the interaction as well, especially when the patient is rather different from the doctor in terms of his social class position. On many hospital services interns and residents "rotate" to a new ward every few months. Often, after such a change, a hostile, aggressive ulcer patient from a working-class background—who has been regarded by the ward staff as a special cross to bear—alters his behavior markedly in response to a new physician who does not show anger or irritation. Occasionally such a patient's physical state then improves rapidly.

We might sum up this section by saying that social class differences can provide a distortion in perception of the *ideal roles* of doctor and patient and interfere with optimum communication between the two, with detriment to the best medical or psychotherapeutic relationship.

Effects of Ethnic Group Membership

Cutting across the lines of social class division within a complex society like the United States are the various ethnic groups, each with its own customs and values about life. Two unskilled laborers, working together on the same construction job would be classified as being in the same social class grouping but might come from quite different ethnic groups. They might bring different foods in their lunch boxes, perhaps hold different religious beliefs, feel differently about their place of authority in the home, and disagree about the extent to which one should express himself on important matters. Ethnic group is therefore another broad but important consideration in the perception that the patient has of medical situations.

A beginning illustration can be drawn from an article by Spiegel; it concerns two dissimilar people who are both filling the role of patient and both are interested in soliciting the interest of the physician. One is an eastern European Jew, the other an Englishman.

> In the first situation the patient states his complaints with great drama, emphasizes his suffering with loud moans and groans, and considerably exaggerates the degree of disability. The doctor will most likely respond with tolerant sympathy and reassurance, telling the patient that he will take care of the difficulty and that his suffering will be relieved. In the second case the patient reports his complaint in an offhand manner and minimizes his suffering or treats it humorously. In this pattern, the doctor may very probably warn the patient that he must take better care of himself, but that if he follows orders and keeps his appointments, the situation will be cleared up.[27]

Expressive emotional reactions, especially to suffering, have great value to the eastern European Jew and can be counted on to gain the interest and support of another person. Calmness in the face of adversity, the "stiff upper lip," and consideration for others have high value for the Englishman. In the relationship with the doctor, the eastern European Jew may unconsciously fear that if he does not make a convincing case of his suffering, the doctor will not take him seriously, while the Englishman may fear that overexpression of his suffering will cause the doctor to lose interest in him.

A different facet of ethnic group custom and values can be seen if we consider two women patients of an obstetrician in a New York clinic, one a recent immigrant from Puerto Rico, the other a second or third-generation American of French and English background. This is the first time the physician has seen either patient. Both are asked to undress and lie on his examining table. The woman from Puerto Rico shows obvious displeasure, even fear, and refuses to comply in spite of the doctor's assurances. The other patient has no hesitancy in following orders and allows herself to be examined. In the first case, the physician is likely to regard his patient as difficult, uncooperative, and a disturbing interference with his busy schedule. The second patient will strike him as the ideal kind for obstetrical practice, and he will wish that all his patients were cooperative.

The family structure and customs of the groups to which these two patients belong show differences that have a direct bearing on their behavior in the obstetrician's office. Among the Puerto Rican group sexual matters are not a common topic of discussion between husband and wife, and women are taught that reticence on sexual matters is important.[28] Furthermore, Puerto Rican women place high value on modesty. Many of them are ashamed to undress before their own husbands. Because of the strong male authority in Puerto Rican families, the woman learns to be wary of strange men and does not feel comfortable in their presence. The American woman of English and French background, of middle social status position or higher, has grown up in a cultural situation where sexual matters are rather freely discussed;

she has little hesitation in talking with her husband, or even other men, about the topic. Although she maintains a "proper modesty," it does not seem wrong to disrobe to be examined by a doctor. This is one of the things that doctors have to do. In some ways she is likely to feel more comfortable in being examined by a doctor whom she does not know.

A final illustration concerns a physician in the southwestern United States, whose practice includes a number of Spanish-American or Mexican-American patients from rural areas. He is annoyed by the fact that they do not have the habit of being punctual in keeping appointments; and he suspects that they are not following his directions accurately with regard to the prescriptions he gives them, in spite of their assuring him that they have no difficulty understanding him. To his time-conscious, punctual way of life, this deviant behavior is hard to understand.

The rural Mexican-American[29] is oriented differently toward the present and future, toward time commitments. Not too long ago his ancestors lived in an agricultural society that ran by the seasons rather than by the clock. What one did on a given day did not matter particularly, so long as the activities during the season were accomplished. Life being simple, there was no need for the complex interrelating of activities for which close time schedules are necessary. Little value was placed on preciseness of time, and many tasks could be put off till another day. This did not mean that the person was "lazy," but merely that he was oriented toward the affairs of the present rather than the future. In the light of this cultural orientation, many of the doctor's directions can be ambiguous or of little meaning. "Take every four hours," "come in next Wednesday at ten o'clock" may not be perceived in the same way by doctor and patient. Also, it may be difficult to understand the doctor's insistence on certain procedures, for example, inoculations when the person is presently healthy. The future will take care of itself.

These three illustrations show some of the important effects of ethnic group influences, customs, and attitudes toward expressiveness of emotions, modesty, and time orientation. Others could be cited,[30] such as the particular set of beliefs about folk medicine, the structure and solidarity of family life, or the meaning and value of work. In each case, the patient brings something with him from his cultural background that determines the way he perceives his relationship with the physician and that facilitates or impedes the interaction and communication between the two.

WORDS AND KNOWLEDGE: OTHER BARRIERS TO COMMUNICATION

In the previous sections we have discussed a number of factors that can distort perception in the relationship between physician and patient and impair the process of communication between the two. The psychological reactions that arise out of the illness, the effects of social class position, and the effects of ethnic group membership influence the way in which the patient perceives his doctor and initiate a feedback process that in some cases may lead only to further distortion. Before considering the implications of these for the role of the physician, a further determinant of perception in the doctor-patient relationship must be discussed. The simple matter of the meaning of words and knowledge about disease and the body often interferes with adequate communication.

To illustrate the importance of words, we can refer to a comment of the late Alfred Kinsey as he looked back on the interviewing experience of the two studies on sexual behavior.

> Vocabularies differ in different parts of the United States and there are differences among individuals belonging to different generations. Sexual vocabularies may differ among persons in different portions of a single city, depending upon their social levels, occupational backgrounds, racial origins, religious and educational backgrounds, and still other factors. In each community we had to discover the meanings that were being attached to particular terms, and learn which terms might be used without giving offense. In order to establish rapport, one has to learn to use the local vocabulary with an ease and a skill that convinces the subject that we know something of the custom and mode of living in his or her type of community, and might be expected, therefore, to understand the viewpoint of such a community on matters of sex.
>
> For instance, one has to learn that a person in a lower level community may live common-law, although he does not enter into a common-law marriage with a common-law wife. As we have noted

in our volume on the male, we have had to learn that a lower level individual is never ill or injured, although he may be sick or hurt; he may not wish to do a thing, although he may want to do it; he does not perceive although he may see; he may not be acquainted with a person, although he may know him. Syphilis may be rare in such a community, although bad blood may be more common.[31]

Words in the medical situation can be highlighted with a story that is told by Eichenlaub in an article on "Clichés That Confuse the Patient."[32]

A local eye doctor (would you *insist* on calling him an ophthalmologist?) tells me his sister phoned him recently to ask some questions. "That surgeon you sent me to is awfully nice," she said. "But I couldn't get his instructions straight, and I was too embarrassed to admit it. Would you translate his orders into schoolgirl English for me?"

"Shoot," the doctor said.

"Here's what I'm supposed to do first: elevate my hand. Do I keep it straight up in the air, or what?"

"Keep it higher than the base of your heart."

"Which is where?"

"An inch or two below the top of your breastbone."

"How do I keep my hand there day and night?"

"When you lie down at night, rest your hand on top of your chest or on pillows at your side."

"Why didn't he say so? But don't go away: I'm also supposed to use hot compresses. What exactly are they?"

"Hot, wet cloths."

"Oh, yes. And I'm to irrigate the wound three times a day."

"Wash it out."

"You're a dear! Just one further question: Do *you* speak Greek to your patients?"

Eichenlaub notes that even worse than the standard medical terms used in his story are the abbreviations that creep in, the common ones like BMR and EKG, those like D and C, RBC and WBC, and countless others that most workers in the health professions could enumerate. Too often in response to their use, the patient may nod his head as if in understanding, but the blank look on his face betrays his ignorance. Like the ophthalmologist's sister, he may be too embarrassed to admit his lack of knowledge.

In the course of a study of ward-round teaching, Romano[33] asked 50 patients in the hospital to define a list of 60 medical terms and abbreviations that might be used in the bedside teaching conference. Most, he found, were misunderstood or unfamiliar to the patients.

A more extensive investigation was carried out in a publicly operated general hospital by Samora, Saunders, and Larson,[34] using a list of medical terms common to interviews between physician and patient. The words were embedded in simple sentences, and the respondent asked the meaning of the key word in each sentence. Patients tested were predominantly from lower social status groups and were Spanish-American, Negro, or "Anglo" in terms of ethnic group. In their report of findings, the authors noted that no respondent defined all 50 words correctly, and the mean score was 28.9. Variation in knowledge of the terms was associated in major part with two social variables, amount of formal education and membership in a certain ethnic group. Those who had graduated from high school could identify 75 per cent of the terms correctly, while those who had less than seven years of school could identify only 38 per cent. At the same time there were differences between Spanish-Americans and the other two ethnic groups. When education was held constant, the scores of those from the Spanish American group were still lower than those from the Negro or "Anglo" group. On the basis of the data from this hospital, the authors concluded that a good deal of what was said to the patients by the medical staff, and perhaps by other services, was not clearly understood, even by patients of average or better educational background.

Another study of medical terms is reported by Redlich,[35] using 25 patients in neuropsychiatric practice who were asked to define 60 medical terms and abbreviations. In accounting for the variation in knowledge, Redlich listed such factors as general intelligence, interest in the disease, degree of anxiety, hypochondriacal tendencies, curiosity, age of patient, cultural and ecological background, duration of disease, and rewards or punishments for previous explorations in medical terminology. He found that there were many terms which patients did not know and that some of them give rise to confusion; that is, different meanings are attached to them by physician and patient. Hypnosis is an example. Other terms lead to a fear response on the part of the patient, as in the use of tumor. The "linguistic environment" of the patient is a term used by Redlich to indicate an area about which many physicians know little, but one which may have a significant effect on their relationship with patients. A patient can hardly perceive his doctor correctly if he does not understand him.

Closely allied to an understanding of terminology is knowledge about the etiology, symptoms, and treatment of common diseases. Pratt, Seligmann, and Reader[36] asked 214 patients in a metropolitan medical center about these aspects of tuberculosis, diabetes, syphilis, arthritis, asthma, cerebrovascular accident, stomach ulcer, leukemia, and coronary thrombosis. Phrased in the form of a multiple choice test, the investigation revealed that on the average patients could answer about 55 per cent of the questions, with considerable range among individuals as well as among diseases. The test was then administered to 89 physicians in the same clinic to find out how much they thought *patients ought to know* about the diseases. The physicians indicated 82 per cent, a considerable discrepancy from the actual level. They were then asked how much they thought the *patient did know*, and the majority of the physicians tended to underestimate the level of patient knowledge, low as it was. Furthermore, it was found that those physicians who seriously underestimated level of patient knowledge did not often discuss the illness at any length with the patient. In general, the patients were not aggressive in finding answers to their questions, although there appeared a latent desire on their part to learn more from the doctor than was usually the case. In attempting to assess some of the implications of these results for the doctor-patient relationship, the authors found that those patients who were given thorough explanations of symptoms, etiology, and treatment participated more effectively with the physician and were more likely to accept completely the way the physician was handling the case.

These findings take on more meaning if we go back to some of the attitudinal statements about doctors which were reproduced in Table 4 on page 221. Especially to be noted is: "They don't tell you enough about your condition; they don't explain just what the trouble is." Nearly half the respondents, with little variation between social status groups, agreed that the statement was true of most doctors. Thus, from the NORC-HIF survey and the study by Pratt, Seligmann, and Reader there is ample evidence that patients would like to know more about their disease condition, would like to understand the situation more fully, but feel that communication from the physician is inadequate.

The gap in communication is most certainly influenced by language, as the studies cited here have clearly indicated, and verbal symbols interfere with an optimum relationship between physician and patient. The implication of the material in this section can perhaps best be summed up by quoting one of the concluding paragraphs from the paper by Samora, Saunders, and Larson.

> A question could be raised about the necessity of adequate communication between patients and those who treat them in hospital and clinic. Certainly no one has demonstrated that those patients who understand everything that is said to them get well faster or more certainly than those who do not. Perhaps, if the goal of medicine is the diagnosis and treatment of disease, the quality of communication between practitioner and patient makes little difference so long as an adequate medical history can be obtained and the necessary cooperation of the patient in doing or refraining from doing certain things can be assured. But if the goal is more broadly interpreted, if the concern is with the person who is sick and the purpose is to relieve, reassure, and restore him—as would seem to be increasingly the case—the quality of communication assumes instrumental importance, and anything that interferes with it needs to be noted, and if possible, removed.[37]

THE PATIENT AND OTHER THERAPISTS

A rather different approach to the problem of the doctor-patient relationship can be had by looking at the interaction of patients with other kinds of therapists, particularly those outside of medicine, for example, the chiropractor, naturopath, or faith healer. The satisfactions derived from this interaction, be they psychological or physical, may indicate some of the strains to be found in dealing with the physician. Like the psychologist's figure and ground designs, this is essentially a contrast situation where new perceptions are elicited by shifting from figure to ground, or vice versa. Studying the relationships with other healers may give new insights about the relationships with physicians.

A good example can be found in the chiropractor, a therapist found almost universally throughout the United States and utilized by sufficient numbers of people to make a study of his relationship with patients worthwhile. Data about use of the chiropractor come from two studies to which we have already referred, the NORC-HIF survey of health attitudes and the Koos report on Regionville. In the former case, respondents were asked: "Have you (or your spouse or children) received medical care during the last year from any chiropractors or other people who were not regular doctors?" Ten per cent answered "yes," and when asked about the kind of person they consulted, a chiropractor was mentioned 66 per cent of the time. The proportion answering "yes" varied according to sections of the country, nearly twice as high in the North Central and West as in the South and Northeast, and higher in small metropolitan and rural areas. Interestingly, the rate increased with higher education and income of the respondent. Also, the rate was twice as high for those who were rated as average or below average health as compared with those who were judged to have good health.

Nearly 90 per cent of the respondents indicated that someone in the family had visited a physician during the past year. The rate for the chiropractor seems small in comparison, but among certain groups in our population significant numbers of people are represented. To this must be added the findings from another question: "Are there any conditions for which you yourself might go to one of these other kinds of medical persons in the future?" Nearly 25 per cent said "yes," and the chiropractor was named as the one that would be visited 71 per cent of the time.

In Regionville, Koos reported that 19 per cent of the illnesses in a given period had been treated in whole or in part by visits to the chiropractor or to other nonmedical personnel. In assessing attitudes toward the chiropractor within the three social status groups in Regionville, 2 per cent in Class I, 10 per cent in Class II, and 58 per cent in Class III said they would use the chiropractor for any illness. When this question was limited to illness involving the back, muscles, or joints, the "yes" replies were 9, 40, and 14 per cent, respectively. Those who replied that they would not use the chiropractor for any illness (a slightly different kind of question from the first one), constituted 60 per cent of Class I, 22 per cent of Class II, and 9 per cent of Class III.

The people in Regionville were inclined to use the chiropractor to a greater extent than respondents in the national sample, but regional and local variations in such matters are bound to be high. Also the study of Regionville was more detailed, involving repeated interviews with the same respondents; and perhaps it built a rapport that allowed for greater freedom of response. From both studies, however, we have a picture of considerable use of the chiropractor, in most instances by people who also use the physician.

The chiropractor does not have the unqualified acceptance accorded the physician. Many come to him as a last resort only after visits to a physician have provided no relief. Others visit him for a limited range of conditions when there is pain in the back or arms or legs. However, there are some people who perceive the chiropractor to be as competent as the physician, and in their relationships with him apparently they find satisfactions which they feel do not accrue from a visit to a physician. This latter group can be called the "positively oriented" and Koos has reported data from his interviews about their motivations toward the chiropractor.

The following reasons were given for using the chiropractor. First, the respondents believed that he knew the real cause of illness, and they did not find his theory of disease incongruous with other theories of disease. They reported that he took more time with them than did the physician, that he was more "professional" in treating them, and that they felt "important" to him. They also reported that it was not so difficult to get to see him and that his fee was more moderate. Roughly, these perceptions fall into those based on knowledge of disease, emotional gratifications in the chiropractor-patient relationship, and convenience, of which the latter two are especially pertinent for our discussion here.

Other patients might be classified as the "halfway" group, that is, those who used both physician and chiropractor and the latter for special conditions. Koos reported that it was his impression that some of the patients were hypochondriacs or mild neurotics, for whom the usual busy physician had impatience or even distaste. The "listening" for which the chiropractor took time provided a mental catharsis, and there were both psychological satisfaction and physical relief in the "adjustment." The chiropractor "did something" for their complaints in the form of a manipulation or adjustment. Much the same conclusion comes from a study by Wardwell[38] where he suggests that the neurotic or hypochondriac may find in visiting the chiropractor a *legitimization of the sick role* which the physician is not willing to grant. The NORC-HIF survey showed that use of the chiropractor was higher in people with average or poor health as compared to those with good health. These may be just the people with aches and pains in the back, with headaches, vague symptoms from a diagnostic point of view perhaps, but conditions for which chiropractic promises help and makes legitimate as sickness while medicine may not.

Wardwell also reported that friendship rather than professionalism seemed to be more characteristic of the chiropractor-patient relationship, that the chiropractor was more oriented to the patient than to the illness. Chiropractors seemed to deal with patients more informally, putting emphasis more on themselves as people than as incumbents of a special role. In sociological terms, the chiropractor tends to emphasize what might be called primary group aspects of the relationship as opposed to strictly professional secondary group aspects.

Implications for Doctor-Patient Relationships

Utilization of alternative sources of treatment to that of the physician indicates three factors that can interfere with adequate communication between physician and patient. First is the matter of conditions that can be considered sufficient to place an individual in the sick role. The physician and patient may disagree on the conditions or symptoms that make one really "sick" and the physician may justify his position to himself by the pressures of time and of the number of seriously ill people who need his care. In the process, however, people with mild or vague complaints may not be helped toward achieving optimum health unless they turn toward other therapists.

The second factor concerns professional manner. Some patients feel that the chiropractor is more friendly and less professional in his approach than the physician. This does not necessarily reflect a fact about the practice of physicians in general, but it does say that some patients are repelled rather than reassured by a professional manner. Professional status and the behavior that accompanies it can weigh heavily on the shoulders of those who carry it, especially if they feel insecure. Again, to use sociological terms, certain of the expectations of the role (professional manner and emotional neutrality) can be overemphasized to the detriment of other aspects of the role (warmth, interest in the patient as a person, and other orientation). By and large, the prestige of the physician's role and the respect granted it by the laity makes unnecessary an overemphasis on professional manner when a friendly manner might be therapeutically more indicated.

Finally comes the problem of convenience. From Table 4 on page 221 the reader will remember that 40 per cent of the respondents in the NORC-HIF survey felt that most doctors made their patients wait entirely too long. In interviews with those who utilized the chiropractor, many said that it was easy to see him, that there were no long waits in his office. Again the busy physician may justify his office procedures on the grounds of his workload, and ignore or regard as unimportant the hostility that patients feel. This hostility, however, can impair the effective communication process and enhance latent ambivalence toward the physician.

Strains frequently do occur in the doctor-patient relationship, strains that can be highlighted by the satisfactions accruing in the relationship with other kinds of healers. For the handling of certain kinds of patients, for the giving of optimum medical care, attention to all the variables that can disrupt communication is in order.

SUMMARY

At the beginning of the chapter emphasis was placed on the fact that the role of the physician is empty until he deals with a patient. Demands and expectations for behavior of the physician are brought out sharply when he treats sick people. There are certain expectations of the patient role, or sick role, which mesh with those of the physician's role, leading to what sociologists refer to as *role reciprocal* expectations. When something occurs to alter or distort the perception of the other's role, usually of the physician by the patient, then the role cannot be carried out fully or to its optimum expectations. If, for any number of reasons, the patient misperceives the role of his physician, there is likely to be disturbance of communication and an impaired doctor-patient relationship. We have pointed out that distortions of perception can occur through the effects of psychological reactions that accompany illness, through the effects of social class and ethnic group membership, and through the level of understanding of medical terms and facts about disease. We have also noted from looking at the relationship of the patient to other kinds of therapists that legitimization of the sick role, professional manner, and convenience can disrupt optimum communication between physician and patient. These factors rarely operate alone. Usually there is a dynamic interaction among them that defies analytic breakdown, and thus every patient is to some extent unique. We have tried here to sketch some of the broad outlines within which that uniqueness appears and to indicate theoretically and concretely some of the variables that are of importance to the physician in his relationship with patients.

NOTES TO CHAPTER 7

1. Every role in society has this reciprocal aspect, that is, it has meaning only as it is articulated with another role, or series of other roles. To this extent, social structure presents a balance of forces. The role of stage actress is only a void without an audience, and each has a set of expectations of the other. The same reciprocal relationship applies to father and children, worker and boss, senator and citizen, doctor and patient.

2. Henderson, L. J., "Physician and Patient as a Social System," *New England Journal of Medicine*, vol. 212, May 2, 1935, pp. 819–832.

3. Joseph, Alice, "Physician and Patient," *Applied Anthropology*, vol. 1, July, 1942, pp. 1–6.

4. Parsons, Talcott, *The Social System*. The Free Press, Glencoe, Ill., 1951. Material pertinent to this chapter is found in Chapter 10, Social Structure and Dynamic Process: The Case of Modern Medical Practice.

5. For ideas similar to those of Parsons, the reader is referred to Lederer, Henry D., "How the Sick View Their World," *Journal of Social Issues*, vol. 8, no. 4, 1952, pp. 4–16. Reprinted in Jaco, E. Gartly, *Patients, Physicians and Illness*, The Free Press, Glencoe, Ill., 1958, pp. 247–256.

6. Parsons, Talcott, "Illness and the Role of the Physician: A Sociological Perspective," *American Journal of Orthopsychiatry*, vol. 21, July, 1951, pp. 452–460. Here deviant behavior is defined as that which fails in some way to fulfill the institutionally defined expectations of one or more of the roles in which the individual is implicated in society. By being sick the individual is not able to fill his social roles in a normal way. The reader is also referred to another of Parsons' articles, "Definitions of Health and Illness in the Light of American Values and Social Structure," in Jaco, E. Gartly, editor, *Patients, Physicians and Illness*, The Free Press, Glencoe, Ill., 1958, pp. 165–187.

7. See Joseph, Alice, *op. cit.*

8. Lederer, Henry D., *op. cit.* The reader is referred to Lederer's quotations from Charles Lamb's essay, "The Convalescent" as apt illustrations of patient reactions.

9. Dichter, Ernest, "A Psychological Study of the Hospital-Patient Relationship," *Modern Hospital*, vol. 83, September and October, 1954 issues. The actual data from the investigation are obscured in the presentation and interpretation, a procedure that makes one cautious in accepting the findings. The conclusions, however, are in agreement with material presented by other writers such as Lederer, cited above.

10. Aitken-Swan, Jean, and Ralston Paterson, "The Cancer Patient: Delay in Seeking Advice," *British Medical Journal*, vol. 1, March 12, 1955, pp. 623–636.

11. Paterson, Ralston, "Why Do Cancer Patients Delay?" *The Canadian Medical Association Journal*, vol. 73, December 15, 1955, pp. 931–940.

12. Cobb, Beatrix, and others, "Patient-Responsible Delay of Treatment in Cancer: Social Psychological Study," *Cancer*, vol. 7, September, 1954, pp. 920–926.

13. Titchener, James L., and others, "Problem of Delay in Seeking Surgical Care," *Journal of the American Medical Association*, vol. 160, April 7, 1956, pp. 1187–1193.

14. Of the 200 patients in the study, 24 had the diagnosis of cancer, 17 of which were judged to have delayed in coming for medical care.

15. Titchener, James L., and others, *op. cit.*, p. 17.

16. Branch, C. H. Hardin, "Psychiatric Aspects of Malignant Disease," *CA: A Bulletin of Cancer Progress*, vol. 6, May, 1956, pp. 102–104. The reader is also referred to Meerloo, Joost A.M., "Psychologic Implications of Cancer," *Geriatrics*, vol. 9, April, 1954, pp. 154–156.

17. Murphey, Bradford J., "Psychological Management of the Patient with Incurable Cancer," *Geriatrics*, vol. 8, March, 1953, pp. 130–134.

18. Personal communication from H. Jack Geiger. The physician quoted was once interviewed by Dr. Geiger.

19. Neuberger, Richard L., "When I Learned I Had Cancer," *Harper's Magazine*, vol. 218, June, 1959, pp. 42–45. The reader should keep in mind the cultural relativity of the reactions cited here and, indeed, the cultural relativity of much of the material in this section on psychological reactions to severe disease. We learn to fear cancer and death as part of the process of cultural conditioning. Fear of death or of suffering is not necessarily a universal human response, because an individual can be culturally conditioned to accept death, even to anticipate it with a certain amount of eagerness. In the culture of which Senator Neuberger was a part, death is feared because it illustrates how far we fall short of being the masters of the destiny that is part of the prevailing image of ourselves. In other cultures where man views himself as subjected to nature, death may be much more of a "natural" occurrence.

20. Simmons, Ozzie G., *Social Status and Public Health*. Social Science Research Council, New York, Pamphlet 13, May, 1958.

21. Koos, Earl Lomon, *The Health of Regionville*. Columbia University Press, New York, 1954. See especially Chapter 3, The Use of the Physician.

22. *Ibid.*, p. 77.

23. The reader is referred to note 33 in Chapter 4 for the source of these data.

24. Simmons, Ozzie G., "The Clinical Team in a Chilean Health Center" in Paul, Benjamin D., editor, *Health, Culture, and Community*. Russell Sage Foundation, New York, 1955, pp. 325–348.

25. Robinson, H. A., F. C. Redlich, and J. K. Meyers, "Social Structure and Psychiatric Treatment," *American Journal of Orthopsychiatry*, vol. 24, April, 1954, pp. 307–316.

26. Gallagher, Eugene B., Daniel J. Levinson, and Iza Erlich, "Some Sociopsychological Characteristics of Patients and Their Relevance for Psychiatric Treatment" in Greenblatt, Milton, Daniel J. Levinson, and Richard H. Williams, editors, *The Patient and the Mental Hospital*. The Free Press, Glencoe, Ill., 1957, pp. 357–379. I am grateful to Dr. Levinson for allowing me to work with some of the raw data from this study, and, therefore, I must take responsibility for the conclusions I have drawn.

27. Spiegel, John P., "The Social Roles of Doctor and Patient in Psychoanalysis and Psychotherapy," *Psychiatry*, vol. 17, November, 1954, p. 371.

28. For a fuller discussion of relationships between men and women in Puerto Rican culture, the reader is referred to Stycos, J. Mayone, "Birth Control Clinics in Crowded Puerto Rico" in Paul, Benjamin D., editor, *op. cit.*, pp. 189–210.

29. See Saunders, Lyle, *Cultural Difference and Medical Care*. Russell Sage Foundation, New York, 1954.

30. For an illustration of the way cultural differences in medical practice are presented to physicians, the reader is referred to Letters to a Young Physician, "The Patient's Cultural Background," *Pfizer Spectrum*, vol. 5, February 1, 1957, pp. 84–85.

31. Kinsey, Alfred C., and others, *Sexual Behavior in the Human Female.* W. B. Saunders, Philadelphia, 1953, p. 61.

32. Eichenlaub, John E., "Clichés That Confuse the Patient," *Medical Economics*, vol. 34, December, 1957, pp. 242–256.

33. Romano, John, "Patients' Attitudes and Behavior in Ward Round Teaching," *Journal of the American Medical Association*, vol. 117, August 30, 1941, pp. 664–667.

34. Samora, Julian, Lyle Saunders, and Richard F. Larson, "Medical Vocabulary Knowledge Among Hospital Patients," *Journal of Health and Human Behavior*, vol. 2, Summer, 1961, pp. 83–92.

35. Redlich, Frederick C., "The Patient's Language: An Investigation into The Use of Medical Terms," *Yale Journal of Biology and Medicine*, vol. 17, January, 1945, pp. 427–453.

36. Pratt, Lois, Arthur Seligmann, and George Reader, "Physicians' Views on the Level of Medical Information Among Patients," *American Journal of Public Health*, vol. 47, October, 1957, pp. 1277–1283.

37. Samora, Julian, Lyle Saunders, and Richard F. Larson, *op. cit.*

38. Wardwell, Walter I., "A Marginal Professional Role: The Chiropractor," *Social Forces*, vol. 30, March, 1952, pp. 339–348.

Chapter 8

The Nurse

A SOURCE OF DEEP EMOTIONAL SATISFACTION, the focus of disruptive stresses, the object of many psychodynamic projections—all these things, and many more, can be said of the role of the nurse. Based on a long tradition of service to humanity, the position of the nurse is secure among those who treat disease and care for the sick. Yet at the same time nurses are uneasy, aware of new demands being made upon the role, and searching for definition of a revised role and ways of educating students for it. Many forces within nursing seek to change it from an occupation to a profession and the strains attendant upon such change are considerable.[1] Nursing is in transition, and in our analysis of the role of the nurse we must take into consideration the effect of transitional pressures on perception of function, not only by the nurse but also by her professional colleagues, her patients, and the public at large. Our task in this chapter is to examine the various features of the role of the nurse, both those that are well defined and those that are ambiguous, to indicate the areas of strain, and to draw implications for the process of perception.

There are dangers in talking about nurses without some kind of qualification as to type. Nurses work not only in hospitals but also in physicians' offices, in schools, in industrial settings, and in public health agencies or visiting nurses' associations. Much of the discussion in the following pages will apply primarily to the hospital nurse, although, of course, many of the points to be covered apply to all nurses. However, the reader should be aware of the problem of speaking about nurses in general and that caution will be introduced from time to time.

NURSING AS A WOMAN'S ROLE

More than any other role within the health professions that of nursing is defined as belonging to women. Some men enter nursing, but they constitute only a small proportion of the total number and are never quite fully accepted by the public as really being nurses. In fact, the male nurse is a good example of a marginal role, much more so than the psychiatrist or public health physician, to which we referred in Chapter 6.[2]

From a historical point of view a number of factors undoubtedly have contributed to assignment of the nursing role to women. Devereux and Weiner[3] note three such factors, the first of which is that in almost every society caring for children is a woman's job. Inasmuch as the sick are like children in many ways, it is easy to equate the roles of caring for children and caring for the sick. The English language, for example, does not differentiate nursing babies and nursing the sick. In our cultural tradition men have usually functioned as nurses only when they have renounced their sexual role, as in various monastic orders, or when they have demonstrated their masculinity in striking ways, or when circumstances do not permit women to work in a given situation. The medical corpsmen of our Armed Forces during the war serve as one example. Being called on to rescue wounded while under fire, and not allowed to bear arms with which they could fight back, has signified courage. In addition, the corpsman has some of the characteristics of the physician as evidenced by the Navy nickname of "Doc" and the fact that he is the only representative of the medical department on small ships and on some submarines. In the Army the corpsman institutes first aid procedures until the wounded can be transferred to aid stations. Then, of course, there are "real nurses" on the hospital ships and in field hospitals.

The second historical factor is the assumed relationship between femininity and kinds of work that might be characterized as drudgery. The uncomplaining housewife who cleans and scrubs and picks up after the children, a picture that is common throughout the world, carries on activities that seem to fit with the job of tending the sick. Certainly bathing patients, emptying bedpans, and changing dressings are not exciting tasks, and it has seemed appropriate that they be performed by people who are used to somewhat similar jobs. The familiar expression, applicable to the household, that a woman's work is never done, could easily be changed to "a nurse's work is never done," and most nurses would heartily agree.

A third factor relates to the cultural belief that women are less independent, less capable of initiative, and less creative than men, and therefore need masculine control and guidance. Responsibility for the diagnosis and treatment of sickness has long resided in the male physician, and with the development of a role that has been subservient to that of the physician in the care of the ill, it is easy for this role to be filled by women.

To these factors must be added the observation that in most societies women have the task of managing the household while men provide food, shelter, and protection. Historically this has been true as well as in the present day. Into the task of household management care of the sick falls quite naturally, if for no other reason than that women are around to do it. In broad perspective, then, we might say that the professional role of nursing has developed historically out of what was originally a household chore.

Through the years nursing as a woman's role has been steadily enhanced. Certainly the starched white uniform and crisp cap bespeak femininity as does the picture called forth by the phrase "angel of mercy." Recruiting posters always feature an attractive young woman in nurse's uniform, and when the patient asks for a nurse he expects to have a woman answer. In the role of nurse the variable of sex is more than an auxiliary characteristic; rather, it constitutes one of the primary or formal aspects of the set of role expectations. Going farther, we can be sure that nurses who have strong masculine traits will be perceived by professional colleagues as more fitted for administration than for bedside nursing. Perception by the patient of a "good" nurse will depend in part on the extent to which she exhibits feminine characteristics in looks, dress, and mannerisms. It might not be unfair to say that the more secure the nurse is in her role as a woman, the more likely she is to be perceived as a capable nurse by physicians, other nurses, and patients.

GENERALIZED FEATURES OF THE NURSE ROLE

In common with the physician there are expectations regarding the nurse role in terms of technical competence, orientation toward others rather than self-interest, and emotional neutrality. Variations within these broad categories occur, however, which distinguish the nurse role from that of the physician. Furthermore, in one of these categories, that of technical competence, are to be found many of the changes that led to the statement at the beginning of the chapter that nursing is in transition. Each of the categories will now be discussed in turn, with somewhat more detailed attention being given to the first.

Skills and Knowledge—Technical Competence

Certification as an R.N. requires that a nurse be educated in a number of areas of knowledge, some of which are specific to nursing while others are not. Of prime necessity is the attainment of a certain level of *proficiency in the natural sciences*, because in this field lies the basis of diagnosis and treatment in scientific medicine. As we shall see in a later section of this chapter, the nurse provides a continuity of care for the patient in the hospital and thus must be alert to the physical status of the patient at all times. Although training in the natural sciences does not approximate that of the physician, the nurse must be knowledgeable concerning basic physiological processes and the signs and symptoms of altered physical state.

Concurrently, the nurse must be able to *carry out a great variety of medical techniques*, such as taking blood pressure, inserting a needle in a vein, operating a suction machine, and giving a variety of medications, including narcotics. Other procedures must be mastered, for example, the sterilizing of equipment and preparation of medications, procedures that are not carried out directly with the patient. The growing sophistication and complexity of medical care has brought an increase in the variety as well as the complexity of medical techniques. Herein lies one of the changes in the role and one of the sources of strain. Nurses have been given increased responsibilities for carrying out many of the technical procedures and for supervising the condition of patients in the absence of a physician. One example can be found in the staffing and action in recovery rooms where the surgeon may not see his patient for some hours after the operation and where the nurse may carry out most if not all of the immediate post-operational procedures. As a result of the increased responsibility, the nurse may be more proficient at certain techniques than the physician. Furthermore, the overlap in skills may lead to ambiguity as to whether the nurse or the physician should carry out a given procedure, such as giving intravenous treatments or blood transfusions. While both physicians and nurses may perceive the nurse role as greatly expanded in terms of technical skills, the limits of this expansion may be differently perceived by the two groups and lead to strain in the social system of the hospital.

Knowledge of the natural sciences and of medical techniques is a common feature of both the physician and nurse roles, although the level of knowledge varies. Specific to nursing, however, is an area of knowledge that might be called *nursing skills.* Here nurses would define their activities with patients as an art, the art of helping people feel better. Thelma Ingles, a nurse, writes that good nursing conveys an unspoken message to the patient that he is being taken care of because the nurse wants to help him feel and get better. The message says further that the patient can be himself with the nurse, that he is safe with her.[4] There are countless ways in which the nurse can demonstrate this message to the patient, feeding or bathing him, changing dressings, fluffing up a pillow, helping him change positions in bed, reassuring him before surgery, running small errands, or just passing the time of day. A good nurse makes the patient feel that he is being taken care of in a manner unmatched by any other health professional.

The contribution of nursing skills to the field of medical care can be understood more fully by making the distinction between *cure* and *care* functions.[5] The former concerns activities of diagnosis and treatment primarily, establishing the nature of the disease or injury and instituting procedures to arrest the disease or promote processes of healing. For example, diagnosis of lobar pneumonia involves auscultating or listening to the patient's chest, noting speed of respiration and pulse, body temperature, evaluating the sound of coughing, and perhaps utilizing the data from blood count or bacterial culture, as well as evaluation of other physical signs. Treatment may involve the giving of antibiotics, bed rest, and the use of an oxygen tent or other procedures. These activities fall within the cure functions in medical care.

Care functions are directed primarily toward the establishment of a positive therapeutic milieu that will facilitate the cure functions. Here nursing skills become of paramount importance. Although some activities of nurses are direct cure functions, as in the giving of medication or the changing of dressings, a great majority are care functions. Not only do the nurse's activities make the patient more comfortable in a physical sense, they also give him emotional support and reassurance, making him more comfortable in a psychological sense.

A slightly different approach to understanding the place of nursing skills in medical care is to view the social system of health services as having *instrumental* and *expressive* aspects. Johnson and Martin[6] have applied this kind of analysis to the nurse role, defining the instrumental problem as that of getting the patient well and the expressive problem as that of managing the tensions of members of the social system. They view these tensions as generated in part by the activities that are necessary to restore the patient to health. In some though not all respects the instrumental-expressive distinction is comparable to the cure-care functions noted above. Although some of the nurse's activities can be regarded as instrumental, she is really the expressive specialist and is mainly responsible for establishing the therapeutic environment. In this regard Johnson and Martin note that many of the nurse's physical acts of care are primarily significant as reflections of her attitudes toward the patient. Here is the art of making people feel better. The result is to help the patient maintain his motivational balance while he is undergoing the technical procedures necessary to bring about a return to health.

The kind and amount of education necessary to assure adequate technical competence in the areas we have just described has been a matter of increasing concern to many nurses. For example, an adequate knowledge of the patient, which is basic to the effective application of nursing skills, requires a grounding in the behavioral as well as the natural sciences. If the nursing staff is to make a nursing diagnosis and to formulate a plan that will mesh with the physician's treatment plan, knowledge about the patient's cultural background, his beliefs about disease, his life values, his psychological needs and defenses may be necessary. The well-trained nurse will therefore need preparation in anthropology, psychology, and sociology.[7] At the same time, knowledge of physiological processes is expanding and medical procedures are becoming more complex. To fulfill her role efficiently the nurse needs more time for preparation in these areas. As a result of these pressures and of the increasing responsibility given the nurse in medical care, a longer period of training seems warranted. Consequently, there has been an increase in "collegiate" programs, with four years of education leading to a bachelor's degree, and more nurses have been obtaining master of science degrees as requisites for teaching, supervision, and administration.[8]

Cross pressures have also been operating, brought about by the growing shortage of nurses. In the United States and other western countries the steady rise in the standard of living and the expansion of medical insurance plans has made good medical care available to ever-increasing numbers of people. Sufficient nurses to meet the problem have not been available. Consequently, hospital and junior college programs of two years in length have developed in addition to the traditional three-year programs.

Herein lies another of the changes in nursing, a differentiation by kind and length of education. The effect on perception is most important. Most of the lay public and even some health professionals probably still perceive nurses as an undifferentiated group from an educational point of view. Many nurses, however, perceive each other as having levels of technical competence that are related to their educational background and should lead to differential rewards in terms of responsibility, pay, and prestige. At the present time this is a transition phase in nursing wherein certain aspects of the role are being redefined, first by nurses themselves, and secondarily by hospital administrators and physicians.

Application of Skills and Knowledge. In the preceding section mention has been made of the increase in responsibility that characterizes present-day nursing as compared to the past. This is an aspect of technical competence, its application, which requires further discussion if we are to understand the complexity of the nurse role today and the manner in which it is changing.

Within the hospital, nurses occupy a key position in terms of supervising and giving care to patients, especially in providing a *continuity of care* over time and across different professional groups. The nurse has a great deal of direct administrative responsibility for patients and at the same time is a coordinator of patient care.

Some examples may clarify this point.[9] In the operating rooms of many hospitals, nurses have the responsibility of scheduling operations, keeping the equipment in proper condition, including its sterility, and assuring aseptic procedures. These tasks are not to be taken lightly in importance, although they are often taken for granted by physicians and even by hospital administrators. On the ward the nurse is the chief arm of the hospital administration, and during the night shift in many hospitals she may be the only representative of management present. Here she carries out the rules and policies of the hospital and the orders of the physician. Neither of these may be simple matters. In the latter case she must often interpret orders to the best of her ability and in keeping with the condition of the patient. Orders for medication are often written to be administered at the discretion of the nurse. Standing orders like "bed rest" or "force liquids," as well as many others, offer a considerable latitude of interpretation. The nurse must also decide when a patient's condition necessitates calling a physician. House staff and attending physicians usually are busy people and unnecessary demands on their time cause annoyance, yet there are often subtle cues to a serious change in a patient's condition that a nurse must recognize and upon which she must act.

On the matter of coordination the nurse stands at the juncture of the cure and care processes in the hospital.[10] Although her role definition emphasizes important care responsibilities, she must also coordinate these with cure functions. Laboratory and x-ray work must be scheduled for her patients, contact made and followed through with the dietary staff, or with physical therapy or social service. Housekeeping services, laundry, and plant maintenance must be dealt with constantly if the ward is to function smoothly and patient care to proceed without interruption and efficiently.

Her position as a coordinator of care means that in the application of skills and knowledge the nurse may have considerable administrative responsibility. One further aspect of this responsibility that we have not mentioned is the supervision of other personnel who are involved in direct care of patients, the practical nurse and the nurse's aide in particular. Here the role of the nurse is undergoing marked transition. To meet the demands of patient load in hospitals there is not only pressure for a shorter training program for the R.N.'s, but also for the utilization of personnel who do not have training as extensive as that of the registered nurse. Being responsible for patient care she must supervise these people, even though at times the result is a growing separation from her direct contact with patients. Later in the chapter we shall return to this problem and the difficulties in nursing that arise from it.

In summary, nurses have responsibility for running a good share of the hospital, a responsibility that grows as the complexity and extent of medical care increase. Again, the majority of the lay public and many health professionals, including physicians, may not realize or may overlook the importance of the nurse in the hospital social system. Resulting perceptions on the part of nurses and their colleagues often lead to stress and to tension.

Many physicians continue to see the nurse as their handmaiden, carrying out their orders and being subservient. They expect willing obedience and are reluctant to accord the nurse the prestige and even the deference that she feels should go with her responsibility.

As pointed out at the beginning of the chapter, the hospital is not the only place where nurses are to be found in our present society, even though the image held by many people of the nurse has a hospital somewhere in the background. Nurses also work in doctors' offices, while countless others are in public health agencies, school systems, and industry. Both in industry and in public health agencies, the nurse often has a great deal of autonomy, doing minor treatment, perhaps delivering babies, giving advice, and calling a physician or recommending his use when she considers such action necessary. For these nurses the physician does not play as active a role in their professional lives as for their colleagues in a hospital situation. When health services broaden, so do the responsibilities of public health and industrial nurses.

Adjustment to the changes we have noted results in a redefinition of the nurse role and of the self-image nurses have of themselves. Nursing is becoming more independent and self-directing, less reliant upon medicine for direction and goals, eager to take a more forthright place in the system of medical care. One indication of the new sense of autonomy was found in the willingness of the American Nurses' Association to support legislation for medical care of the aged through social security, in spite of the opposition to this bill by the American Medical Association. As an editorial states in the *American Journal of Nursing:* "We call ourselves a profession. Essential to this professionalism is the capacity to make independent and forthright decisions on matters relating to the public a profession must serve."[11]

Psychological Support—Orientation Toward Others

When young women enter nursing school many of them say that they want to become a nurse in order to help people, to take care of them. The psychologist would say that these young women are expressing a need for, or a value concerning, nurturance which they feel can be fulfilled in nursing. Psychological support of others and emotional commitment to the patient, often called "tender, loving care," constitute an important aspect of the expectations of the nurse role. Orientation toward others is the general theme, with variations, however, from the other-orientation aspects of the physician role.

Referring once again to the article by Ingles, good nursing is the art of making people feel better and conveys an unspoken message to the patient that the nurse wants to help him get better. Good nursing therefore implies an emotional commitment to take care of the patient, a commitment that is directed primarily to the person as a patient. However, around emotional commitment there is a coalescence of psychological needs on the part of both the nurse and the patient with the expectations of the role.

We noted in the preceding chapter that when a patient becomes ill he tends to regress emotionally and to seek strong narcissistic gratification. His emotional reactions in illness are more like a child's than an adult's. Under these circumstances he tends to perceive those who take care of him in the hospital much as a child perceives his family, especially his parents. He may see the physician as a father image, having characteristics of omniscience, authority, and the giving of a sense of security. He may see the nurse as a mother image, comforting, protecting, supporting, meeting his need for succor. The anthropologist, Weston LaBarre,[12] has characterized this aspect of the nursing role *vis-à-vis* the patient as the *id mother*. In contrast, he feels that the medical social worker can become the *ego mother*, a point that will be discussed more fully in the next chapter. Being the id mother in fantasy, the nurse becomes the focal point of strong needs and reactions, not only for succor and comfort but sometimes for rage and frustration. To the extent that she accepts these needs without being disturbed, and responds to them with interest and loving care, she can do much to speed physical and psychological recovery from illness.

A similar characterization of the nurse role in terms of psychological involvement has been made by Schulman when he distinguishes between the *mother surrogate* and *healer* aspects of nursing.[13] Healing activities center about those tasks that are specifically necessary to combat the patient's affliction and return him to a healthy state. In the main, these activities are the same as those which Mauksch calls cure and which Johnson and Martin call instrumental. Mother surrogate activities center about the everyday tasks of living which the patient must have others do for him. Interaction with the patient is much like that between mother and child in its emotional impact, emphasizing tenderness and compassion. Mother surrogate activities are essentially feminine in nature, while those of the healer are essentially masculine. The nurse fulfills both kinds of activities, often at the same time, and one of her problems is to keep them from clashing, or keep one from dominating the other.

Part of the public image of the nurse lies in the area of her emotional commitment. Data from the survey conducted by Community Studies, Inc., of Kansas City show that the public expects a businesslike relationship more frequently from the schoolteacher or social worker than from the nurse.[14] The author concludes that "the image of the nurse still seems to maintain predominant elements of one whose function it is to provide human companionship (and compassion) and personal services." Not only are many women recruited into nursing because they feel they want to help people, but a good proportion of the public expects that they will exemplify this sort of behavior.

A word of caution is in order again lest the reader assume that nurses are an undifferentiated group in the extent to which they want and have a close emotional relationship with patients. Emphasis on the mother surrogate or id mother aspects of nursing is most likely to occur in a hospital setting, whether it be a general or a psychiatric hospital. In some ways it will be most acute for the private duty nurse who spends all of her working shift with one patient. Nurses who work in industry, doctors' offices, schools, or public health agencies are in situations where the healer aspects of the role are more likely to be emphasized. Emotional commitment to the patient is not so vital a part of the medical care process in these situations because the patient is not as seriously ill and the opportunity for emotional regression on his part is limited. Do these nurses have different psychodynamic needs from their colleagues in hospitals? Do patients perceive hospital nurses differently from nurses in other settings? These questions have not yet been answered; but when they are, more light may be shed on variations in nurse role expectations relative to orientation toward others.

Part of the transition and conflict in nursing today concerns the extent to which the nurse is being pulled away from direct patient care and placed in administrative positions. As we have noted, frequently she is asked to supervise practical nurses or nurses' aides, these two groups often taking her place in terms of emotional involvement with the patient. For the nurse with strong needs for nurturance, conflict between the application of her technical skills and fulfillment of her psychogenic needs can lead to frustration and job dissatisfaction.

Turning to the experimental literature, Argyris found in his study of Cancer Hospital[15] that in their human relations the nurses wanted to be indispensable, self-controlled, and harmonious. They felt that behaving in this way toward patients was necessary and rewarding but that these dispositions could not be fulfilled successfully in administration. Staff nurses resisted administrative responsibility. Furthermore, Argyris concluded that head nurses and supervisors tended to internalize their feelings about subordinates, to be hesitant about discipline or checking up on performance, and to maximize nursing rather than administrative standards.

Results of a rather different nature from those of the Argyris study come from projects about nursing care in two different parts of the country. The first is found in a report by New, Nite, and Callahan[16] concerning hospitals in Kansas City. The investigators altered the staffing patterns among nurses in two hospitals, using two variables, the ratio of staff nurses to auxiliary personnel and the ratio of all nursing personnel to patients. Work activities were observed and questionnaires administered to both hospital personnel and patients. Among other findings, it emerged that when more staff nurses were on the floor they did not spend more time with patients but did other things. Much of the direct patient care was still left to the aides. From the attitudes of the nursing personnel the investigators suggest that a number of nurses who received their training recently regard themselves as highly professional nurses, which they define in terms of technical skills and the assumption of educational, administrative, and supervisory responsibilities. The net result is an emphasis on indirect contact with patients.

New Orleans was the site of the second study, which is described in a series of reports edited by Reissman and Rohrer.[17] Nurses in Charity Hospital expressed the value that direct bedside care is the most important role behavior for a nurse but in the majority of instances the investigators observed that patients received a rather impersonal, assembly-line type of care. Furthermore, in test instruments where role performance could be assessed there was an absence of any reference to bedside care, these tasks being delegated to the nurse aide. In this hospital it appeared that graduate nursing was concerned primarily with the performance of highly technical procedures and supervision of other personnel who would provide the direct patient care Nurses were still indoctrinated with the value of giving that care themselves but in actuality were not trained for it and did not perceive themselves as doing it.

That the three studies just cited vary in results and conclusions is indicative of the kind of change and strain that can be found in nursing today. How to keep the psychological satisfactions that are inherent in direct patient care but yet to supervise the technical aspects of patient care as it becomes more complex and extensive, is a fundamental question facing all of nursing. It may mean changes in the kinds of persons recruited for nursing, or in educational procedures, and in the perception which most nurses have of their role. All of this is related to the transition question posed at the end of the section on technical competence. Moreover, it is a variation of it, though an important one, for it reaches to deep levels of satisfaction or frustration within the personality.

Controlled Involvement—Detached Concern

One of the aims of good medical care is to return the patient to health as soon as possible and to bring every resource to bear that may contribute to the accomplishment of this end. At other times the aim may necessarily be to make the terminally ill patient as comfortable as possible or to aid a patient to adjust to an irreversible physical handicap. Inherent in the role of the nurse, as in that of the physician, is the requirement that she give the best care possible to every patient under her responsibility. She must not let dislike of a patient interfere with her nursing duties. We are dealing, then, with the concept of *detached concern*, but it is a complex variable in the role of the nurse and bears careful analysis. In brief, the nurse is expected in her role to give strong emotional support to the patient, yet at the same time certain features have to be built into her role to protect both her and the patient from emotional involvement that is too deep or of the wrong kind. Thus, she is not expected to be emotionally neutral in the sense that she shows no emotion, but in the sense that *all* patients have a right to her emotional support and that there are clear limitations on her emotional involvement.

The emotional needs and the projections of the patient cannot be allowed to get out of hand. Therefore, the nurse must be warm and feminine as a mother but reserved as a woman. Concern for a sick patient and his needs in the hospital must not be allowed to extend to involvement with a real person and his life outside the hospital. Each patient has strong emotional ties which he brings with him to the hospital; these cannot be broken or tampered with by the ministrations of the nurse. The patient is vulnerable to emotional exploitation during his emotional regression and must be protected, but so must the hospital and the nurse herself.[18]

Nurses who are personally insecure may react by being as aseptic in their emotional involvement with patients as they are in their operating room technique. They cannot give tender, loving care because they cannot draw a line between the sick patient and the real person whose emotional ties extend into the world outside the hospital.

One protection to both nurse and patient is the proscription against falling in love with a patient, one of the *mores* of nursing. The nurse who falls in love with a patient and marries him is perceived as betraying her trust in the eyes of her colleagues. It implies that she has taken advantage of the patient's vulnerability and given preference to private interest and emotional gratification over professional obligation.[19] As we have said, the nurse is expected to regard each patient emotionally the same as all others lest she be unable to take care of all her patients to the best of her ability.

Another kind of protection, which is more of a *folkway* because it does not carry strong social sanctions, is a tendency to refer to patients as cases: "My jaundice case in number 117 is coming along nicely." This does not necessarily mean that the nurse has depersonalized her relationship with that patient; rather, the statement may signify only a protective emotional reserve. A closely allied technique is the use of the pronoun "we" in talking with a patient about his condition or his care. "How did we sleep last night?" has been uttered to many a patient when the morning shift comes on, or the nurse might say in a friendly way, "Are we ready for a bath and back rub?"

The amount of emotional reserve or social distance that is used as a protective device in role fulfillment depends in part on the stage of the patient's illness. In the early stage, when the illness is acute, the nurse can give freely of warm, tender affection, catering to the infantile needs for succor and care. At this stage the patient is not responding emotionally as an adult, but as a child. When the patient begins to convalesce, her techniques for increasing social distance must be brought into play. The cartoons about patients with roving hands apply to that stage of illness when the patient has begun to lose his narcissistic preoccupation and to take an interest in the world about him once again. When this stage is reached everyone knows that the patient is on the road to recovery, and nurses sometimes have to learn to be masters of the quick "brush-off."

Dealing with male patients is different in some respects from dealing with female patients. In both cases the nurse can function as an id mother, granting recognition to the emotional needs of the patient and responding with support and gratification. She has the problem of leading the patient back emotionally to an adult status, of changing dependence on her to dependence on self, of shifting orientation from the sickroom to the world outside. It is in this process that her role as a woman enters her dealings with male patients and she may need to show more social distance from them than from her patients who are women. Perhaps, at this stage, she has to shift from the symbolic mother image to the symbolic sister relationship.

Giving of warmth, sympathy, and loving care to the ill patient—emotional involvement with the patient as the id mother—cannot be done without some cost to the nurse. There must be strong sources of these positive emotions within the nurse because involvement with patients in a therapeutically effective way involves a continuous emotional discharge or output. Nurses who genuinely want to help people and are secure in their own personality integration can provide the attachment, but even for them a line must be drawn. If a nurse were to take every case to heart, or carry her cares home with her, the load would be impossible. Patients do suffer intensely, and some die, frustrating the best efforts of medical and nursing care. Therefore, built into the nursing role is what the sociologists call *functional specificity.* The emotional commitment, part of the nurse's function, is specific to the sickroom or hospital situation, and to the stage of illness when the patient needs loving support. The nurse is expected to leave her cares at her place of employment, not to take them home with her. When she goes through the door of the hospital, she must think of other things. Also, once the patient has gone beyond the stage of severe illness, the nurse must disengage herself emotionally and concentrate her energies on those who are more in need of this kind of help.

Another illustration of functional specificity comes from the different manner in which nurses often perceive blood donors in distinction from patients, for the blood donor hardly falls into the patient or sick role. At such times a jocular, often flirtatious manner may be used along with the businesslike approach to the technical aspects of the job. For one thing, the encounter is a short one; for another, the patient is not in pain or suffering, not emotionally regressed. The nurse can be a woman as well as a mother figure without danger. However, let one of the donors be admitted to the hospital as a patient and a perceptible change in attitude will occur, the mother figure remaining but the woman subdued.

Private duty nurses are perhaps more vulnerable to the perils of emotional involvement than their colleagues in general duty nursing, for the latter have so many patients that attachments to specific ones do not occur as easily. The private duty nurse must be especially careful to draw a linc between her job and the rest of her life, to be quite functionally specific in her emotional involvement; otherwise the strain may be too great.

Role Rewards and Attendant Problems

From a sociological point of view adequate role performance involves rewards of some kind: money, prestige, power, security. From a personality point of view psychological satisfactions must accrue from the role performance, or other rewards must be present, if the individual is to perform the role without conflict and tension. In roles where there is considerable outgo of emotion, as in the service professions, adequate rewards are necessary to keep frustration within normal limits. For the nurse one of the best kinds of reward is appreciation by the patient, openly expressed, for what the nurse has done—symbolically a return of love. Most hospitals, or nurses themselves, have rules against the practice of tipping; so that appreciation must be expressed through the spoken or written word, or some other kind of action. Many nurses can attest to the response that comes from good and thoughtful care, but can also tell of the frustration that arises when the patient takes this attention as a matter of course and makes no return.

For rewards of prestige in society, money, or power, the nurse may be at some disadvantage as compared to other professional groups, which is certainly true in the case of the physician. In the hierarchy of most hospitals the nurse is considerably below the physician in terms of prestige, although in some institutions those nurses who occupy top positions of responsibility receive due recognition for their status. In the world outside the hospital, the nurse is likely to have less prestige than persons in some other occupations that fall into the same salary range. One study of a sample of registered nurses in the state of Ohio sought to compare nursing with schoolteaching and social work.[20] In answer to the question, "Which occupation do you think is more respected by the public?" nearly half the nurses indicated schoolteaching, while only 18 per cent selected nursing. The Kansas City study of public images of the nurse[21] showed that schoolteachers were given a better Occupation Evaluation Index than the nurse by all socioeconomic groups except the lowest, and in this group the difference was not statistically significant.

There is no question that the prestige which nurses feel will vary from one hospital and community to another, and that the statements made above have only general validity. The tone set by the hospital administration and medical staff toward the nursing service will make considerable difference in the degree to which individual nurses perceive that they have an important and valuable place in the medical system.

The type of reward found in income places the nurse in the same category as a number of other occupational groups, including schoolteachers, social workers, clergymen, and some college instructors. Although salaries in nursing have increased in recent years, they have not kept pace with the relative income of physicians or of certain skilled occupations that have become unionized. Consequently, nursing as a career does not have the same income attraction as even good office jobs or other occupations. Actually, the main rewards from nursing seem to be the intrinsic psychological satisfactions of the job of caring for patients and certain secondary aspects, such as the preparation which nurses think their training gives them for marriage and the possibility of a satisfactory job for extra income once the children are in school.

The problems of reward for role fulfillment, reflected in prestige and income, are the source of some of the noticeable stresses in nursing today that create uneasiness on at least the upper levels in the profession. We will defer a discussion of these strains, however, until later in the chapter.

EMPIRICAL STUDIES OF NURSING ROLE

Discussion of the role of the nurse up to this point has been largely theoretical, although a few references have been made to empirical studies. When we turn to the research literature we find that there are a number of studies that deal with personality characteristics of nurses, with the perception that nurses have of their role, with attitudes of the public toward nursing, and with the ways in which nurses might be differentiated according to personal goals and values rather than according to functional variables of the work situation.[22] The studies discussed below cannot be regarded as definitive in terms of their representativeness of the profession as a whole. They are limited by area of the country, sampling, and range of variables considered; but they nevertheless add a dimension to the theoretical discussion of the nurse role, and suggest gaps in our knowledge of factors underlying the role perception and performance of the nurse.

Personality Patterns

Adequate performance in a given role demands a congruence between the social expectations of the role and the personality structure of the role incumbents. In the previous sections we have outlined the generalized role expectations for nurses; now we turn to data that indicate broad personality patterns in certain groups of nurses. We referred on page 252 to the study by Argyris of nurses in Cancer Hospital. In addition, there are studies by Mauksch and by Cleveland, which compare nurses with other kinds of people, and a study by Lentz and Michaels, which compares two different kinds of nurses, medical and surgical.

Mauksch compared nursing students and graduate nurses with college students, using the Activities Index.[23] The test is designed to measure the strength of psychogenic needs in the Murray definition, as listed in note 13 of Chapter 2, and is the same test used in differentiating gynecologists and pediatricians, to which we referred in Chapter 6. Mauksch found that the need profiles of both groups of nurses were different from those of the college students. In the area of interpersonal warmth and association the nurses were higher on affiliation, succor, and nurturance. In the area of internal controls and anxiety the nurses were higher on deference, order, blamavoidance, harmavoidance, and infavoidance. Mauksch concluded that nurses could be described as strongly motivated to be with people, while at the same time exhibiting a concern for internal controls and for security. From interviews with nurses there was evidence that the affiliative and nurturant needs were consciously formulated and strong; in other words, they might be called goal-defining needs. The control and security seeking needs were not so clearly formulated, and probably functioned in subtle ways to influence the choice of conditions under which the defined goals might be sought.

Utilizing projective test material Cleveland compared groups of nursing students and graduate nurses with dietitian interns and staff dietitians.[24] His study has an advantage over many others in that successive groups of nursing students and dietitian interns were tested, which gave him a good measure of reliability in his findings. The particular test used was the Thematic Apperception Test, administered in a group situation, and scored quantitatively for the presence of certain themes or the use of certain categories of words. In addition, all groups were asked to indicate the reasons for choosing their particular vocation.

Dietitian interns exceeded nursing students in themes that stressed achievement and success. The latter group also liberally sprinkled their statements with emotionally toned words involving feelings of suffering, discomfort, and anguish, and used words denoting sadness and loneliness. A greater number of nursing students than dietitian interns referred to parental enforcement in the TAT stories and generally attributed negative attitudes to parental figures. The same overall thematic patterns were found at the staff level but the differences between nurses and dietitians were not so striking as between the students. Also, the staff groups did not differ significantly on the parental attitudes and the "sad-lonely" words.

On the questionnaire nurses placed self-sacrifice for the suffering high on the list of reasons for choosing nursing, some of them reporting that a strong urge impelled them toward nursing. The dietitians gave answers indicating more of an interest in intellectual gratification in a field of science, and a desire to achieve prestige at a professional level.

Grouping together the Mauksch and Cleveland studies with that of Argyris, we have three studies from different parts of the country which are rather remarkable in showing common features in the personality patterns of nurses. On both a fantasy and a conscious level there is an emphasis on empathy with other people, on the need for nurturance, and an awareness of strong emotional feelings. At the same time there are internalized controls, probably represented in a strong superego, which keep the emotions in check. When we consider the role expectations of emotional commitment and orientation toward others, coupled with the necessity for emotional neutrality and control, there appears to be congruence between the social demands and personality patterns.

Within the hospital situation different medical care requirements mean variation in tasks for the staff that are perhaps best fulfilled with people who have different sets of personality patterns. Medical and surgical wards are cases in point, and we noted in Chapter 6 that there appeared to be variation in personality characteristics between surgeons and internists. Do differences also exist between nurses who prefer one type of ward over the other? Lentz and Michaels seem to think that they do.[25] They first asked a panel of physicians and nurses if they thought there were differences, and found that specialists in both the medical and surgical areas were inclined to say they could be found. Medical nurses were described as having a higher liking for people, more tolerance for those needing psychological support and for older or cranky patients. Surgical nurses were described as more tolerant of the impersonality involved in rapid turnover of patients, more satisfied with techniques than relations with people, quicker acting, and more inclined to enjoy physical activity.

Next, the investigators studied a group of nurses with a strong medical syndrome and a group with a strong surgical syndrome, and found different interests expressed by each group. The former preferred coronary cases, patients needing tender, loving care, occasional psychological problems in patients, diagnoses that are puzzling, a slow turnover, and a quiet work station. They also preferred to be talkative. The nurses with the surgical syndrome preferred accident cases, self-reliant patients, especially those with no psychological problems, a clear diagnosis, fast turnover, and a busy work station. They also preferred not to be talkative. One can speculate at the differences that might have been found if the investigators had also used projective techniques.

Although there are general expectations for the nurse role, there are task differences within nursing. Those who enter the profession apparently get sorted to some degree, according to differences in personality characteristics, into groups requiring varied task performance. To understand this procedure more explicitly we need to know much more about the selection process, and to include in our studies public health nurses and private duty, industrial, supervisory and administrative, as well as surgical and medical, nurses.

Role Rewards, Job Satisfaction, and Attitudes Toward Nursing

Consideration of the satisfactions which nurses derive from their jobs and their perception of the profession constitute another group of studies. To a certain extent they overlap those just cited, but provide interesting data from a somewhat different point of view.

The general duty nurse in the hospital is the focus of a study by Stewart and Needham,[26] a social scientist and nurse team, carried out in ten general hospitals in Arkansas. The investigators were mainly interested in nurse function, but also report some data that are useful here, mainly in terms of the rewards which the nurse perceives as important for role fulfillment. The hospitals from which the material came were representative of the state in that some were large, others small, some sectarian, others private or county controlled. Nurses, physicians, and patients were interviewed and nursing procedures carefully observed.

Nurses were asked if they would recommend nursing as a career to a younger sister or daughter. Ninety-two per cent gave an unqualified "yes," their reasons falling into the following categories in order of importance. The personal, psychological satisfactions to be gained from the work, interest in bedside nursing, constituted the largest group. In second place was the opportunity for service which nursing offers, helping those who cannot help themselves. Next came reasons classified as the general value of nursing education and experience for life, the good background for marriage and rearing a family. Finally, the income, prestige, and occupational security which nursing offers was given as a reason, but by only 14 per cent of the sample, compared to 66 per cent giving the first reason. Interestingly, among those physicians in the study who would recommend nursing as a career to sister or daughter, the reasons fell in just the reverse order. Most of the physicians indicated the income and prestige reason, whereas only a few indicated the psychological satisfaction reason.

Further support for the perception of rewards in terms of psychological satisfaction can be found in answers to the question about desirability of promotion to nursing supervisor or director of nursing service. Eighty per cent indicated they did not want such promotion, a finding similar to that by Argyris in Cancer Hospital. Reasons for the rejection could be classified as dislike of the responsibilities involved, administrative and patient-oriented responsibilities, especially in hospitals where there were no residents or interns; and secondly, as unhappiness in removal from bedside nursing. Also, in studying complaints of nurses, it was found that the most general complaint centered on the belief that they were not being given enough bedside nursing in their daily work.

A second study has already been cited, that by Bullock.[27] He drew a sample from the files of the Ohio State Nurses' Association and gathered his data by the use of a questionnaire administered by mail, which obtained a response rate of 60 per cent. His results are based on a final population of 500 cases. Although the aim of the study was to gather information about job satisfaction, there are data on expectations of the nursing role, the rewards that go with the role, and nurses' impressions of public attitudes toward their occupation.

The consensus of the respondents was that hospital nurses felt they work under more rigid discipline than women in other occupations and have fewer opportunities for social activities. They must take and follow orders more frequently, must more often accept criticism without complaint, and must show more obedience. Also, they felt that nurses have more rules to abide by than women in other occupations, and that their work requires more precision.

The great majority did not agree that nurses become more hardened and less feminine than women in other occupations, or that they become old-maidish. However, they did not feel that the profession provides a good steppingstone to other kinds of work.

Other features of role perception, especially in relation to rewards for role fulfillment, appeared when the nurse was asked to compare her occupation with schoolteaching and social work on a number of variables, occupations that have comparable status and are most open to women. Nearly 90 per cent felt that it was the best preparation for marriage and family life, a finding similar to that of the Stewart and Needham study. In terms of its value as a part-time occupation, a great majority indicated that nursing was superior. Many saw nursing as a desirable way of supplementing their husband's income. Again, the results agree with those of Stewart and Needham.

The features of any role always include the expectations of the role incumbent regarding other people's attitudes toward the role. In this study the consensus of the respondents was that nurses thought the public perceives nursing as a profession, that nurses are hard workers, alert, devoted, and independent or self-directing in the use of considerable technical knowledge. At the same time, the respondents indicated that nurses are not properly appreciated and are looked upon somewhat as servants who engage in a rather unpleasant occupation. About 50 per cent agreed that the public thinks nurses are "freer" in sex matters than other women.

Whether or not these expectations represent reality is another question. However, they do constitute "psychological reality" for the nurse in her role, and that is the important point for role perception and performance.

Studies by Deutscher in Kansas City dealt with public images of the nurse and with the image which physicians have of nurses.[28] A subsample of respondents from a representative sample of the metropolitan area was utilized, data being gathered by means of a standardized interview schedule. Results were analyzed against the variables of socioeconomic status and sex, and images of the nurse were compared with those of the social worker and schoolteacher on a number of variables.

The sample was divided into four socioeconomic groups: I, representing upper-middle or professional and executive people; II, lower-middle or white-collar people; III, working or blue-collar; and IV, the lower class, people who live on a bare subsistence level. On the basis of an Occupation Evaluation Index, it was found that evaluation of the nurse became more favorable as one moved down the socioeconomic scale. Furthermore, open-ended questioning revealed that the images at the top and bottom of the socioeconomic scale concentrated on different elements.

In essence, the core element of the opinions of Group I concerned the sex role. Professional nursing is not ladylike, for it exposes young ladies to intimate contact with strange males and hardens them. Nurses were described as cynical, unsympathetic, not so refined as the average woman, and brusque—a picture almost completely lacking in interviews with the lowest socioeconomic group. There was a positive side to this picture, however; for at the same time nurses were thought to be composed, competent, and emotionally stable. Considering both negative and positive aspects, the conclusion reached was that there was "sufficient evidence to indicate that the top ISC group image of the nurse centers around the divorce of the young woman from what is considered her traditional feminine role."[29]

Most respondents in the lowest socioeconomic group described nurses as sympathetic, kind, understanding, more patient than most people. Hardly any respondents in the top group made such comments. Thus, the lower-class person saw the nurse more as a mother figure, the upper class more as a servant figure.

Women evaluated the nurse more favorably than did men. Men were inclined to perceive the nurse as different from other women in terms of her training, education, and knowledge. Some men gave this positive value; others saw it as indicative of encroachment on traditional male superiority. Women did not perceive the nurse in a competitive, resentful way; rather, they saw her as less self-oriented than most women are usually thought to be, and as more interested in the problems and well-being of other people. In the case of both men and women, these are general pictures with individual variations being found. They do represent a consensus of the respondents.

Comparisons of teachers, social workers, and nurses showed that teachers were evaluated slightly more favorably than nurses, but that social workers were rated much less favorably than the other two groups. This evaluation was consistent for both men and women, and for the various socioeconomic groups, except Group IV, which gave a slightly more favorable rating to nurses than to teachers.

Each respondent was asked to react to three descriptive phrases for each occupation: "kind and sympathetic," "businesslike and efficient," and "blundering and incompetent." Each was asked to indicate the phrase best describing the way nurses are, and the one describing the way they ought to be, and to do the same for social workers and teachers. The results indicated that the respondents agreed that nurses should be kind and sympathetic, although not all thought they are; and that teachers should be more businesslike. Respondents indicated that though the nurse is regarded as a professional person this does not mean social distance between herself and the patient. *In their image of the nurse the predominant element is that of providing human companionship, compassion, and personal services.*

A different phase of the Kansas City study dealt with the image of nurses held by physicians. A sample was drawn from the directories of the medical societies in the area, and data were gathered by the use of a questionnaire administered by mail.

Though some of the physicians were critical of the growing professionalization of nursing, the majority still gave a positive evaluation of the nurse. Type of specialty had little effect on the evaluation, but it was found that older physicians were more favorably inclined toward the nurse than their younger colleagues. When the sample was divided into a series of age-groups, it was found that the break in attitude came about age fifty-five, which suggests, the investigators believe, a generational difference in evaluation. The older men tend to remember the nurse more as a faithful, obedient, subservient subordinate, and are not so aware of the trends toward professionalization.

The physician sample was asked to react to the attributes "kind and sympathetic," "businesslike and efficient," and "blundering and incompetent" as applied to nurses. The majority preferred the ministering angel type, although the proportion was smaller among the younger men. Physicians indicated that nurses were not as kind and sympathetic as they should be, but were at the humanitarian pole as compared with schoolteachers and social workers.

To summarize some of the major points in this section, most nurses feel that there are psychological satisfactions to be gained from the practice of their skills, emotional gratification from giving bedside nursing to others. Here they reflect the orientation toward others rather than toward the self which is part of the role. The public image seconds this. People expect companionship and compassion from the nurse, although this is more true for women than for men and for people in the lower socioeconomic groups.

Nurses feel that their education and training provide good preparation for marriage and the rearing of a family, a perception that is shared by women among the general public. Nurses also look upon their work as a way to supplement family income after marriage, as a skill that is not lost by time.

On the other hand, nurses feel that they are not always appreciated, that some parts of the public place them somewhat in a servant class. The Kansas City data show that people in the higher socioeconomic groups do have a tendency in this direction. Thus, the psychological rewards which nurses find in role fulfillment are a bit tainted and a potential source of frustration and dissatisfaction to the insecure incumbent of this role.

Work Attitudes: Typologies of Nurses

Although there may be broad personality patterns in common among those who enter nursing, we have indicated that different task requirements within nursing may be associated with variations in personality variables. Another kind of differentiation may also be made, one based on the attitudes that the nurse has toward her job rather than the functional requirements of that job. Variation among nurses in the way they approach their work can be important in terms of interaction with patients and of the impression nurses make on the public.

In the course of their study of the general duty nurse in Missouri hospitals, Habenstein and Christ[30] evolved three types or categories of nurses, based on work attitudes and the place of nursing in the individual's life. Their typology draws on data from only one kind of nurse, general duty, and the dimensions they use do not exhaust the field, but their conclusions are interesting and may stimulate further research.

First, they describe the *professionalizer*—a nurse who focuses not so much on the patient as on the techniques, mechanical and psychological, that must be used to facilitate the healing process. The basic sciences present the nurse with a set of tools to use and the key to treatment, therefore, is knowledge. Professional prerogatives are important, as are membership in organizations, symbols of status, and trust by society for the job she is asked to do.

> The trust she receives implies her use of judgment; but the judgment of the professionalizing nurse is not felt by her to be subject to public review; her function, through the use of such judgment based on training, accrued medical and clinical experience, she believes, *is to create appropriate therapeutic* (healing) *situations.* In the drama of healing, she stage-manages adroitly, and although the doctor demands his dramatic prominence and always plays the lead, she is the "stalwart character who must always be ready to pick up a missed cue."[31]

A second type is called the *traditionalizer*, representative of a sense of devotion in the image of Florence Nightingale. Her approach to nursing is based on the wisdom of accumulated traditional experience, with the new suspect and the old always preferable. If new ideas are to be accepted, they must prove themselves better than those they seek to replace.

Her focus is on the patient, as an individual and as a personality, to whom she brings the healing arts as long practiced in home and community. She is a selfless adjunct to the physician, showing him complete and unquestioning deference, a dedicated "saint of mercy" to the public, and a personality resource to the patient.

Finally, there is the *utilizer*, a type motivated by short-term goals, with no particular dedication to an ideal, and no life philosophy in which her work occupies a central role. Her work role begins at the start of her shift and ends as she leaves the institution at the end of the day. Innovations or changes are accepted or rejected on the basis of their immediate return in the form of time, labor, or personal effort saved. The main concern is the job and to get the job done adequately. On this basis she asks to be judged by her colleagues and the public. Her involvement in nursing as a collective image outside herself is minimal; rather, she is more attuned toward community and family.

A rather similar typology was developed by another investigator. In a study of nursing students Waik[32] speaks of the *theoretician*, who sees nursing as a means to something else, who is critical of all facets of nursing, who seeks recognition and is concerned with professional values and attitudes; of the *practitioner*, who sees nursing as an end in itself and finds satisfaction in bedside care, and where qualities of motherliness and femininity are strong; and of the *individualist*, who is a nonconformist, cynical, and has little eagerness to learn.

Most of the changes in nursing, which arise within nursing itself, come from the professionalizer or the theoretician. Most physicians prefer the traditionalizer or practitioner, and older physicians, in particular, hark back to the days when most nurses were of this type; while both they and their younger colleagues decry the drive toward professionalization. Finally, it must be remembered that much nursing is still done by the utilizer, who seeks to supplement her husband's income and to fill her life with things to do as the children grow up.

CHANGES AND STRAINS IN NURSING

In his provocative article about the occupation of nursing, Lyle Saunders has this to say:

> A final point to be made about nursing as an occupation is that it is changing. And the rate and direction of change are possibly largely outside the control of nurses themselves. The past fifty years have been years of moving away from a concentration on sick people to a concentration on the mechanical and technical aspects of therapy and care. They have witnessed the change of the nurse from a self-employed entrepreneur to a salaried employee; from a person who worked largely alone and self-directed to one who shares in a minute and highly specialized division of labor; from one whose relationships with those she worked among were close, intimate, and personal to one whose working relationships with both patients and colleagues are subjected to strong pressures toward becoming both impersonal and segmental; from one whose skills and functions were generalized, to one whose skills and functions are very highly specialized.[33]

Throughout the chapter we have pointed to areas in nursing where change is taking place, and where strains are likely to occur in self-perception and in relationships with other health professionals. At the risk of some repetition a concluding section on changes and strains is appropriate, summarizing points made earlier, expanding the discussion in some cases, and drawing implications for other health professionals as well as for nurses.

Behind the changes in nursing lies the growing complexity of medical care, complexity in terms of medical techniques and treatment, in terms of bureaucratic structure in hospitals and other medical care facilities, and in terms of the utilization of medical care by the public. Taking care of the sick is no longer a simple matter.

The major changes are therefore in *responsibility* and *function* relative to patient care. Within these two factors there are three interrelated aspects: an increased scope of responsibility for cure and care activities related to patients, increased supervision of auxiliary health personnel, and a greater emphasis on the co-ordinating function.

A number of examples have been cited that illustrate the broadening of cure and care activities: supervision of the recovery room, administration of the operating room, carrying out new technical procedures, taking over procedures that once had been performed almost exclusively by physicians, making a nursing diagnosis to be integrated with the physician's treatment plan, and providing a continuity of care for the patient among a variety of specialists and over a period. In hospitals where there is no house staff the nurse must often make decisions about cure or care procedures in the absence of medical authority. Also, there are many times during a twenty-four-hour-period, especially at night, when she may be the only representative of administration in the hospital. It is not unfair to say that nurses make the hospital run, and in larger medical centers the nursing service has an increasingly autonomous role.

Utilization of auxiliary personnel in the form of practical nurses and aides means that nurses have the task of supervising their activities. Ideally, auxiliary personnel have been viewed as performing tasks that consume a great deal of time of the highly trained nurse, yet do not require her technical competence—tasks like emptying bedpans, bringing meals and beverages, giving back rubs, making beds. Operationally speaking, the practical nurse in some hospitals has taken over other tasks such as the giving of certain medications, even taking and recording various physiological measurements. Great variation in the use of auxiliary personnel will be found between hospitals, but the net effect has been to involve the registered nurse in more supervisory activities, or in the technical procedures of medical care. When she does have an opportunity to come to the patient's bedside, it may be for the purpose of performing a complicated treatment procedure or to check on the activities of one of the auxiliary personnel. Not only does the nurse take on more supervisory activities, she has less chance to give direct patient care.

The position of coordinator of activities that impinge directly or indirectly on the patient is more and more often applied to the nurse, especially in large hospitals. Besides direct patient-care tasks, there are housekeeping activities to be integrated, records to be kept, supplies to be ordered, teaching to be done, and other professional services to be integrated with the eating, sleeping, and medication schedule of each patient. Although the hospital administrator will be concerned with some of these tasks, throughout the hospital it is the nurse who must articulate them on the patient floors. Often she must know something about hotel administration, group dynamics, business finance, and pedagogy as well as the art of nursing skills. The demands of coordination are high but ambiguous, and the frustrations are many.

Some noticeable strains occur along with these changes in responsibility and function. First among them is the inability to do more bedside nursing. Stewart and Needham found that even the general duty nurses included in their study spent only 22 per cent of their time in direct patient care, with a larger proportion being taken by supervision of other personnel, record-keeping, and care and procurement of supplies and equipment. The nurses did not like the situation and often complained about it. Argyris noted in his survey of Cancer Hospital that staff nurses resented the adding of administrative responsibilities to their work, in part because it took them away from contact with patients. Numerous studies have shown that the psychological satisfactions in taking care of patients are of prime importance to many nurses. On the other hand, the studies from Kansas City and New Orleans, cited earlier, indicate that many nurses perceive their tasks more as supervising direct care or the carrying out of technical procedures. Many did not spend time with patients when they had the opportunity. A conflict obviously exists in this area and some nurses may feel that they are not meeting those needs that originally motivated them toward nursing. Furthermore, if the nurse-patient relationship is to be important in recovery, the nurse must continue to have some kind of close personal contact with the patient. At the same time, she cannot be a good supervisor of auxiliary personnel in patient care if she does not have a continuing experience in that function herself. A great many nurses are bothered by the dilemma thus presented, but as yet it has not been solved satisfactorily.

A second strain lies in the ambiguity of responsibility for procedures, between the registered nurse and practical nurse, on the one hand, and the physician on the other. Merton[34] has referred to this as the *zone of ambiguity*, a lack of clarity about who can do what. Physicians often expect the nurse to carry out a greater variety of cure tasks, yet have not been specific in granting authority or defining limits. Registered nurses are reluctant to have the practical nurse do more of the traditional nursing, yet admit that good patient care in a modern hospital requires more effort than the number of registered nurses alone can supply. In many cases the overlap in task performance by the two kinds of nurses is considerable, yet ill defined.

That registered nurses should feel ambivalent toward the practical nurse is hardly surprising. Often bitter in interviews, the registered nurse says, in effect, why devote three years or more to fulfilling the R.N. requirements when one can become a practical nurse in a much shorter time and yet do all the same things. Distortions of perception do occur on the part of the nurse toward some of her colleagues, and many nurses will be anxious and unhappy until a clearer definition of function relative to other role categories is established.

Concurrent with the shift in responsibility and function have come changes in the educational preparation of many nurses. The basic hospital program of three years' training has remained, and continues to train the great majority of nurses. However, the baccalaureate program, in which the nurse spends four years in both hospital and college, has grown steadily.

In the other direction, there has been pressure for a two-year hospital program to help meet the demand for more nurses. We have noted that one of the results of this variation in education is a differential perception among nurses of each other, a potential source of strain. In addition, a somewhat different result may be inherent in the differences in educational background. Three-year hospital schools of nursing usually operate on a modified apprentice system where the nursing students fulfill important service functions for the hospital as well as having an educational experience. This system was adequate to train the majority of nurses in the past but it may not be adequate to train nurses for the added responsibilities that go with nursing today in the larger medical centers. We have pointed to rather substantial changes in the role of the nurse, calling for an autonomous, self-directing, professional person, a role model or an image which the nurse who is trained in a hospital program may be inadequately prepared to fulfill.

In addition to functions related to patient care, other changes in the role are also occurring. For one, nurses are becoming interested in research, in doing research themselves, either on their own or as active members of an interdisciplinary team. Reference to the book by Hughes, Hughes, and Deutscher,[35] to that by Stewart and Needham,[36] or to many studies in the United States Public Health Service shows that nurses have become active participants in or directors of research projects. One of the characteristics of a profession is continuing inquiry into its function and research that leads to an expansion of the body of knowledge peculiar to that profession or underlying a number of professions. In nursing, as in social work, participation in research is an important aspect of the attempt to reach professional status.

Strains occur, however, in this new aspect of the nurse's role. For one thing, the research nurse realizes that she is a different kind of nurse from her colleague who is on general duty, and she may wonder where her identification lies. Is she really a nurse or is she a scientist? The research nurse, therefore, may be another example of a marginal role with all the tensions attendant on the ambiguity in that status. In the second place, nurses do not receive training in research design or scientific method as part of their regular education. They may feel inferior to researchers in other fields and other research scientists may perceive the nurse as an inadequate colleague. Nurses who participate in research with physicians, especially if they do not have full partnership in planning the study and the analysis, seldom are mentioned as collaborators on the title page of a published paper, even though other physicians who lent only moral support are given such recognition. Dissatisfaction and frustration by the nurse are logical consequences. The nurse in research is, therefore, in the position of proving her worth; consequently, schools of nursing are now offering graduate courses in research design, and nurses frequently seek doctorates in one of the scientific fields basic to medicine or nursing. Regretfully, some feel that they are no longer nurses when they finish.

Participation in research is only one part, however, of the general concern about professional status. Many within nursing see the role as achieving the level of a profession and through advanced education and increase in responsibility for the nurse seek to advance that end. Not all nurses are at ease with this definition of the role, nor are many physicians or other health professionals willing to admit the nurse to full professional status. At the same time, Goode[37] questions whether nursing will be able to gain standing as a profession, defined in sociological terms. The issue will not be solved quickly and in the meantime will continue to generate strong emotional reactions by nurses and by those in other fields.

Running through all the changes in the role of the nurse is the question of reward. Her role requires long training and high technical competence; the public expects service, devotion to duty, and emotional support; and most physicians want willing obedience. Her main rewards are the psychological satisfactions of ministering to sick people, but she finds herself being pulled farther and farther away from the patient. Her financial remuneration is low, often not commensurate with her responsibilities, and varies considerably among different kinds of hospitals. Her prestige often is in the shadow of the physician, often reduced by the auxiliary roles, practical nurse and nurse's aide, that are developing in the medical care field. She is eager to be regarded as a professional and willing to invest the additional time for education toward that end, yet needs the prestige recognition of a professional to make the task worthwhile. Expansion of her technical competence and responsibility leads many a nurse to feel that she deserves more of a colleague and less of a handmaiden status in her relations with physicians. To be sure, these remarks do not apply to all nurses, perhaps not even to a large proportion of them. They do apply, however, to increasing numbers and to those in the profession who are and who will be its leaders. In the long run they will affect young women who have an interest in nurse's training. Rewards for role performance remain a strain for the nurse and of important consequence to all those who work closely with her.

NOTES TO CHAPTER 8

1. For a discussion of the difference between an occupation and a profession the reader is referred to Goode, William J., "Encroachment, Charlatanism, and the Emerging Profession: Psychology, Sociology, and Medicine," *American Sociological Review*, vol. 25, December, 1960, pp. 902–914. Goode states that occupations lie along a continuum of professionalism. The core aspects of professional status lie in a prolonged specialized training in a body of abstract knowledge, and a collectivity or service orientation. From these core features certain sociologically derivative traits can be noted, including high prestige, power, income, and control of standards by members of the profession. Goode maintains that nursing has yet to demonstrate its claim to a body of abstract knowledge that is sufficiently different from that of medicine, and therefore does not fully qualify as a profession.

2. A study of the male nurse as a marginal role is one that, so far as I know, has been neglected thus far. There are potential data in such a study for contemporary role theory and for the interrelation between personality and social systems.

3. Devereux, George, and Florence R. Weiner, "The Occupational Status of Nurses," *American Sociological Review*, vol. 15, October, 1950, pp. 628–634.

4. Ingles, Thelma, "What Is Good Nursing?" *American Journal of Nursing*, vol. 59, September, 1959, pp. 1246–1249.

5. See Mauksch, Hans O., "The Nurse: A Study in Role Perception." Unpublished doctoral dissertation, University of Chicago, 1960.

6. Johnson, Miriam M., and Harry W. Martin, "A Sociological Analysis of the Nurse Role," *American Journal of Nursing*, vol. 58, March, 1958, pp. 373–377.

7. A recent book by Frances Macgregor was written for the express purpose of providing social science teaching material for nursing students. Material in the book was drawn from a course which Mrs. Macgregor has given for a number of years to students at the New York Hospital-Cornell University School of Nursing. See Macgregor, Frances, *Social Science in Nursing*, Russell Sage Foundation, New York, 1960.

8. Bridgman, Margaret, *Collegiate Education for Nursing*. Russell Sage Foundation, New York, 1953.

9. For a broader discussion of the responsibilities undertaken by the modern hospital nurse in the United States the reader is referred to Brown, Esther Lucile, "Auxiliary Personnel: An Essential Link in Nursing Services," Russell Sage Founda-

tion, New York, February, 1960; mimeographed. See also Dr. Brown's *Newer Dimensions of Medical Care*, Parts I and II published by Russell Sage Foundation in 1961 and 1962.

10. An extensive discussion of the nurse as coordinator can be found in Mauksch, Hans O., "The Nurse: Coordinator of Patient Care," Department of Patient Care Research, Presbyterian-St. Luke's Hospital, Chicago, 1960. Mimeographed.

11. Editorial, "Taking a Stand," *American Journal of Nursing*, vol. 59, September, 1959, p. 1245.

12. LaBarre, Weston, "The Patient and His Families," *Casework Papers 1958.* Family Service Association of America, New York, 1958, pp. 61–71.

13. Schulman, Sam, "Basic Functional Roles in Nursing: Mother Surrogate and Healer" in Jaco, E. Gartly, editor, *Patients, Physicians and Illness.* The Free Press, Glencoe, Ill., 1958, pp. 528–537.

14. Deutscher, Irwin, *Public Images of the Nurse.* Community Studies, Inc., Publication 96, Kansas City, Mo., 1955. See Chapter 4, Nurses, Teachers, and Social Workers: A Comparative Analysis, pp. 31–40.

15. Argyris, Chris, *Diagnosing Human Relations in Organizations.* Labor and Management Center, Yale University, New Haven, Conn., 1956.

16. New, Peter Kong-ming, Gladys Nite, and Josephine M. Callahan, *Nursing Service and Patient Care:* A Staffing Experiment. Community Studies, Inc., Publication 119, Kansas City, Mo., 1959.

17. Reissman, Leonard, and John H. Rohrer, editors, *Change and Dilemma in the Nursing Profession.* G. P. Putnam's Sons, New York, 1957.

18. Thorner, Isidor, "Nursing: The Functional Significance of an Institutional Pattern," *American Sociological Review*, vol. 20, October, 1955, pp. 531–538.

19. *Ibid.*

20. Bullock, Robert P., *What Do Nurses Think of Their Profession?* Ohio State University Research Foundation, Columbus, Ohio, 1954. See Chapter 7, What Rewards Do Nurses Expect? pp. 60–76.

21. Deutscher, Irwin, *op. cit.*

22. A comprehensive report of a series of studies sponsored by the American Nurses' Association is to be found in Hughes, Everett C., Helen MacGill Hughes, and Irwin Deutscher, *Twenty Thousand Nurses Tell Their Story*, J. B. Lippincott Co., Philadelphia, 1958. Some of the studies reported in the present book are to be found in Hughes, Hughes, and Deutscher, but in addition there are many on a variety of topics.

23. Mauksch, Hans O., "The Nurse: A Study in Role Perception." Unpublished doctoral dissertation, University of Chicago, 1960.

24. Cleveland, Sidney E., "Personality Patterns Associated with the Professions of Dietitian and Nurse," *Journal of Health and Human Behavior*, vol. 2, Summer, 1961, pp. 113–124.

25. Lentz, Edith M., and Robert G. Michaels, "Comparisons Between Medical and Surgical Nurses," *Nursing Research*, vol. 8, Fall, 1959, pp. 192–197.

26. Stewart, Donald D., and Christine Needham, "The General Duty Nurse." University of Arkansas, Fayetteville, Ark. Mimeographed.

27. Bullock, Robert P., *op. cit.*

28. Deutscher, Irwin, *The Evaluation of Nurses by Male Physicians*, Community Studies, Inc., Publication 93, Kansas City, Mo., 1955; *Public Images of the Nurse*, Publication 96, 1955.

29. Deutscher, Irwin, *Public Images of the Nurse*, p. 22. ISC means Index of Status Characteristics.

30. Habenstein, Robert W., and Edwin A. Christ, *Professionalizer, Traditionalizer, and Utilizer*. University of Missouri, Columbia, Mo., 1955.

31. *Ibid.*, pp. 41–42.

32. Waik, Elvi, "Becoming a Nurse—Socialization into an Occupational Role." Master's thesis, University of British Columbia, Department of Anthropology, Criminology, and Sociology, October, 1957.

33. Saunders, Lyle, "The Changing Role of Nurses," *American Journal of Nursing*, vol. 54, September, 1954, pp. 1094–1098. This article is recommended for its lucid presentation of the characteristics of nursing and of its stresses and strains.

34. See Merton, Robert K., "Issues in the Growth of a Profession." Paper presented at the 41st Convention of the American Nurses' Association, Atlantic City, N. J., June 10, 1958.

35. See note 22.

36. See note 26.

37. Goode, William J., "The Theoretical Limits of Professionalization." Paper read at the Fifty-Sixth Annual Meeting of the American Sociological Association, St. Louis, 1961.

Chapter 9

The Medical Social Worker

In the fall of 1905 two Boston hospitals hired social workers, quite independently of each other and with no knowledge of the other's activities. That move, soon to be followed in the eastern medical centers of Baltimore and New York, represented a growing feeling that social factors were an important part of disease and its treatment. Some physicians, for example, Dr. Richard C. Cabot at the Massachusetts General Hospital, realized that much more than bedside nursing might be required in the successful convalescence of a patient, and were eager that the resources of society outside of medicine be brought to bear on the diagnosis and treatment of problems faced by patients.

Medical social work in the United States got its start from situations similar to that in Boston, often arising out of a working relationship between an astute physician and a social worker who had vision, and an ability to make social data meaningful to her medical colleague. Dr. Cabot and Miss Ida M. Cannon at the Massachusetts General Hospital were one such team, but there were others as well who collaborated on the utilization of resources within the individual and his environment for more effective handling of the patient's problems in relation to his illness. Since social work did not develop its own body of professional knowledge, values, and method until later, at this early period medical social workers had to make their way by trial and error. Their task was to bring clarity out of the diffuseness of their theoretical goals, win suspicious or resistant physicians by the force of personal encounter and contribution, and move away from the context of nursing to a new and different dimension in patient care. Only from about 1940 has strong impetus come for the full professionalization of social work, including medical.

Speaking in terms relative to medicine and nursing, medical social work is a new profession, one that is still developing. The situation is different from that described in the preceding chapter. The nurse has a well-defined role in the medical setting. The medical social worker does not have as clearly defined a place. The latter might be described as a professional looking for a place in the medical setting, while the nurse has a place but is looking for increased professional status. Changes in medical social work are part of the initial role-defining process, building a consistent and systematic set of expectations for the role which can be understood and utilized by social workers and other health professionals in the process of medical care.

Since medical social work is still in the developmental stage professionally, it faces the problem of variation in expectations among different sets of role definers, physicians, nurses, hospital administrators, and the general public. In some situations, the role definers may not have a clear idea of the technical competence of the medical social worker, may not be able to differentiate social work in general into subprofessions, of which one is medical social work. In other situations, the role definers may have worked primarily with medical social workers who were inadequately trained, and from this experience gained a limited, perhaps even inaccurate expectation of the contributions an able worker can make. The major task of this chapter, therefore, is to define the expectations of the role from the point of view of leaders in the profession, for this is the focus around which a consistent set of role expectations will emerge that can be shared by all health professionals. We shall use the same general categories that were applied to the physician and nurse—technical competence, other orientation, and emotional neutrality or detached concern—indicating in some detail how the medical social worker differs from the physician and nurse in each of these respects. Discussion of guiding values in the profession and problems of role performance and reward will comprise the remaining sections of the chapter.

GENERALIZED ROLE EXPECTATIONS

Prior to a presentation of the detailed aspects of the medical social worker role, some general comments are in order about the scope of activities encompassed.[1] The social needs and problems of individual patients who are receiving care in hospitals or clinics constitute a primary focus, but in addition the medical social worker will be concerned with the social and health needs of the patient's family, of groups of patients, of the community in which the patient lives, and of the broader society.

Within this framework the functions of the medical social worker, may be divided into three categories, of which the first is an understanding of the *natural history of the disease process.* Through a knowledge of social and psychological variables in the patient's situation the medical social worker can often provide important data to supplement those obtained from the laboratory or from physical examination, data that the physician may not be sensitive to, that he may not be trained to obtain, or that are beyond the limit of his available time. Understanding the natural history of disease is important for diagnosis and treatment plans in individual cases, but application in research efforts is also a major concern of the medical social worker. There is, secondly, a concern for the *consequences of the illness in the social functioning of the patient* or his family, and for the personal and social variables that influence adaptation to the illness. Here the medical social worker uses casework procedure or group work procedure as part of an overall treatment plan which in many cases is developed in collaboration with the physician and other members of the health team.[2] The third function is the process of *health planning*, in which individuals are helped to develop personal resources or to alter their environments in order to prevent the onset or the recurrence of disease or injury and to minimize disability, or in which community efforts are directed toward the alleviation of conditions that contribute directly or indirectly to the occurrence of disease among groups of people. In the latter case the medical social worker's knowledge of community organization theory and practice will be utilized.

A somewhat different but equally important function is that of teaching, not only social work students but also medical students, nursing students, public health students, and others who contribute to the process of medical care. In the early part of this century the work training of medical students in charitable institutions showed the need for competent people to teach them about the effect of social factors on disease and its treatment. With a broadening scope of medical education, social workers became important contributors to the educational experience of students in many types of situations and now are utilized in the curriculum of nearly all medical schools. They are finding their way onto the faculties of schools of public health and nursing and, of course, provide the bulk of instruction for students in their own profession.

Hospital and clinic, inpatient and outpatient services, and rehabilitation units are places where the medical social workers are concentrated most heavily. Since about 1920 a slow but steady development of social work has occurred within public health programs. Here the major function of the worker is one of consultation to colleagues in medicine and public health nursing, but in some situations social casework may also be utilized. Research teams constitute another place where medical social workers are to be found, most often in the setting of a medical school. Finally, in terms of community planning, medical social workers often work outside a medical setting, on boards with civic responsibilities or within the framework of a public agency for community service. The skills required in these situations will vary, as indeed individual workers vary in aptitude or training, but there are broad expectations for role performance which apply generally across these situations. In that direction we now turn our attention.

Knowledge and Functions: Technical Competence

Within the medical care situation a social worker has a number of responsibilities that reflect her specific technical competence.[3] As described by Eleanor Cockerill they are as follows. First comes an authoritative definition of the social situation of the patient. Relationships among family members, effects of the job situation, cultural effects of the ethnic or class group of which the patient may be a part, previous patterns of handling stress in the family, financial strengths or liabilities, and the attitude toward and understanding of the illness by the patient, all these enter the social definition of the problem. The social worker must have the requisite background to know what information is necessary, the skills to gather it, and the experience and judgment to weigh findings and place them in proper perspective within the problem description.

Identification of social and psychological factors in the natural history and treatment of the patient's illness situation constitutes a second responsibility. Relationship of this responsibility to that described in the previous paragraph is evident. Within the broad definition of the social situation comes the identification of specific factors that must be modified in an adequate treatment program. Earlier in the book, in Chapter 1, we discussed the idea of necessary and sufficient cause, pointing out that many disease conditions cannot be understood and properly treated without knowledge of one or more sufficient causes. Frequently these causes are social or psychological in nature, and the medical social worker should be sensitive to them and take the responsibility of bringing her findings to bear on the case. In long-term illness or disability, the social and emotional factors which are involved in the interaction of the patient with others will be key variables in treatment and patient adjustment. At the same time, there are factors in the patient's social situation that will have an important effect on treatment plans. A patient and his family may not have the financial resources to follow a certain therapeutic regimen, may not be able to understand the physician's instructions, may be prevented by other kinds of commitments from attending clinics or seeking private treatment, may distrust or be overtly hostile to a physician or hospital, or may hold values about life and illness that differ from those of the medical team. A regular treatment plan might not work at all under some of these circumstances and the medical social worker must be ready to suggest alternate courses of action which will be acceptable to the patient yet fulfill insofar as possible the requirements of the medical situation. In passing we might note that the social worker no longer has the field to herself in identifying social and psychological factors in the natural history of illness and the treatment situation. Physicians and nurses are more sensitive now to the patient's psychological world and often are skilled in identifying and even modifying social factors. In some ways this makes for stress in the medical social worker role, yet in other ways a favorable climate is produced that can lead to more thorough definition of the problem and more adequate treatment plans.

A third major responsibility is the selection of methods of intervention in the situation that can modify the etiological factors previously identified. Often the major effort is toward the patient himself, using interviews; or other procedures can be followed—including interviews with the family or obtaining services from public or private agencies, such as employment services, welfare agencies, or special schools. Methods of intervention will depend on the worker's assessment of what steps the patient can take himself, with what readiness, at what tempo, and with what kind of support from the environment or with what kind of stimulation from family and other social groups. Through training and experience the medical social worker is often in a position to help the patient in ways not available to other members of the health team, but we shall be more specific about that shortly.

The first three responsibilities are best brought to fruition by joint evaluation and treatment planning sessions, in which information and suggestions from various professional areas are integrated. Formal case discussions may not be necessary, but the social worker has the responsibility of communicating her knowledge of the patient to the physician and nurse, in terms they can understand, and of being authoritative about the difficulty or value of various approaches to the patient or different therapeutic actions. As one might expect from what has been said about the role expectations of the physician and nurse, there are often stresses inherent in this responsibility. In part these arise from a limited vision of the patient's illness situation which may be held by some physicians, from an unwillingness of the physician or nurse to accept advice from another profession, or from an inadequate perception of the knowledge and skills that the social worker has to offer. From the other side, the medical social worker may be so in awe of the physician, or perhaps so tied up in status conflict, that she cannot make an authoritative statement about the patient's condition, especially if her contribution is at variance with that of the medical team. Furthermore, the knowledge base of social work has been slow to develop, in contrast to the use of skills, and social workers often have not had adequate concepts that could be used in making an authoritative statement to other members of the health team. Not only has this caused difficulties in communication, but it has contributed to a feeling of insecurity on the part of many workers.

Finally, the medical social worker has a responsibility for carrying out treatment within the goals and structure of a plan which has been worked out with the physician, nurse, and other health professionals. In the treatment process the social worker often must move back and forth between the medical and social aspects of the situation. At times she will deal with factors that have direct medical implications, such as resistance to diet prescription or x-ray, while at other times the factors will be more indirect or long range, for example, helping the patient work through his feelings about an altered work role or helping a family utilize community services without disruption of a sense of pride and autonomy. Consequent to these actions is the fact that the medical social worker often works quite independently of the other members of the medical team, making decisions or following courses of action in her area of competence. Although this gives her a feeling of professional competence in her own right, the physician and nurse may perceive her as someone apart, a member of the team only in a tangential sense. Moreover, social problems in an illness situation often take the worker outside the hospital into the home or community, whereas the physician and nurse are more often limited to action in the hospital or clinic, except, of course, in the case of public health activities. However, in clinical situations where there are able medical social workers, and where there is understanding between team members, the social worker may be able to move between the social and medical aspects of the situation with ease.

The primary technique in dealing with the patient is that of the *interview*. Here the interpersonal relationship is important, consciously utilized by the worker to enable the patient to handle his problems more effectively. The social worker will emphasize the giving of psychological support, accepting the patient and his feelings for what they are, not criticizing or forcing him into some course of action. In nontechnical terms this is known as "starting where the patient is." Expression of feelings is encouraged, especially those of hostility or fear, for these emotions often block the effective handling of problems arising out of the illness situation. If the patient can feel comfortable with the social worker and can express to her the things that are bothering him, he may then be in a better position to come to grips with his problem or to adapt to the therapeutic measures proposed by the physician and nurse. By use of the interview relationship the worker hopes that the patient can alter his perceptions of the problem facing him, of his own capabilities, or the contributions others can make to help him.

As part of the casework process the medical social worker is in a position to translate the hospital's efforts into language the patient can understand. Patients have beliefs and fantasies about their condition, about medical personnel, and about medical procedures that are sometimes distorted from reality and may block the patient or his family from being willing to accept the care offered. Being sensitive to social and psychological variables that could be responsible for reaction patterns by the patient, and having an interpersonal relationship in which he can feel safe to express negative feelings or variant opinions and beliefs, the social worker often can interpret the hospital and medical care situation to the patient.[4]

Interviews are not limited to the patient; indeed the focal person in the social situation surrounding illness may not be the patient, but some member of his family. Pediatric illness comes readily to mind as an illustration, but adult illness is also often fraught with tension and difficulty. For example, when the domineering, decision-making husband in a family is hospitalized for a long-term disease, his wife—unused to or incapable of planning for the family—may find that anxiety about managing the family is as great as anxiety about her husband. Here the social worker will find that casework interviews with both the patient and his wife may be crucial to adequate handling of the illness situation. The patient will need help in facing and dealing with his feelings concerning dependency, the wife with feelings about autonomy and independence.

The relationship with the patient, or his family, in the casework situation is quite different from that between either the physician or the nurse and patient. Although both physician and nurse may be quite aware of the psychological implications of the interpersonal situation, they do not ordinarily utilize the relationship in the same way or to the degree shown by the medical social worker as part of the treatment process. By necessity the physician must concentrate most of his energy on the disease process. The nurse has cure and care functions that are related intimately to the doctor's work and to the immediate illness situation. As we noted in the preceding chapter, many of her actions can be regarded as falling under the symbol in fantasy of *id mother*. The social worker, on the other hand, functions more as an *ego mother*, orienting the patient toward the realities of his illness and the social situation outside the hospital. The casework interview operates largely on the level of ego functioning, encouraging the expression of painful emotions, weighing alternate courses of action, and facilitating the self-determination of the patient. In short, the task of the social worker is to help the patient face his problems realistically and solve them. The immediate goal may be to deal with crises, while the long-range goal more often is one of maximum self-realization and growth.

In addition to the casework interview the social worker has a second technique, that of providing environmental service. We have already mentioned this skill in passing but it bears emphasis here. There are many agencies in society that have been founded to help people in distress, providing financial help, homemaking services, job placement, or foster-home care for children. The patient may not be aware of these services, may not know how to make contact with them, or may not have the time and effort to bring them into action on his behalf. The social worker can assess the needs of the patient and his family in relation to community agencies and make the necessary contacts, thus providing help that is beyond the capacities of those in the illness situation. The contribution of the social worker in this regard is again one that the physician and nurse are usually not able to make owing to limitations of both knowledge and time. Unfortunately, in some medical situations the colleagues of the social worker see this as her main contribution, especially in terms of making financial arrangements for medical care. Where there are inadequately trained workers such a limited perception of function can be continually increased. Thus, the technical competence of the medical social worker can play a part in making for a narrow perception of her role if it is allowed to dominate her activities. One of the major strains in the role lies here, a point to which we will return later in the chapter.

In addition to casework interviews with patient and family, and the giving of environmental service, the medical social worker contributes to the treatment plan in still another way. This lies in the relationship she has with other members of the medical team—in particular with the physician or nurse, but is not limited to these two persons. We mentioned earlier that the social worker has the responsibility of communicating her knowledge of the psychological and social situation of the patient to the other members of the health team. In this, her activity becomes one of interpreting the patient to the hospital and medical team. She brings data regarding the effect of the illness on the patient as an individual personality, functioning in his various social roles, presenting the meaning of the situation from the patient's point of view. Again the relationship with colleagues in medicine and nursing is important, as well as the information and professional insights which the social worker has to offer. She can often help the physician or nurse work through negative feelings about the actions of a particular patient, or about a professional colleague, or can indicate how certain behavior toward a patient produces withdrawal or resistance to the medical situation. These are delicate matters because the prestige of professional roles and the inviolacy of personalities are at stake; therefore, a careful utilization of interaction dynamics, including the social worker's own feelings, is required. A well-trained medical social worker should have the technical competence to work with the other members of the medical team in this way.

Actions expected of the medical social worker according to the role definition thus far described presuppose a fund of knowledge somewhat different from that possessed by the physician or nurse. In brief, the worker must have a working understanding of the physiological processes of the organism in health and disease. Of necessity she will have less knowledge of these processes than her medical and nursing colleagues, but sufficient to indicate the significance of various signs and symptoms, or the potential course of a given disease. Concurrently, a comprehension of personality development and functioning will be required. As we have indicated, this knowledge must not only include an understanding of personality theory in general; it also must embody some insight by the worker concerning her own preferred personality needs, patterns, and defenses. The profession of social work, in general, has depended heavily in the recent past on the psychoanalytic frame of reference for an understanding of personality functioning. Although some of the leaders in the profession feel that the dependence has been too great,[5] it has provided a consistent and usable theory available for understanding human behavior. Besides personality theory, knowledge is required of social system functioning and cultural patterns and effects. We have pointed frequently to the influence of social class or ethnic group membership on beliefs, attitudes, values, family structure, and other variables. The social worker is many times the expert in the medical situation on these matters, and her contribution must be based on good sociological and anthropological theory. The educational background leading to the achievement of the role—a bachelor's degree and a master's degree in social work and training under supervision in a medical setting—is crucial to adequate technical competence in the areas we have noted, as defined by leaders in the social work profession.

Other Orientation

Like the other helping professions, medical social work puts the interests of the patient first. The variation in this role expectancy from medicine and nursing is a subtle one, yet most important to the way that the physician or nurse may perceive the social worker, or to the preconceptions that they may bring with them about medical social workers. From the beginning the wider profession of social work has been interested in social welfare, in the social bases of crime, poverty, and general degradation. From a historical point of view social work developed from problems created by the industrial revolution and the need for social vehicles to help unfortunate members of society. At first, this was seen in individuals who fought for humane treatment of the insane, in the development of settlement houses, or in organizations designed for the relief of the poor. The philosophy of action that emerged was a recognition that many of the social ills responsible for human suffering might be prevented and that an individual could be helped to live a fuller and richer life by better utilization of his resources in his own way. A social consciousness was thus important in the development of social work and in the early days the profession put a great deal of energy into social reform as well as into treatment or help for those who had run into calamity. As a result, built into social work tradition and shared by members of the profession, is the implicit expectation that they should contribute to the development of more adequate community services as well as help individuals solve their problems. Although some physicians and some nurses have exemplified similar orientations toward social problems, the profession of medicine is essentially conservative so far as social change is concerned, especially fearful of any actions that look like socialism. To the minds of some, probably on an unconscious level, social consciousness and socialism are not too far apart. Also, the image of the social worker as a "do gooder" may be repugnant to conservative physicians, who wish no alteration of the social order or interference with the privacy of the individual. Thus, they may be suspicious of the medical social worker on "general principles," and show a resistance to utilizing her skills to the fullest extent until by personal encounter she has convinced them that the service she can render is constructive and helpful.

Self-Determination and Emotional Neutrality

Part of the expectations of all three roles—physician, nurse, and medical social worker—is that emotional distortions should not interfere with the handling of a case, and that the patient should be accepted for what he is even though the health team members may disagree with him on any number of issues. Within this general expectation the social worker exercises a permissiveness and acceptance toward the patient that is not so true in medicine or nursing. We noted earlier that the function of the social worker can be thought of as ego-related, turning the patient toward reality in the social situation; but in this process the self-determination of the patient is a key issue. The physician and nurse both approach the patient much more as a passive object. The doctor gives "orders" for the patient's treatment, and although permission must be elicited for certain treatment procedures like surgery, the patient often does not know what is being done to him or why. In contrast, the medical social worker provides psychological support, helps the patient assess his problems more effectively, and provides services in the community that the patient otherwise might not obtain; but all these are done with the patient's knowledge, adjusted to his speed and with his full participation. Consequently, one might speak of the social worker's relationship to the patient as authoritative rather than authoritarian. Under these circumstances a rather remarkable degree of permissiveness and acceptance is required, and the worker must be aware at all times of the significance of her reactions to the patient. Training in dynamic psychology and in psychoanalytic theory, as we mentioned earlier, is part of the technical competence of the role, and it makes possible the kind of emotional neutrality that we are describing. Only by self-insight and repeated emphasis on places in the interpersonal relationship where distortions of perception and reaction are likely to occur can the medical social worker be objective, emotionally neutral, yet permissive and accepting.

There may be times, however, when the social worker will need to be authoritarian as well as authoritative, but a decision to act in that manner will depend on a careful analysis of the patient's personality and cultural background. For example, the husband of a Mexican-American family from a rural area was hospitalized for a long-term illness. His wife had no close male relatives on whom she could call for the making of decisions about the family, yet the culture in which she had been reared was one that emphasized the importance of decisions by a male in time of crisis. The medical social worker, who happened to be a man, realized that optimum adaptation to the situation by both the patient and his wife could best be achieved by an authoritarian approach on his part. Had a permissive approach been used, a serious maladjustment to the illness situation might have ensued.

Even though the social worker must be willing to allow the patient considerable latitude and move at his speed, she also must keep one foot planted firmly in the medical situation and with her colleagues on that team. At times the worker can be forced in two directions and find that her situation is rather stressful. For example, the physician and nurse may become quite impatient with expressions of hostility toward them or the hospital by a patient, or by the slowness by which a patient seems to move in following the medical plan. The temptation may be for a coercive decision or a termination of the relationship, to which the medical social worker may need to raise firm opposition. In so doing, the frustrations of the medical team may be generalized to her as well as the patient. However, she is the only member of the team who can go quite so far in accepting negative feelings and deviant behavior without disrupting the program of diagnosis and treatment, and thus often forms a helpful bridge between the difficult patient and his doctor and nurses.

VALUES AND PHILOSOPHY

The values espoused by a person are exemplified in his behavior; so too are the values or philosophy of a given profession carried out in the expectations for members of that profession. The values associated with social work, and particularly medical social work, have been stated implicitly in the preceding section, but they bear singling out here even at the risk of some repetition.

Importance and uniqueness of the individual underlies social work action. The focus is on the total individual, functioning in a social situation. Disability, whether biological or social, is reflected in all aspects of the person: his physical state, his emotional well-being, his effective participation in social life. By studying or treating only one aspect of the individual not only is the most comprehensive treatment neglected, but the importance of the individual person is lessened. Medicine also places emphasis on the importance of the individual; but concern with a particular disease condition can narrow the focus of the physician to the immediate aspects of that condition. In part, this is due to the limited time many physicians can devote to patients individually; but in part it is due to the effect of the historical tradition of single cause or specific etiology in disease, which is only slowly being replaced. Medicine often has this narrowed focus on the individual, while medical social work emphasizes a broader illness situation.

Closely allied is the importance of *self-realization* on the part of the individual, which the social worker carries over into treatment plans. Basically, everyone should have the opportunity for self-realization of the full potential of his physical and emotional resources. Action by the individual in fulfilling that potential is an essential factor. Insofar as possible the social worker will encourage the patient to work out his problems in his own way. Although she may work with the family or give direct service by dealing with community agencies, the main focus is problem-solving by the individual. Characterizing medical social work as fulfilling an ego function is one way of expressing this value in terms of role expectations. There is a subtle difference here between medicine and nursing, on the one hand, and medical social work on the other. Physician and nurse are more inclined to view the patient as a passive object, often deliberately withholding information from him, making the majority of decisions for him during his hospitalization, even invading his privacy at will. Much of this is quite a necessary part of good and efficient medical care, but in the process attempts at self-realization by the patient can be slowed up. Emphasis on the individual and his problem-solving capacities by the medical social worker can therefore provide an important balance in medical care.

The importance of *social and emotional aspects of illness* constitutes a second major aspect of the guiding philosophy of medical social work. Although we have made this a primary issue in the previous pages, it takes a number of forms that have not yet been spelled out specifically. For example, illness and the process of medical treatment may be a threat to the integrity and to many of the social roles of the individual. Radical surgery, loss of function, inability to work, these and many other outcomes may have serious consequences for the individual's self-esteem and for the adequate fulfillment of his role as father, husband, or community leader. Illness may also be a way of solving life situations or emotional problems; it may be used to gain advantage over others or to fulfill deep-seated psychogenic needs. In assessing a particular case the medical social worker will be particularly interested in determining how far and in what way illness has, or has not, become linked with the patient's life situation and family equilibrium. Destructive linkages can occur, even to the point where the individual's whole life centers around illness, but these the social worker hopes to prevent or to alter. Finally, illness and disability involve a considerable social component in terms of community attitudes toward various diseases or handicaps. Mental illness, alcoholism, and venereal disease are rather extreme examples of conditions in which there may be much fear, disgust, or moral disapproval. As we have pointed out previously in this book, disability in the form of loss of limb, difficulty in speech, or disfigurement may cause other people to avoid the patient, withdraw emotional support, or even ostracize him. Furthermore, the attitude toward disability may vary from one subgroup to another, as for example between Irish and Italian communities, or between mountain folk and city dwellers. Assessment of the reaction to disability in the patient's community will be an important aspect of treatment plans, especially in discharge planning. Because this is an important component of the philosophy behind medical social work, the social worker will be sensitive not only to social and emotional factors in the natural history of illness but also in the handling of illness and later adjustment.

Emphasis on health and its fulfillment rather than death and disease was one of the trends we discussed in the first chapter. Although not clearly articulated yet in the basic philosophy of medical social work, this trend is becoming an important value in that profession. The social worker evaluates the implications of the medical situation for the patient and his family, the problems it presents, and the potential stresses that may accrue, but at the same time she assesses the strengths in the situation, the skills possessed by the patient to solve the problem, and the forces that can be marshaled for optimum adjustment. These are more likely to be salient for the social worker than are the pathological aspects of the case. To be sure, pathology and health can rarely be regarded as separate entities in a medical situation, and emphasis on health over pathology may be one of small degree; but it may be a key emphasis and one to be made more by the medical social worker than by other medical personnel.

As in any value system there is likely to be close relationship among various values. The four we have singled out here show a marked interdependence, even to the extent that there is difficulty in differentiating them except for didactic purposes. They are the basis for much of the behavior seen in medical social workers and are carefully incorporated into the expectations for the role which the profession itself is developing.

PROBLEMS OF ROLE PERFORMANCE AND REWARD

In a medical situation the social worker must work closely with other professional groups, particularly physicians and nurses. Also, she is often in contact with physiotherapists and occupational therapists, with hospital administrators, and with the auxiliary services, such as the Grey Ladies, Red Cross workers, or community volunteers. Working relationships with these groups are a potential source of strain in role performance, in that the social worker may be blocked in performing the role as she sees fit, or she may not receive adequate rewards, especially in terms of recognition or prestige. The term "role deprivation" may often be applicable.[6] Any new role that still is in the developing, defining process faces the possibility of stress or deprivation; but inasmuch as this may lead to tension and reduced adequacy in role performance it is important to throw as much light as possible on the sources of conflict. Some of the factors that are important in producing stress are outlined below.

A team approach is usually a necessary part of the activity of the social worker in a hospital or clinical situation. Ordinarily her entry into the case will be through a referral by the physician, although in some instances she may be approached by the nurse or by the family. Also, the decisions she makes concerning social treatment plans will usually have medical implications and need to be coordinated with the therapeutic plan proposed or being carried out by the doctor. The problem then arises: How independent or dependent should the social worker be in relation to the other team members, especially the physician? Relative to the physical condition of the patient she must depend, of course, on the judgment of the physician. For example, she cannot ask the patient to undertake responsibilities that will overtax his capacities or will interfere in any way with limitations on his activity that may be imposed by his physician. Also, she cannot make the decision as to when the patient enters or leaves the hospital, although in a good team situation she may have much to say about the latter. On the other hand, in casework with the patient the social worker should have initiative and independence. As we pointed out earlier, she must be prepared to allow the patient to express his feelings about the medical situation: his fears, his hostilities, his thoughts about the way things should be done, his ideas about the cause or the cure of his condition. Inasmuch as these feelings and ideas may be at variance with the position taken by the medical team, the social worker may move some distance from her team members in the casework interviews, although keeping one foot with her colleagues. In order to perform this task successfully, and help the patient to a more realistic appraisal of his problem, she must exercise considerable independence. Stress may come in two ways in this situation, first, from the limited expectations of the doctor and nurse, and, second, from the hesitancy of the social worker to assert independence. Many doctors expect the social worker to be useful only in untangling financial problems that impinge on the patient's case or in making arrangements with community agencies for services beyond those provided by the hospital. They do not understand her skills in casework and may regard her interviews as a waste of time, perhaps even harmful. When the social worker has to deal with a physician who has this limited perception of her role, she may be hampered in acting independently by lack of support and cooperation on the part of other team members. Stress may accrue, however, from the feeling of superiority which the worker may impute to the physician, leading her to await his permission before making moves in the treatment situation. Her position as a woman in a subculture that has traditionally had male domination may contribute to her unwillingness to take the initiative; but in any case the perception of limited functioning by the worker is enhanced in the doctor's mind. Closely allied is the fact that physicians are trained to make relatively firm and quick decisions, while social workers are more hesitant to indicate the cause and propose a course of action. In ward rounds the various physicians will give their diagnoses and recommendations for treatment, while the social worker may not be ready or able at that time to make definite judgments to her medical colleagues. The physician may attribute her hesitancy to lack of skill or may unconsciously view it as evidence of the proper deference due his position.

One factor that should not be forgotten in relationships with other professional colleagues is that there are strong equalitarian tendencies within medical social work, both in the way patients are viewed and in the way interaction patterns with colleagues are structured. Social workers tend to reach a first-name basis much more quickly than do physicians, and to be less concerned about formal modes of address in face-to-face relationships or in conferences and meetings. A willingness to question authorities in the field more often occurs among social workers than among physicians, also to try new and different procedures. Then, too, social workers may not be quite so concerned about their status in the eyes of the public as physicians are, although as we shall see shortly they may have more of a problem in this area. Medicine as a profession is conservative, has rigid status hierarchies, and changes but slowly. Social work is a change-oriented profession and has much less rigid status hierarchies within itself. Finally, the relationship with the patient may often be less authoritarian among social workers than among physicians. Equalitarian and liberal tendencies can lead the physician to perceive the social worker as too folksy and lacking in professional dignity and as we have already pointed out, too disruptive of the established social order. On the other hand, the social worker may perceive the physician as too formal, too committed to tradition, and often resistant to more effective and comprehensive medical care. These perceptions do not always occur in relationships among members of the health team, but they may operate at an unconscious level and result in a role deprivation that is role-centered rather than person-centered.

In many hospitals medical social work has a clearly defined place on the team with professional independence, a fact that is usually true in larger hospitals and those under government control. Furthermore, where there are social service departments, a good share of activity by social workers is devoted to casework.[7] Yet there are still a sizable number of hospitals where medical social workers are utilized in only a limited way and have not been able to maintain professional identity within the collaborative pattern, or where the medical social workers themselves have not demonstrated their capacities for independent action even though there is a readiness to grant it to them. These situations constitute a continuing source of stress for individual social workers and for the role-defining process of the profession at large.

A second major factor that contributes to difficulties in role performance and reward arises from the fact that social work has been a middle-range status position. We noted that the ranks of the profession have been filled largely by women and that women still outnumber men to a considerable extent in many areas. In our society high-range status positions have traditionally not been filled by women, and within medicine we have noted the difficulty faced by the woman physician. Also, many social workers come from minority groups, racial or religious, or from middle and lower-middle socioeconomic groups. Although it is true that social work more than nursing has attracted women from upper-class families, these people constitute only a small proportion of the total profession. Medicine has drawn its members primarily from middle-class groups or those of higher social status, and has held a position of prestige in our society that is very high. Moreover, the competence and educational qualifications of social workers have become visible only in recent years. Although standards of the profession now require a master's degree and some workers also hold a doctorate, there are still many who do not have these qualifications. In contrast, medicine has a longer history of high educational requirements, and nursing presents a clear picture of the length and degree of professional training. The ambiguity in the past of educational requirements for social work has contributed in no small measure to the middle-range status position. Finally, the salaries paid to social workers have often not been commensurate with the length of education now required and, generally speaking, are below those of psychologists, physicians, and administrators. Financial reward is one means by which prestige and status are determined in our society and therefore contributes a great deal to a middle-range status position for social work.

Relationship between the physician and medical social worker can be affected by the social status position of the two roles, quite apart from the personal capabilities of the individuals occupying the roles. Deference may be expected because of status considerations even though not congruent with the demands of a particular case situation. As a consequence, the social worker may feel frustrated and demeaned, unable to make her full contribution to the treatment situation. Under these circumstances she may project her insecurity into the working relationship and perceive the physician as inflexible, unjust, or overbearing.

Social status position as well as knowledge, or its lack, about functions performed probably contributes among other things to the attitudes which the public has about social work. Although perhaps not as important as the attitudes of working colleagues, favorable public attitudes can be an aspect of reward in role performance. One study throws some light on this, the survey from Community Studies, Inc., in Kansas City, to which we referred in the preceding chapter.[8] Nurses, teachers, and social workers were compared on the basis of scores on the Occupation Evaluation Index, a technique which allowed the research team to assess how favorably or unfavorably each occupation was regarded by respondents. Social workers were rated significantly lower than either nurses or teachers, a finding that held across age, sex, and socioeconomic groups among the respondents. However, the rating assigned social workers became more favorable as one went from higher socioeconomic groups to lower ones, the same being true of nurses but not of teachers. Respondents were also asked to rate those belonging to each occupation on such characteristics as "kind and sympathetic," "businesslike and efficient," and "blundering and incompetent," first as they are and then as they should be. None of the three groups was rated by many respondents as being blundering and incompetent, whereas all were thought to be less kind and sympathetic than they should be, and overly businesslike and efficient. However, two-thirds of the sample agreed that both social workers and teachers have the qualities they should have, and a smaller proportion felt the same way about nurses.

A factor that may have affected the somewhat unfavorable rating given to social workers as compared to teachers and nurses was that over half the respondents said they had friends who were nurses or teachers, while only 26 per cent were able to say this about social workers. Most people know teachers or nurses, but fewer have equal acquaintance with social workers. Also, the survey did not ask about different kinds of social workers, such as psychiatric or medical. Although it is a moot question as to how far the public can go in making such a differentiation, the application of the Kansas City study to medical social work is thereby limited. These data do point, however, to a potential stress in the reward system for the social work role.

SUMMARY

Expectations of the medical social worker role as described in this chapter in some ways constitute an ideal picture, exemplified by many workers, not by others. The contribution of social work to medical care is still in the developmental stage, and role definition is still going on. Inasmuch as the major effort in the defining process comes from leaders in medical social work, we have presented in essence their conception of the role. The reader should remember that other health professionals may have somewhat different expectations, and that herein lies a strain in role performance.

Emphasis was laid on the interest of the social worker concerning social and psychological variables in the natural history of the patient's illness situation and in his reactions to that situation. Her contributions to diagnosis and treatment were seen to fall primarily in this area through a case evaluation worked out with other members of the medical team, especially with the physician and nurse. In working with the patient her efforts were seen as directed toward helping him understand the hospital environment and solving the problems in his life that might result from the illness situation. In this regard the activities of the social worker were described mainly as ego-related. Work with members of the patient's family and with various public and private agencies in the environment constituted further aspects of the technical competence of the worker.

Like the physician and nurse, the social worker is expected to be emotionally neutral, but she utilizes in her work the psychodynamic aspects of the relationship with the patient to a greater extent than her medical colleagues. Self-realization by the patient is one of her goals, and she must be prepared to accept the patient's feelings even though they be hostile to the medical situation. Often she has the difficult task of keeping one foot with the health team and one foot with the patient.

Finally, the medical social worker has problems of role performance and reward growing out of dependence on, or independence from, other members of the health team, equalitarian tendencies within social work, and the middle-range status position of social work among professional groups.

The trend toward more comprehensive medical care indicates growing opportunities for the use of medical social workers, indeed the necessity for utilizing them. The role-defining process therefore assumes central significance.

NOTES TO CHAPTER 9

1. Many of the ideas presented in this chapter grew out of discussions with Miss Harriett M. Bartlett of Boston, Miss Eleanor Cockerill of the Graduate School of Social Work, University of Pittsburgh, and with members of the medical social work faculty in the School of Social Work, Tulane University. I have also drawn on published materials, particularly those by Miss Bartlett and Miss Cockerill. These publications and others of general relevance are cited below. The individuals I have mentioned have been most helpful and patient, but it would be hardly fair to hold them responsible for the way the material is presented in this chapter, in terms of content or organization.

For references the reader is referred to: Bartlett, Harriett M., *Social Work Practice in the Health Field*, National Association of Social Workers, New York, 1961; *Idem*, *50 Years of Social Work in the Medical Setting*, National Association of Social Workers, New York, 1957; *Idem*, "Toward Clarification and Improvement of Social Work Practice," *Social Work*, vol. 3, April, 1958, pp. 3–9; Cockerill, Eleanor E., "Medical Social Work," in Kurtz, Russell H., editor, *Social Work Year Book 1960*, National Association of Social Workers, New York, 1960, pp. 375–382; Hemmy, Mary L., "The Use of Medical Social Service in the Total Treatment of Patients," *Hospital Management*, vol. 74, August and September, 1962, pp. 98–102, 111; 129–134; Goldstine, Dora, *Readings in the Theory and Practice of Medical Social Work*, University of Chicago Press, Chicago, 1954; *Idem*, *Expanding Horizons in Medical Social Work*, also published by the University of Chicago Press, in 1955.

2. Social casework might be defined as a problem-solving process that has three aspects. First is the establishment of a good working relationship between caseworker and client, in which there is warmth and objectivity on the part of the worker and trust combined with a willingness to share the work by the client. Secondly, the caseworker is responsible for a social diagnosis in which the parameters of the problem are defined and the accessible resources to solve the problem are determined. Finally, there is treatment in which such therapeutic and material supports as are deemed necessary are utilized. The process of casework is an interaction process between caseworker and client which enables the latter to see the problem objectively, aids in bringing in the necessary material resources, and helps the client "work over" his emotional reactions to the situation.

Social group work might be defined as the systematic process of guiding social and group interaction to achieve specified goals. Clients are helped in and through the group itself toward a better social functioning. Through the group experience positive social relationships may be formed which aid individuals in their social maturation. The caseworker must have a thorough grounding in the theory of group dynamics.

For a concise description of both social casework and social group work the reader is referred to Perlman, Helen Harris, "Social Casework" and Cogan, Juanita Luck, "Social Group Work"; both articles appear in *Social Work Year Book 1960*, National Association of Social Workers, New York, 1960, pp. 535–549.

3. Medical social work is a branch of the general profession of social work, and has skills which are unique. For purposes of convenience, however, the term "social worker" as used throughout the chapter refers to medical social work and not to the

profession of social work in general. One other stylistic comment should be made. In referring to the physician one conventionally uses the pronoun "he"; when speaking of the nurse one uses "she." In the case of the social worker the convention is less clear. Inasmuch as most social workers in the past have been women, it might seem easiest to use "she" in referring to a social worker in the abstract. However, increasing numbers of men are entering the profession and in many social work articles "he" is used. I have made an arbitrary decision to use "she" largely because of tradition and because there are still more women than men in the profession. The fact that an arbitrary decision is necessary, however, reflects one of the strains in a professional role which is not yet so stabilized as that of the physician or nurse.

4. For some illustrations of the way in which the medical social worker can interpret the environment of the hospital for the patient, see Cockerill, Eleanor, and Helen M. Gossett, "The Cooperative Venture Between Hospital and Patient," *Smith College Studies in Social Work*, vol. 14, September, 1943, pp. 184–196.

5. Although a controversial article among social workers, there is a presentation of extremes to which the profession may have extended itself in Sanders, Marion K., "Social Work: A Profession Chasing Its Tail," *Harper's Magazine*, vol. 214, March, 1957, pp. 56–62.

6. For a discussion of the problem of role deprivation in the health professions, the reader is referred to Brown, Esther Lucile, "Role Expectations and Deprivations: Their Implications for Patient Care and Health Service," a paper read before the Massachusetts Public Health Association, January 30, 1958.

7. *Social Work in Hospitals*. United States Public Health Service, Publication 510, Washington, 1957.

8. Deutscher, Irwin, *Public Images of the Nurse*. Community Studies, Inc., Publication 96, Kansas City, Mo., 1955.

PART FOUR
THE PLACE WHERE DISEASE IS TREATED

Chapter 10

The Hospital: An Analysis in Terms of Social Structure

THERE WAS A TIME when many people believed that a hospital was a place where a person went to die. The fear and dread associated with this institution were often as disabling as the effects of disease itself, and many families preferred to let the patient die quietly at home rather than endure what they considered to be the tortures of the hospital. Nowadays only a very few individuals have such a belief; indeed, the hospital is more likely to be regarded as a haven. Near miracles take place within its walls, relief of pain is to be found there, and considerate attention by skilled hands is the expectation. Going to the hospital has become a commonplace experience. This does not mean to say that going to the hospital has become an experience free from emotion, or that people are able to look at hospitals in a dispassionate way. One needs only to take note of casual conversation over the bridge table, at the woman's club, or at a cocktail party to realize that feelings about hospitals can run high.[1] The reason is not surprising. Contact with the hospital occurs in the framework of emotionally laden experiences arising out of the illness situation and the consequent disruption of normal social and emotional relationships. Under these circumstances the patient and his family are unduly sensitive to experiences of all kinds that occur in the hospital, with the result that normal perceptual processes sometimes change to those of perceptual distortion.

The hospital, on the other hand, is not a passive institution onto which the patient and his family project their feelings. Rather, it is a dynamic social organization with customs, values, and expectations to which the patient must make some adjustment. The patient, his family, and hospital personnel are all involved in a process of social interaction to which each brings a set of perceptual expectations. Perceptual distortions can occur on the part of hospital personnel as well as in the patient or his family.

Medical care in the hospital must be considered within the context of social interaction and perception, because social and psychological variables can have a number of effects on the treatment process, both in immediate and in long-range perspectives. For example, the adjustment of the patient to the hospital may affect his willingness to accept the treatment offered him or to stay until it is complete. It may hinder his recovery, in that he may not respond properly or fully to prescribed therapy. Future relationships with hospitals and medical personnel may be impaired, with reluctance to give financial and other kinds of support to appeals for funds or labor. Thus, the adjustment of the patient and his family to the hospital world may range in its effects from matters of immediate moment that have direct bearing on life and death to future situations that deal with public and community relations.

An analysis of the major factors that influence the process of social interaction between patient and hospital will be the topic of this chapter and the one to follow. First, the hospital as a social institution will be examined in terms of goals and functions, both those that are manifest and those that are latent.[2] Hierarchy of functions and differential perception of function by various roles within the structure are important to this aspect of the analysis. Next, the social structure of the hospital will be examined with special emphasis on authority lines in administration, conflict between various roles in the structure, and patterning of relationships between personnel. The functions and structure of the hospital will be considered in relation to the patient and his family, both as to the effect that function and structure have on the perception of patients by hospital personnel and the problems they pose for the patient in his attempts at adjustment.

Chapter 11 will deal with the hospital as a subculture, presenting a way of life that has its own customs, language, values; moreover, it is a unique world in terms of sights, sounds, and smells. The important psychological and cultural variables in the patient will then be discussed as these bear on his attempts to adjust to the hospital subculture.

By its very nature the analysis of the hospital as a social institution must be phrased in general terms, for hospitals differ as to type and as to character or style. Perhaps the most familiar type is the *voluntary* hospital, supported by the community or by religious groups, and often dependent on endowment and public subscription, as well as fees from patients for operating funds. For the great majority of members of our society this is probably the kind that comes to mind when the word "hospital" is mentioned. There are also *proprietary* hospitals, owned by one or more individuals, who are usually physicians, and operated by them for their benefit, which includes realizing financial profit, if possible, and providing a convenience for treating their patients. Often the general public does not differentiate the proprietary from the voluntary hospital. Finally, there are *publicly owned* hospitals, administered by the city, county, state, or federal government. Although these may be general medical and surgical hospitals, as in the case of those administered by the Veterans Administration, many are run for the care of patients with tuberculosis, mental illness, or other long-term conditions—the so-called chronic diseases.

Within these broad types hospitals differ much as do personalities, exemplifying specific kinds of problems and structural variations, or "images," embodying degrees of warmth, friendliness, efficiency, and concern for patients. Probably the analysis in these two chapters will not be exemplified fully in any one hospital with which the reader is familiar. The material is therefore primarily a set of guidelines, generally applicable to the hospital as a social institution, that may open up to the reader new ways of looking at familiar situations and a set of analytical tools for studying his own organization.

FUNCTIONS AND GOALS

Written into the bylaws of every hospital, emphasized in speech and story, presented as the core of fund drives, the major purpose of the hospital is the *care of patients*.

> In a hospital environment the patient is the ultimate end of all activity. His needs must take precedence over everything else. In a word, the patient is the *raison d'être*. Patient-centrism may thus be described more succinctly as an approach which establishes patient needs as the precept for all policy and all activity.[3]

These words by Wooden, taken from a description of a project on organization and patient care, clearly define a goal that can be applied to all hospitals. Many times it may be an ideal not fully realized or only approximated in action. Nevertheless, here is a tacit assumption shared by hospital personnel and public alike as to the major function of the organization.

Phrased in another way, the primary function of the hospital is *service*, a feature shared with other social institutions, such as the church and school. In our culture high value is placed on the worth of the individual as an individual. Service to a person implies giving him that recognition, and not regarding him as a number or merely a body in bed.

The function of patient care and service tends to reach through all levels of the hospital social structure, affecting even those who may not have direct contact with patients. Orderlies, clerical workers, cooks, stationary engineers, and others more often than not have a feeling of satisfaction that their work contributes in some measure to the care of patients. Though not always expressed, and often competing with other goals, service to patients does provide a unifying force at all levels of the hospital organization.

Furthermore, in this function the hospital realizes a responsibility to give patient care in time of emergency regardless of the patient's ability to pay for its cost. Since the Middle Ages religious orders have provided care for the sick and impoverished, and many hospitals had their beginnings under these circumstances. Among lay groups that founded hospitals within the past century, one can find the care of the indigent as a partial motivation, evidenced even now in the endowment of beds or wards for patients who could not otherwise afford hospital care. As the standard of living has risen, as more people have come under the protection of hospital insurance plans, and as civic responsibility for all citizens has heightened, hospitals have had fewer and fewer charity patients. They are still cared for in most hospitals, however, which involves the time of physicians, nurses, and social workers, the allocation of beds and equipment, and contributes to the continued perception of hospitals as service institutions.

A number of other functions can be seen in hospitals, secondary to that of patient care, and sometimes in conflict with that primary function or with each other. One of importance is *teaching*, especially as it is applied to nursing students, medical students, interns, and residents in various specialties. Not all hospitals fulfill this function, particularly those that are small or located in rural areas, but where it is fulfilled the teaching function is crucial to the continuation of the health professions, especially medicine and nursing. Learning from textbooks is only part of the process of making a good physician or nurse; learning by doing is of equal importance. The medical student must listen to the sounds from many hearts before he can differentiate pathology from normality and make a differential diagnosis. The presenting picture of symptoms rarely approximates closely that seen in textbooks, and the physician in training must see many variations of the same disease picture in order to be certain of his therapeutic action. One experience of examining and treating a patient with any disease is worth many lectures without benefit of patient. For the nurse, skillful handling of physical procedures and of psychological support grows out of constant practice with people who are ill. Only gradually can she recognize the signs of a subtle but serious shift in a patient's condition, which makes it mandatory that she call the physician in charge.

Hospitals that are connected directly with medical schools and with university schools of nursing usually have the facilities for fulfilling the teaching function to a high degree. In these circumstances the patient may receive a type of care somewhat above the ordinary, even though his financial resources are limited. Nevertheless, the relationship between the two factors is delicate, and again the potential for conflict is present.

Another important function is *research*. Mention was made in Chapter 4 of the emphasis in scientific medicine upon experimentation with new ideas and treatments, a willingness to discard the old ways when the evidence strongly indicates new approaches. Scientific medicine could not long endure without research, and the hospital is one place where it is carried out. New surgical techniques, new drugs, new diagnostic procedures although developed in the laboratory must eventually be tested on patients when the element of risk has dropped to a reasonable level. Research is more likely to be conducted in large medical centers, especially those connected with schools of medicine; thus, this function can be ascribed to only a portion of our hospitals. However, research is a function with high value attached to it, because of the eventual implications for patient care.

The hospital is sometimes viewed as a *workshop for the physician* engaged as an entrepreneur in the private practice of medicine. Included here are both the general practitioner and various kinds of specialists. Under this function the hospital provides beds, equipment, and services that are put at the disposal of the physician for his work. He may call upon hospital personnel beyond the ordinary range of their responsibility toward patients in the hospital organization, as in diagnostic workups in the outpatient department or in requests for x-ray and laboratory reports on patients not admitted to the hospital. Proprietary hospitals fulfill the function of a workshop for the physician quite specifically, but in some voluntary hospitals the medical staff assume a relationship with the hospital that places them in a category that allows privileges beyond those extended to a "guest of the hospital." This is not so important or universal a function as teaching or research, and varies greatly among hospitals. Where it is strong, however, one may find the local practitioner using the emergency room for routine treatment of his patients, or manipulating the concept of "emergency" in order to get his patients admitted.

Custody and control are functions that can be discerned in certain kinds of hospitals, especially those devoted to chronic disease and to the mental diseases. Here we use control as it relates to the application of coercion on the behavior of patients as a result of deliberate policies. Variation may occur among different categories of hospital personnel in the deliberateness with which control is exercised, but patients still feel its effects. These functions may also appear in large general hospitals on wards that are devoted to chronic disease, or even with individual patients whose stay in the hospital seems likely to extend over a long period. Hospital personnel must work out ways of getting along with these patients on a kind of social interaction basis that is somewhat different from the ordinary patient-nurse or patient-physician pattern. Perhaps one might phrase the new pattern as having a factor in common with the hotel or boarding-house pattern of relationships, but still leaving control in the hands of the "innkeepers."

When the custody function is pursued, activities are directed more toward keeping the patient happy, allocating housekeeping services, and establishing patterns of behavior that keep interpersonal friction to a minimum than toward the more traditional patient-care procedures.

Our large publicly owned mental hospitals often exemplify the custody and control functions to a high degree. Although great changes have been taking place in the care of mental patients, there are still many wards that are operated under the "Legend of Chronicity."[4] Patients are not expected to get well and are typed according to their usefulness in getting ward work done and in keeping the level of excitement at a low state. Restraint, through wet packs or the seclusion room, emphasizes the control that staff can exert over patient behavior in order to keep the system steady.

The functions discussed up to this point are concerned with the relationship of the hospital and the larger social system. There are two internal functions that are also important to our discussion, functions that are concerned with the ongoing activity of the organization *per se*. The first of these is the *business* or *operational* function, and the second, *keeping the system going*.

Hospitals have become complex organizations; they have actually reached the state of "big business" when one considers the capital investment in buildings and equipment, the dollar turnover in goods and services, and the annual payroll for personnel. Owing to the size of the business transaction, as well as the increasing costs of equipment and medicines, not to mention staff salaries, efficient management of the organization is necessary. The hospital that is run inefficiently cannot long continue without a reduction in its services, which, in turn, results in a decline in quality of patient care and the loss of its patients to other hospitals. Therefore, training in business administration is an important part of the education of the professional hospital administrator, a role that has emerged only recently in the medical care field.

Discharging the duties of a good business manager involves many things, in the operation of a hospital. Efficient purchasing and cost accounting, effective use of personnel, and allocation of materials are necessary in conducting the food services and laundry and in running and maintaining the physical plant, as well as in the more traditional patient-care areas of nursing, pharmacy, x-ray, and laboratory. In many hospitals the line between "breaking even" and incurring debt is thin, especially when there is little in the way of endowment or gifts from wealthy benefactors. If the hospital administrator is a good business manager, his institution may be able to stay out of debt, maintain its buildings and equipment, buy the new equipment needed to keep up with advances in diagnosis and treatment, and compete successfully in the labor market for essential personnel such as nurses and laboratory technicians.

The business or operational function is of major importance in the modern hospital, second only to that of patient care and service. Ideally, business should be complementary to service, as indeed it is in many hospitals, but because of the different implications of the two functions, there is a built-in potentiality for conflict between them. We shall turn to a discussion of that conflict shortly.

Common to many social organizations is concern with keeping the system going, perpetuation of jobs, prerogatives, networks of relationships, and rewards. The routine of patterned activities has value in and of itself; it provides a sense of security, all of which can be threatened by the introduction of strange personnel, rearrangement of activities within the system, or the injection of new procedures. Perpetuation of the system is a *latent function* in Merton's terms,[5] not recognized or necessarily intended by those who carry it out. Inferences about its presence can be made, however, from the actions of hospital personnel that tend to preserve the status quo and do not relate directly either to good patient care or efficient business management.

Hospital Functions and Perception

Although there is general consensus in most hospitals about the function of service and patient care, there will be differential perception of the importance of other functions in relation to that of service. Actions of various people within the hospital social system can be understood in part by reference to their perception of hospital functions and the importance they attach to each. An analysis of this kind can be particularly helpful in explaining conflict among various hospital services and can contribute to techniques for resolving conflict.

Differential perception of the importance of the service and business functions can occur in a number of areas within the social system. Generally speaking, those closest to the patient and most directly responsible for his care will view the service function as paramount. The farther hospital personnel are removed from direct patient care, the more likely they are to perceive other functions as being of some consequence. Also, the training of various staff members is pertinent; when this training is in areas only indirectly applicable to patient care, more importance will be given to functions other than service.

Overemphasis on the business function can have consequences for the patient at the time of admission. Many hospitals, for example, require evidence of financial reliability if the patient does not have hospital insurance, even to payment in advance of part of the anticipated bill.[6] Further, the admission procedure may be long and impersonal, because the emphasis is on administrative record-keeping rather than the comfort of the prospective patient.

Hospital personnel may find themselves working at cross purposes on many issues when they have differential perception of the business and service functions. Nowhere is this more acute than in expenditures for services or new equipment. The service function commands prestige and expenditures are often justified by manipulating this symbol; yet, on the other hand, the statement that "there is no money" is a powerful deterrent to action. Staff members imbued with service to the patient may demand things that are not absolutely essential, while those committed to the business function may block expenditures because they cannot be justified in terms of immediate dollars and cents return.

Perception of hospital function by the board of trustees in a voluntary hospital often affects hospital policy and structures the potentiality of conflict. If members of the board are especially concerned about balancing the books and hire an administrator because of the business acumen he is known to have, the hospital organization may be efficient but cold in its emotional climate for the patient. If the board members see service as the more important function, they may hire an administrator who has the "human touch" with patients but find at the end of the year that the hospital has been operated at a deficit. These two cases are the extremes; neither need happen, for business skill and interest in the patient's welfare can be combined. But in many hospitals one can see variations of these themes when perception of the business or service function becomes dominant.

In hospitals with teaching programs there is likely to be persistent conflict between the teaching and service functions, especially on the nursing service.[7] Nursing supervisors often perceive students as valuable assets in service to patients, while those who are responsible for teaching often feel that patient care should always be viewed in the educational context, believing that the nursing experience helps to educate the nursing student. Serious disagreements can arise between the directors of nursing service and of nursing education as an outgrowth of differential perception of the importance of these functions.

A potential source of conflict in some hospitals is the use to be made of medical students, interns, and residents in the care of patients, especially private patients. The attending physician in these cases may perceive the teaching function as important and be willing to spend time in going over cases with his colleagues in training. In contrast, if he views the hospital primarily as his workshop, he may frustrate the younger physicians by not using them on his cases or giving them insufficient time and details, or responsibility.

Emphasis on the teaching function also has implications for the admission of patients, especially charity or ward patients. If the patient gives promise of being an interesting teaching case, especially if he has some rare disease, he may be admitted quickly and receive the most intensive care, in which medicines, equipment, and staff time are utilized to a degree far exceeding the patient's ability to afford. Conversely, if his disorder is like many others already under treatment in the hospital and is perceived as contributing nothing new to the teaching situation, there may be reluctance to admit him, especially if other hospitals can be found to care for him.

Finally, we must note that hospitals where teaching is done may be perceived with apprehension by some patients. This may be expressed in the phrase, "I don't want to be a guinea pig," or "I don't want any interns practicing on me. I want a real doctor." Although such statements, when overheard may shake the self-image of the newly graduated physician, they do reflect a real fear. In effect, the patient indicates his belief that the doctor when well trained is supposed to know everything necessary, but if not yet completely trained he might make a mistake. When he is so dependent on others for vital decisions the patient wants to be certain that the right ones will be made.

Problems posed by the research function are in a special category, and the physician who has a strong commitment to research often finds himself in a dilemma. Nowhere is this better illustrated than in the recent book by Renée Fox,[8] a sociologist who spent many months as a participant observer on a research ward in a large teaching hospital. The ward was run by a group of young research physicians, specialists in metabolic diseases and in heart and kidney surgery. During the course of the Fox study the physicians tried many new drugs and radical surgery procedures, all of which had gone through careful development in the laboratory but had to be tried on human patients. In each case the physician had to weigh his responsibilities to the patient against his desire for information, and to calculate the risk and the ensuing discomfort against the potential gain for the patient or for future patients. Even with the wholehearted cooperation of the patient in research endeavors, the physician often had to make difficult decisions and work under a stress load heavier than that carried by many of his colleagues in other parts of the hospital.

Conflicts of a wholly different nature can arise between the research function and that of business or patient care. Research is often expensive, and a decision to use regular hospital funds for a research program may depend on the differential perception of the importance of research to the hospital. Even modest expenditures for drugs, or a request to change certain nursing procedures, may run into opposition from those who fear the economic waste in the disruption of an ongoing system of operations, or who have difficulty in perceiving the value of long-term gains as against the costs or inconveniences of short-term changes.

The problem of conflict in function cannot be dismissed without reference to the difficulties that occur when the custodial and patient-care functions conflict. The best illustrations are found in mental hospitals where patients often stay a long time and present difficulties in cure that seem at times insurmountable. Fear of mental illness and of the unpredictability of behavior on the part of the patient also contribute to the potentiality of conflict. Those responsible for the daily supervision of the mental patient and in closest contact with him are the psychiatric aides,[9] a group in whom the conflict between patient care and control often appears. The object of a study by Rubington,[10] psychiatric aides in a Veterans Administration hospital exemplified goals and functions only partially parallel to those of the medical staff who manifested the "official" functions of the hospital. Custody and control as a function was ranked by the aides as more important than patient care, and the former was made evident through attitudinal and behavioral sanctions that emphasized strict conformity to hospital rules and regulations. Less value was placed on understanding the patient than on the ability to compel patient conformity to the authority of the aides. Rubington believed that the function of custody and control became so important to the aides because their occupational mobility was blocked, and because they were under female authority in the form of the ward nurse. Control of the patient thus became a way in which they could prove their masculinity and derive an important self-image. Although the official hospital policy, and that accepted by the majority of the medical staff, emphasized patient care and treatment, those personnel in closest contact with the patient perceived a different function as most important.

AUTHORITY STRUCTURE AND PROFESSIONAL ROLES

In a social organization the reciprocal of function is structure, a system of rules and roles for carrying out functions and goals. Human activities must be coordinated through division of labor and an authority structure in order that the functions of the organization be fulfilled. Structure and function are like two sides of the same coin, each meaningless without the other. In this section we consider the social structure of the hospital, comparing it with the other types of social organizations in our society, looking for sources of stress and strain, and analyzing the effect of structural arrangements on perception.[11]

A rigid status hierarchy geared for emergency action is a brief description that has been applied to the hospital. Though obviously too simple, the statement still contains the core of much that should be said about structure and functions. A high degree of specialization of activity characterizes the modern hospital, these activities being set in *exclusive* positions. The positions are arranged in sets or substructures and organized in a firm power and prestige hierarchy. In most hospitals the main substructures can be identified as administration and housekeeping, medical staff, nursing, professional services (x-ray, pathology, laboratory, and pharmacy), social service, and board of trustees. An individual cannot move from one position to another except in limited cases, usually within the particular substructure of which he is a part. When an individual enters the social structure in a certain position, he tends to stay in that position. That is why we talk about exclusive positions, or say that an important aspect of hospital social structure is the *blocked mobility* from position to position, or more especially, from one substructure to another. It is true that positions within the structure that require only generalized skills can be entered by almost anybody. However, positions that require highly specialized skills, as do those of the physician and nurse, and in some cases the administrator, cannot be assumed without special training which, in turn, calls for specific aptitudes, personality characteristics, and other variables.

By way of illustration, the system does not allow the laboratory technician to shift to the role of physician unless he goes outside the organization for extensive technical training. Dietitians do not become social workers; bookkeepers cannot fill the position of nurse; orderlies may not change to pathologists. An individual cannot work his way up through the hospital structure as he might in an industrial organization. In the latter case it is often considered wise to have filled most of the positions in the system at one time or another as a background for becoming president of the company. From stockroom boy to chairman of the board is a route still fulfilled with sufficient frequency to make it legitimate. Business organizations tend to have more open mobility than seen in the blocked mobility structure of the hospital. Here, then, is the explanation for the use of *rigid* as an adjective in the descriptive sentence above.

Lest the reader think that hospital structure is static in terms of blocked mobility, mention should be made of the fact that changes are occurring, at least in the extent to which important activities are being shifted from one group to another. The nurse, for example, is taking greater responsibility for activities that were once the concern of the physician. Although she may not become a physician, the activities assigned to or assumed by her may be of such importance that the prestige of the role is increased. Mobility from one position to another may remain blocked, but the shift in responsibilities attached to various positions does change, as a result of which there are greater rewards for nursing positions which formerly had lower prestige.

Specialization of activity not only occurs in differences between the substructures of the hospital, but there is specialization of activity within substructures and there can be mobility within these substructures. In nursing there are teachers, administrators, supervisors, head nurses, and staff nurses. Among the medical staff differentiation occurs by reason of age and experience, intern to chief of service, also by reason of general practice or training in one of the specialties. Administration and housekeeping activities are concerned with food services, office staff, laundry, public relations, maintenance, and many other types of service. The larger the hospital the higher amount of specialization, but even in small hospitals differentiation of activity is extensive.

The division of labor represented by specialization of activity carries out the functions and goals of the hospital, patient care being primary. The phrase "geared for emergency action" exemplifies the primacy of patient care and the importance of the concept of emergency. Even though much of hospital activity is not on an emergency basis, the structure is set for that contingency. As we shall see, "emergency" is also a symbol that can be manipulated at times of strain and conflict.

In order to complete the relationship between social structure and function, it is necessary to add another dimension to specialization of activities—that of power and lines of authority. In any social organization activities must be ordered, coordinated, and controlled if all the goals are to be met properly, and this implies systematic provisions for decision-making. The hospital is of special interest in this respect, for it represents a situation where two lines of authority operate, each drawing power from different sources. Often the two lines of authority are in conflict with each other, a situation that is a major source of strain in hospital social structure. To understand the power system we must consider, first, the more traditional administrative or authority arrangements in social organizations within our society; then, we must consider the variations or differences presented by the modern hospital. In this discussion we will draw extensively on a theoretical paper by Etzioni[12] and a study of hospitals by Smith.[13]

As soon as an organization numbers more than a few people or becomes complex in terms of function, authority must be vested in certain positions within the organization. Behavior of individuals occupying those positions consists in defining, integrating, and controlling the activities of individuals who occupy other positions within the structure. These authority positions are usually referred to as managerial and are described as *line* positions. They are organized in a "chain of command" where each person occupying an authority position is responsible to the person above him and has control over those below him. A glance at the familiar table of organization in a business firm, military unit, or governmental bureau shows in graphic form how power is transmitted through the line to meet the goals of the organization.

The authority exercised by the managers or line personnel can be thought of as *formal*, vested in the very structure of the organization and usually grounded on a legal or semilegal base in bylaws, table of organization, and job descriptions.

In addition to the managers and production workers, there are in many organizations *staff* positions, the task of the staff person being to acquire and apply new knowledge, and develop better or more efficient *means* of fulfilling the major goal activities of the organization. Staff positions are filled by *experts* with specialized training and knowledge.

The traditional administrative arrangement thus has authority vested in manager-line positions with the responsibility for fulfilling the major goals and functions of the organization. Staff positions contribute to attainment of goals through development of means that are translated into action by those under the direction of the manager.

In the hospital, however, the situation is reversed. The physician occupies a staff position, not managerial, yet he has ultimate responsibility and authority for the major function of patient care. He may carry out this function personally or may direct semiprofessionals and nonprofessionals in the performance of the activity. Managers or administrators are in charge of secondary activities, providing the *means* by which the major goal activity can be accomplished by the expert. People in managerial positions now are the ones who have limited authority in relation to the major functions of the organization, subsidiary to that of staff personnel in the person of physicians. Etzioni notes that some of the complaints lodged against the expert or staff person in private business are often aimed at administrators and managers in professional organizations. The latter are said to lose sight of the major functions of the organization in the pursuit of their specific limited responsibilities.

Managers in the hospital continue to have formal authority based in the structure of the organization, but the authority of the expert or staff person is of a different kind and more powerful. The physician brings charismatic power with him to the hospital social structure and, along with his legal backing and superior knowledge, this is the basis for his authority in the organization more than any formal power which he may receive from the organization.

Formal and charismatic power are the two types to be found in hospital social structure, the former exercised mainly by the managers and those under their direction, the latter by the physician or experts, and those whom they direct. As we shall see, one of the strains in the social system occurs when the expert or staff people try to exert their charismatic authority over individuals who are under control of the managers, or when people from the "line" try to impose their formal authority on the physician or those directly under his control.

STRUCTURAL CONFLICT AND STRESS

Our structural analysis of the hospital to this point has been largely theoretical, setting forth two major variables; specialization of roles and lines of authority. The previous section, that dealing with functions and goals, was also on a theoretical level. We shall continue somewhat in that vein, yet shall draw more on data about the hospital as an ongoing dynamic system.

Hospitals are full of activity, of constant interaction between different types of individuals, different in terms of the social roles they enact and in terms of their personality characteristics. By looking at studies of ongoing hospital activities, we can learn more about the important variables in a structural analysis, for we can see what aspects of the organization work smoothly and what parts show stress. Three aspects of the social structure come under scrutiny in this section: the medical staff, nursing service, and administration. In each we shall delineate some of the problems of operation, basing the presentation on empirical studies of hospitals in action and other data.

The Medical Staff

Except for physicians who are connected with the hospital on a full-time basis, including the resident house staff, action of the physician in the hospital is dominated by the fact that he is an entrepreneur engaged in the private practice of medicine. As medical care has become more complex there has been greater tendency to use specialists not only in the sense of referring patients to other physicians, but in calling in consultants to aid the attending physician in his diagnosis and treatment. A practitioner from the community, whether he is a general practitioner, an internist, or a surgeon, may refer the case to a gynecologist, urologist, or neurologist; or he may ask for a consultation with a hematologist, an allergist, ophthalmologist, or a psychiatrist. Wherever special skills are available, they are likely to be used by the physician in charge of a case. The question then arises, whom does he call, given a choice between a number of colleagues, and in borderline decisions what factors help him decide to ask for consultation from a colleague? Furthermore, what effect does this situation have upon the hospital and the physician's place in hospital social structure?

To answer these questions we must turn first to a study by Hall[14] of the informal organization of the medical profession to which reference was made in Chapter 6. Among the physicians of a given community the rights to status and power become recognized and upheld, mechanisms of legitimate succession and patterns of recruitment become established. These interactions are never formalized and can only be observed through the *subtle network of obligations* and preferences among physicians. These informal relationships function primarily through sponsorship, whereby the careers of those selected for membership are facilitated by special attention in training, referrals, and consultations, while those not selected are placed in a position where they compete on disadvantageous terms. Sponsorship can apply to the training of a man just entering the profession, or in certain cases to the acceptance of a physician who has had considerable experience elsewhere. Those who are sponsored, accept obligations to their sponsors and expect severe sanctions should these obligations be broken. In some situations the informal set of obligations can become the basis for a clique that attempts to dominate the medical scene in hospital and community. Some data on cliques in hospitals are presented below. However, the point that needs to be kept in mind as a background for much of the material to follow is the importance of informal but powerful sets of subtle obligations and relationships that initiate a bond between the physicians who are engaged in the private practice of medicine.

The informal organization of physicians affects hospital structure in two ways: by influencing or dominating the medical committee that selects those who will be allowed staff privileges or by forming power groups within the medical staff. In the latter case there may be one clique that dominates a given hospital, making it difficult for those outside the clique to utilize the hospital effectively, or there may be two or more cliques that compete for bed space and other hospital services. The informal organization may thus exert pressure through formal channels, as in the case of the medical committee, or may control the situation informally through referrals and granting or withholding favors.

For empirical data we turn to a study of 15 hospitals in a state "east of the Mississippi" which was conducted under the auspices of the Association of University Programs in Hospital Administration (AUPHA).[15] Investigators interviewed many people in each hospital, drawing them from all the substructures that were mentioned earlier under specialization of activity, assuring sufficient numbers for valid generalization about hospital structure. In each interview the principal question was: "Do you now have, or have you recently had, a problem which interferes or might interfere with your carrying on your job?"

In three of the hospitals there was clique formation that presented problems: physicians in the clique excluded independent physicians, referring patients only to each other and controlling bed space. The investigators found that antagonisms were evident among the physicians and hospital routine was often disrupted. Other hospital personnel were affected by the disunity, with the result that general hospital morale was lowered.

Where cliques exist in a hospital the formal power of the administrator is not so effective as the informal charismatic power of the physician, especially when the latter is exercised through a network of relationships among physicians. Members of the clique can bring pressure on the hospital system at many points to serve their own ends, and administration may be unable to control such action. Thus, we see that the power of the physician's role can be disruptive to hospital social structure when it serves ends of personal aggrandizement.

Even though physicians in the private practice of medicine dominate the hospital scene, the number of salaried specialists is increasing, a situation that causes stress and strain in the hospital social structure. Most physicians have tended to resist any form of compensation other than fee for service, feeling that salary tends to detract from the independence that has long been associated with the private practice of medicine. Salary weakens the informal set of obligations and relationships among physicians, these being closely tied to income through fees. Also, it is probably fair to say that in a salary situation the physician loses some of his charismatic authority and comes more under the formal bureaucratic authority of management. In spite of these drawbacks, the security of a regular salary and a limitation on hours of work are most attractive to an increasing number of physicians. In addition, some physicians argue that fees weaken the relationship between doctor and patient, and they feel they can be more effective in the practice of medicine if fees are not involved.

The pathologist is likely to experience this conflict acutely. Not only does he stand outside the network of obligations based on fees if he is on salary, but by the very nature of his work stands ready to challenge the diagnoses of his colleagues. If persistent reports of unnecessary surgery or incorrect diagnoses come from the pathologist's laboratory, considerable strain may be placed on the personal relationship between colleagues, but more importantly, these reports put pressure on the administration to correct the situation. If not corrected, the accreditation of the hospital may be jeopardized. The private practitioner is then likely to feel that one of his colleagues is supporting lay authority in an area that had traditionally been within medicine.

Data from the AUPHA study point to another factor within the medical staff that throws light on structural variables in the hospital. Investigators found that general practitioners and surgeon-specialists predominated in the smaller, more isolated hospitals, and that specialists and surgeon-specialists were in the majority in the larger, urban institutions. In the latter situation conflict existed between the teaching and nonteaching staff, between the medical and surgical staff, and between the general practitioners and the specialists. Members of the teaching staff often had salaried appointments, which created the problems discussed above. With a base of financial security the teaching staff could be more selective about the kinds of patients they treated, selecting the more interesting cases and leaving the routine ones for other physicians. They could also treat fewer patients and do a more intensive workup of each case. In some situations the members of the nonteaching staff felt a little like second-class citizens because their prestige in the hospital structure was less than that of those with teaching appointments. Specialization of activity in any number of different ways leads to differential perception, with the nonteaching physician in this case likely to see his teaching colleague as more secure, as having more prestige, as taking more time than necessary with patients, but perhaps also as being the captive of a system or someone who has violated the tradition of free enterprise.

All the hospitals in the AUPHA study were confronted with the problem of bed space, a commodity of consistently scarce proportions and often the focus of power plays. We shall return to the question of bed space, but at the moment we report that it reflected difficulties between the medical and surgical staffs. Each of the two specialties was inclined to think that the other was able to obtain more than its fair share of beds. To digress from the AUPHA data temporarily, surgeons often feel that internists keep patients in the hospital too long and hospitalize their patients unnecessarily for tests. From the other side, the internists may perceive their surgeon colleagues as "knife happy" and admitting surgical "emergencies" that could well wait until beds were available. In this case a physical factor, number of beds in the hospital, served to bring out a potential strain in specialization of activity within one of the substructures of the hospital system, and again the power of management was limited in being able to control the situation.

The relationship between the general practitioner and the specialist is not confined to the hospital but strains in the relationship occur there frequently. The general practitioners in the AUPHA study felt that they were being excluded from referrals and privileges, inasmuch as they lost their patients to the specialists once the patients had been admitted to the hospital. Physicians in the specialties were inclined to believe that modern medical care required more specialized diagnostic and therapeutic procedures than the general practitioner was equipped to offer.

Hostile feelings between general practitioners and specialists, when they occur, reduce general morale among hospital personnel, thus extending the structural strain from the medical substructure to other aspects of the social system. Patients feel the strain, being hypersensitive to the relationship with a physician at the time of illness, eager to know that one person has basic interest in their case.

Nursing

When the role of the nurse was discussed in Chapter 8, it became clear that one cannot speak of nursing in a unitary sense; there are many kinds of nurses, and they have diverse interests. These differences among nurses must be remembered as we consider their activities within the hospital system and the relationship of this substructure to that of the medical staff and administration.

The nursing substructure, sociologically speaking, is most directly concerned with fulfilling the major function of the hospital —the care of patients—performed under the general direction of the medical staff. Nurses supervise or carry out the actual, physical procedures of patient care, give medications, bed baths and backrubs, take temperatures and blood pressures, make observations concerning the condition of patients, offer psychological support, and in many hospitals perform a long list of technical procedures that may be done by the house staff in teaching hospitals. In addition, they are often responsible for teaching patients about caring for themselves once they leave the hospital, especially in handling physical disabilities. Nurses therefore occupy a key role in hospital structure and, because of the very importance of their work, are probably more susceptible to structural stresses than other people in the institution.

Perhaps one of the most important of these stresses arises from the fact that nursing is the funnel for so many activities. The nurse is often called upon to do things other than nursing, such as filling out forms, assuming responsibility for many housekeeping activities, storing and keeping account of supplies, and being a public relations expert, to mention only a few. A work sampling study by Abdellah and Levine[16] in three Michigan hospitals showed that during the study week 11 to 22 per cent of all the nursing time observed was spent on such things as housekeeping, dietary problems, care of linen, and errands to other parts of the hospital. Clerical activities, devoted mostly to entering material in patients' records, took 12 to 20 per cent of the total nursing time available. Activities other than direct patient care thus consumed at least 23 to 42 per cent of the nurses' time, activities that could be performed by personnel other than professional nurses. Although a pattern of activity in hospitals that combines nursing and nonnursing duties has existed for a long time, nurses are asking more frequently if it is necessary, especially in view of the increase in time necessary for carrying out the technical procedures of modern medical treatment. The nurse is torn between her interests in direct patient care, the time and supervision necessary for treatment procedures, and the demands made by other aspects of hospital life that concern the patient but are not specifically nursing tasks. The conflict is heightened by the persistent shortage or poor utilization of nurses in most hospitals, which was found to be a chronic condition in the 15 hospitals included in the AUPHA study.

Fortunately, changes have taken place in some hospitals and give promise of occurring in others that relieve the nurse of many activities not directly concerned with patient care. Housekeeping services have assumed more responsibility for the "innkeeping" aspects of ward life, and staff secretaries are able to handle a greater volume of record-keeping activities. Greater utilization of new kinds of personnel, such as secretaries, or change in responsibility of established personnel, may lead to improvement in the "shortage" of nurses. At the same time nurses who are interested have the opportunity for greater fulfillment of some of the psychological satisfactions to be gained from bedside care of patients.

Another area of potential structural strain is that of teaching, which raises the perennial problem of utilizing nursing students in service tasks, and of the time that should be spent by staff nurses in teaching or service activities. Those instructors who are responsible for the educational program perceive the patient situation as an opportunity for the student to put theory into practice and to learn by doing. They object to the student spending time on patient care beyond what is needed for a varied and rich learning experience. As a consequence, nursing educators may feel that their students should spend more time in the library and laboratory, acquiring a more diversified clinical experience, or learning how to establish relationships with patients rather than acting as staff nurses in repetitive situations. Those directly concerned with patient care may perceive the student nurse as a seriously needed source of help and feel that the student can learn to be a good nurse only by doing considerable nursing. The meaningfulness of the immediate task for educational goals may not have the same importance for the ward nurse as for the educator.

Difference between the teaching nurse and the staff nurse appears on another level as well. The former is more inclined to have a stronger professional orientation, to be more concerned with the goals of nursing as a profession and somewhat less with the burdens of everyday patient care. Her emotional ties may be stronger to groups outside the hospital than to the hospital itself, what Gouldner has called the *cosmopolitan* rather than the *local* orientation.[17] The staff nurse may thus perceive the nursing educator as having her head in the clouds of theory and being overly concerned with increased professional status.

The structure of the hospital, or at least of many hospitals, enables two major goals to be fulfilled—patient care and teaching—and the activities of nurses are devoted to both. There is division of labor here, specialization of activity within the nursing substructure, but there are also conflicts of interest and variations in perception. The AUPHA investigation found conflict between the fulfillment of teaching and service functions in all the hospitals studied, reporting that nursing service and nursing education were not reconciled in any of the 15 hospitals. Unfortunately, such conflict often consumes emotional energy that could be used effectively in patient care, either in direct interaction with the patient or at the level of coordination of services.

To return to our discussion of lines of authority and sources of power in the hospital structure, the nurse is responsible both to managerial authority and to the physician. In the latter case she receives instructions about the medical care of patients and orders for medication or for instituting certain technical procedures. In this capacity she carries out the work of the expert, under his general direction, and is responsible to him for mistakes in this area, as well as for checking on any mistakes he may have made in the writing of orders for medication. We have already noted, in Chapter 8, that the nurse often has considerable latitude in interpreting orders and must often make decisions about care of patients in the absence of the physician. At the same time the nurse is under both hospital administration and nursing administration authority in terms of rules and regulations concerning patients and general hospital activities.

It is not unusual to find a conflict between the demands made by the physician and those by administration, or to find that commitments to the two authorities are difficult to reconcile or produce tension. Data from the AUPHA study show that physicians sometimes made demands on nurses over and above the prescribed duties of the nurse, action which the nurses perceived as an affront to their self-respect and an unnecessary addition to an already burdened day. Another example was found in surgery; the surgeons were sometimes uncooperative in maintaining schedules, an action that could disrupt seriously a routine carefully planned by the operating room supervisor. In the process of scheduling operations and keeping the surgical suite in top condition, the nursing supervisor is responsible to management; yet, she cannot always persuade the physician to follow rules of time and procedure.

Administration: Housekeeping, Management, or Executive Leadership?

Throughout the chapter we have pointed to structural strains that center on the role of management and the weakness of formal authority versus the charismatic authority of the physician. The problem has become more acute through the increase in operational complexity, and some of the most important changes taking place in the hospital as a social institution concern the role of hospital administrator. A discussion of some of the features of that role, theoretical and functional, is now in order.

The major task of an institutional head is *system integration*, making certain that secondary goal activities do not supersede the major goal activities of the organization, that conflict is kept at a minimum; in other words, that the system is maintained in the most efficient manner possible. Fulfilling this task, as Etzioni points out, can be best accomplished if the manager has a certain set of personal characteristics, the managerial personality so to speak. The role requires that the manager be more skillful in handling people than in handling knowledge, the latter being more in the province of the expert.

In the traditional type of administrative situation, the "manager" is responsible for carrying out the major functions of the organization. In a professional organization such as the hospital this task is in the hands of the "expert"—a physician—means to this end being provided by the manager—a hospital administrator. The manager's task is still that of system integration, however, even though he does not engage directly in the major function of the organization, and his task is complicated by the fact that in addition to the personal characteristics necessary to the managerial role, certain aptitudes and some understanding of the work of the expert are necessary. To some extent there are incompatible sets of orientations here; the expert best understands the major function of the organization but is not trained for the task of system integration, nor is he likely to have the set of personal characteristics necessary to it. Most successful doctors have little desire to become managers, while those who do move into administration often become marginal to their professional colleagues.

The dilemma posed by the conflict between managerial and professional demands has in the past been solved in a number of different ways in hospital organizations. In some hospitals a physician has moved into the role of manager. By and large this has occurred only in large hospitals where the rewards of pay and prestige can be commensurate with the expectations of the physician role, and has been accomplished by people who emphasize the personal qualities necessary to the management role. The policy of many publicly owned hospitals, as in the case of those run by the Veterans Administration, is to appoint a physician to the position of manager, and the same is true of some voluntary hospitals. Unfortunately, the physician as administrator may be a marginal man, except in the psychiatric hospital. Unless his competence as a physician is accepted by his colleagues, he may not be able to form close associations with them, while at the same time he may reject association with other lay administrators because of his having an M.D. degree and an educational background superior to theirs.

Another approach, often used in smaller hospitals, lies in appointing a nurse to the manager's position. The nurse is likely to have an advanced degree. Like the physician, the nurse is trained to carry out the major function of the hospital, patient care, but may not have the training to perform secondary functions in the most efficient manner, especially if the system becomes large and operationally complex. Another difficulty may arise inasmuch as the administrative authority of the nurse is limited by the very fact that some physicians are accustomed to viewing nurses as their handmaidens. Many voluntary hospitals, therefore, have given a more active role to the board of trustees, who provide assistance to the nurse-manager in carrying out secondary functions, especially the business affairs, and back her strongly in relationships with physicians on the staff. Although the intervention of trustees in hospital affairs is often fraught with difficulties, the policy has proved to be successful in many instances.

A third technique that has been tried to advantage is to put the administration of the hospital in the hands of a business manager, especially in situations where the trustees have special concern for the financial stability of the organization. Decisions about the major goal activity of the organization must then be left almost entirely to the medical staff, with a consequent split in responsibility for system integration. Such an arrangement is open to potential conflict unless a working relationship between the administrator and chief of the medical staff can be established, a relationship that must be based on personal factors rather than formal role factors.

The development of the role of professional hospital administrator is a fairly recent occurrence and represents another functional solution to the management problems of a professional organization. The role includes a number of elements, among which are a semi-expert background, training in tasks specific to the administration of a hospital, and a set of personal characteristics that are necessary to the managerial function. The role, however, is still *emergent*, is still being defined, and varies considerably from one hospital to another or from individual to individual.

A number of factors bear on the role of the professional hospital administrator that may have long-range implications for hospital structure and the problem of the dual authority lines. In the first place, a prescribed course of training is now being offered in universities which leads to a master's degree. This is a prerequisite in the background of the professional administrator. Greater consistency in education and more thorough education are immediate results of such university programs, and both are necessary factors to the clarity of role definition, which until recently has been largely lacking in this particular role. Furthermore, the attainment of an advanced degree is a sign of technical competence that allows the expectations of the role to rest more on the office than on the personal characteristics of the incumbent.

Secondly, in both education and practice there is an increasing emphasis on the shift from housekeeping or custodial activities to professional management and executive leadership. The administrator is now more frequently expected to be a coordinator of activities and the initiator of new courses of action. These activities relate quite specifically to what we have called system integration, but it is only recently and only in certain hospitals that the administrator has been given this responsibility in the fullest sense. The administrator may neglect his real function if he becomes preoccupied with the routine crises and concentrates on problem-solving in areas that are remote from patient care. In the face of operational complexity, system integration demands that the administrator not lose sight of the primary goals of the hospital, and that secondary functions be geared to the main purpose, patient care.

If the function of system integration becomes clearly established as the prerogative of the hospital administration, this will lead to a strengthening of formal bureaucratic power in the institution and limit somewhat the informal charismatic power of the physician. Tension within the system, when it does occur, is thus likely to be more overt than covert, and can be dealt with more easily from the administrative point of view.

Cosmopolitan-Local Differentiation

Discussion of the problems of authority in the hospital and the emergent role of hospital administrator leads to consideration of a structural strain that may be acute in some hospitals. We refer to the *cosmopolitan-local* differentiation in latent social identities, a concept that has been discussed in the writings of Gouldner.[18] Within the context of role theory he emphasizes that *latent* roles can be as important in organizations as *manifest* roles and views the cosmopolitan-local differentiation as indicative of latent roles. Those defined as *cosmopolitans* conform to a pattern of three variables: "low on loyalty to the employing organization, high on commitment to specialized role skills, and likely to use an outer reference group orientation." On the other hand, those defined as *locals* are "high on loyalty to the employing organization, low on commitment to specialized role skills, and likely to use an inner reference group[19] orientation."

Under the heading of restriction and exclusion of personnel, the AUPHA study reports that the cosmopolitan-local orientation is the source of real problems in many of the 15 hospitals studied. More likely to be acute in the smaller hospitals, especially those not connected with a medical center, the "home-guard" situation can block the effective utilization of outsiders, many of whom have skills that are essential to the effective operation of a modern hospital.

Locals can be found within the hospital structure in a number of areas, a common bond uniting them in subtle ways across disciplines and social background. The "loyal employees" who have served the hospitals for years and will continue to do so until they die are perhaps the hard core of locals. Members of the board of trustees are often drawn from the pool of lifelong residents in the community, especially those who have high social prestige. Though the horizons of their world may be expanded beyond that of the employees, their orientations are primarily local, especially in the smaller or more provincial communities. Physicians also often have a strong local orientation, especially those who are general practitioners and who are likely to stay in the community for the rest of their careers. To some degree or another, all these groups fit the pattern of variables stated by Gouldner: "high on loyalty to the employing organization, low on commitment to specialized role skills, and likely to use an inner reference group orientation."

Cosmopolitans in the hospital structure are more likely to have strong orientation to their particular professions, to have a readiness for accepting a better appointment at another hospital, and to have rather specialized role skills. The hospital administrator, if he is professionally trained, fits this category well. Though he will very likely be loyal to his hospital, it is more in terms of a professional loyalty than one based on strong emotional ties. When he gets his degree, he probably expects to hold more than one job in the first fifteen to twenty years of his career, to "move up" in terms of salary and prestige. Certain kinds of salaried physicians, particularly those engaged in specialties, and also those who are attached to university teaching hospitals, fulfill the definition of cosmopolitan. The increasing drive for professionalization within nursing means that many more nurses must now be viewed as cosmopolitans than would have been the case just twenty years ago.

The effect of cosmopolitan-local differentiation is to vary perception. Locals will be suspicious of the "outsiders"; perhaps they will view them as threats because they do not give complete loyalty to the organization. Exercise of formal power in the hands of the administrator may be difficult in a hospital where the local orientation is strong and the administrator has a background of professional training in management. Much of the blocking may be quite unwitting on the part of locals, but nonetheless frustrating to the point of exasperation on the part of the administrator.

PATIENTS AND SOCIAL STRUCTURE

An analysis of the social system of the hospital must include that person to whom the hospital directs its primary energies, the patient. He has a definite place in the structure, a role to fill that has reciprocal relationships with other roles in the system. In this chapter we will consider the patient as one element of the whole social structure, and will discuss some of the formal aspects of the role. We will also discuss the structured relationships among patients that often develop and the effect of these relationships on the rest of the system. In the following chapter we will devote our attention to the adaptive process, how the patient as a person tries to adjust to the demands of his role as a patient in the hospital.

In Chapter 7 we discussed some of the formal features of the patient role in our society as described by Parsons. To recapitulate, when he becomes a patient the individual acknowledges that he is not well and cannot fulfill his normal role responsibilities. Society relieves him of these obligations, in exchange for which he is to seek technically competent help for the process of recovery. When the patient enters the hospital he signifies further that he wishes technically competent help, and surrenders decisions about his care to hospital authorities—to the physician and those under his direction, as well as to others in the institution who assume responsibility for his well-being. Decision-making, except in the most minor situations, is taken over by the hospital staff. Even in the case of giving permission for surgery, there is a latent implication that the surgeon is the best judge of the situation, and the patient should accede to his considered opinion.

The assumption of decisions for the patient by hospital personnel has legal and moral connotations that often lead to formalization of routine. Safety for the patient often seems best assured through familiar procedures. For example, in many hospitals every patient automatically has a chest x-ray, a blood count, a complete physical examination, a Wassermann, and other technical procedures that may not be indicated by the specific medical situation. The reliance on routine tends to assure better medical care. Patients sometimes protest some of these procedures and are frustrated when they are told it is "just routine." However, a protection is being provided for the patient against the possibility that emotional involvement by staff will cloud the factors that lead to medical decision. Frequently patients are in pain, badly mutilated, tied to members of the staff by bonds of friendship, all situations calling for detached concern when unpleasant procedures of diagnosis or treatment are involved or quick decisions must be made.

Two other features of the patient role in the hospital must be considered. The emotional and physiological strain brought on by the illness means that the individual cannot cope with problems in the ordinary way and is expected to be more childlike in emotions and more in need of psychological support. Although treatment may emphasize physical procedures, the assumption is always implicit that the patient has psychological needs as well. In addition, one of the values of our society is that each person as an individual should be respected, that he is more important than society and is important in his own right.

Two sets of orientations toward the patient, therefore, are important in the structuring of relationships between hospital personnel and patient: one is the dependency of the patient and assumption of responsibility for him; the other is the need for psychological support and respect for the individual. These are not incompatible orientations, but they do mean that the patient can never be accepted fully as part of the "hospital family." There will always be staff and patients, and the bond that unites staff cuts across the blocked mobility lines between professions. In a sense it is a "we" and "they" situation. Functionally speaking, this is probably a most efficient way of handling the complexities of medical care in the modern hospital, both from the standpoint of the emotional reactions of the people involved and the smooth running of the special system.

These structured relationships between staff and patients have implications for perception. Patients who make too many demands, who try to tell hospital personnel how "to run things," who complain overmuch will be perceived as bad patients and disruptive influences. Basically, these patients threaten the staff's perception of their ability to assume responsibility in a competent manner. The "VIP" patient can be especially annoying on this count, for his demands must be met even though they interfere with established routine. On the other hand, patients may perceive the detached concern of the hospital staff as rejection and be most annoyed that they are not taken "right into the family."

The particular kind of relationship that exists between the physician and his patient can be a source of strain on the structured relationships between hospital personnel and patient. The latter will voice his complaints to his doctor, his gripes about food, poor service, noise, or whatever might trouble him. The physician, being an entrepreneur, is eager to keep the relationship with his patient a happy one and, therefore, may pass the complaints on to nurses, dietitians, or the administrator, perhaps with a little added bitterness if he thinks the complaints are justified. Hospital personnel are often unhappy about this situation, but from the standpoint of the social system, this may be one of the important checks and balances needed to keep the emotional neutrality from becoming real impersonality.

We will return to the adjustment of the patient to the hospital in the next chapter, but before doing that we must consider another aspect of patients and the social structure of the hospital.

When the conditions of time or propinquity are right, patients develop structured relationships among themselves; they constitute a patient society, which must be integrated with the total social system of the hospital. In a ward, or in hospitals for long-term care, conditions are especially conducive to the emergence of patient society.

Generally speaking, the factors that lead to high status and prestige in patient society are different from those that determine prestige outside the hospital. New patients have to go through a process of socialization in which they learn the rules through the process of trial and error, reward and punishment. Finally, patient society may constitute an "ingroup" that draws lines between the hospital world and itself, allowing hospital staff to enter the social interaction process only up to a point. Some relevant studies will illustrate these points.

The orthopedic ward of a large general hospital is the setting for one report.[20] The variety of cases extended from quadraplegics and paraplegics to patients with rather simple fractures, from patients who would have to live with their afflictions the rest of their lives to those who would be healed within a few months. The factors determining prestige were the severity of affliction and the length of hospitalization; in this society the sickest had the highest status. As the author, who was himself a patient, came to know patient society, he found that the rights of those who constituted the aristocracy were simple: to be left alone, to initiate conversation and social interaction only when they wished to do so. In return, their duty seemed to be to provide the horrible example of greater suffering to those less seriously injured. A new patient coming onto the ward would frequently find his friendly overtures to other patients rebuffed because he did not as yet understand the "pecking order," and his days could be lonely, indeed, until he figured out his place in the social system and understood what he was expected to do and not to do.

Another feature of this particular patient society was the secret envy and competition for recovery among the patients. Those having a similar extent of injury tended to pair off and seemed to try to outdo each other in evidences of recovery, one not admitting to the other his weaknesses or his disappointments at setbacks, but secretly rejoicing in every inch gained on the other.

The social dynamics of a small metabolic research ward constitute the data of another report.[21] Here sickness was of quite a different kind from that on the orthopedic ward, but equally serious and in some cases leading to earlier death. One of the most important elements in determining prestige was the ability to conform to the balance regimen, which required accurate account by weight of all intake and output. Patients who had difficulty meeting the demands were considered weak. Length of stay was also indicative of prestige; those who were veterans were proud of their role as orienters and of the number of studies in which they had participated. The interest evidenced by the physicians and nurses in a particular patient contributed to prestige, even the length of time that a patient spent in ward rounds conferences. Rare diseases had more prestige value than common diseases, as did specific physical findings such as those pertaining to the size of spleens and livers, and the like. These were all factors over which the patient had little control, and they loomed large. Personality variables also seemed to influence prestige and perhaps to make the crucial difference between patients when the ascribed factors were equal. Congeniality and forcefulness of personality without unnecessary aggressiveness were highly regarded, as were special talents which contributed in some measure to life on the ward.

Drive for prestige was keen, and the force of social interaction among patients was strong. Disapproval and social sanction by patients had a marked effect on behavior, a fact that could be recorded in physiological data as well as those of a social and an emotional nature. Emotional turmoil affected all patients adversely, especially that growing out of maneuvering for prestige within the group, while periods of quiet and peace contributed to individual feelings of well-being.

Some of the clearest examples of patient social structure come from mental hospitals, where the length of stay is sufficiently long to encourage well-developed social structure and where the aspect of confinement or at least control makes for an ingroup feeling. Caudill's[22] study as a participant observer on a ward of severe psychoneurotic patients in a small private hospital indicated that patient society was an important force in helping the patient adjust to the hospital and in putting his behavior within certain bounds. The patient group exerted pressure on each individual for certain kinds of attitudes toward the self (accepting the reality of the hospital), toward other patients (giving support and being willing to listen), toward therapists (keeping relations with therapist separate from ward life), and toward nurses (not informing on other patients or using nurses for domestic and routine services). Thus, the behavior of any one individual in the hospital could not be understood by reference to his personal dynamics alone; the effect of the group also was influential.

Large state mental hospitals show different kinds of patient social structure, depending on the type of patient on a given ward, the amount of psychological regression present, and the kind and extent of control that hospital personnel exercise. In the book by von Mering and King[23] there are numerous examples of patient social structure, only one of which will be cited here, a type that is found in different variations in all large mental hospitals, "The Family Ward." The authors describe it as being similar to an old-fashioned extended family with a great variety of differentiated roles and a well-established authority hierarchy. The ward society is presided over by one or more ward veterans who take a marked interest in the rest of the patients and are of help to the hospital staff in spotting and controlling deviant behavior, or in encouraging tentative explorations toward more realistic social behavior. Patients find a strong set of values and attitudes to which they must conform, with rewards and punishments clearly established. Although The Family Ward can be most supportive to many patients, it can also provide so many satisfactions to the ill person that it discourages thoughts of taking up life once again on the outside.

The effect of patient social structure can be both functional and dysfunctional to the hospital and to individual patients, although more frequently it is the former. First of all, it can act to help the new patient *structure his perceptions about the hospital*, help him become oriented to a new way of life, sort out the varied kinds of people and their functions, indicate ways of acting toward different personnel. This is beneficial to both hospital personnel and patient, making it possible for the new arrival to fit much more smoothly and quickly into a complex social structure. Schottstaedt and his associates,[24] note that their patients on the metabolic research ward took pride in helping newcomers get adjusted; indeed, this was one of the rights of people with high prestige.

A different effect can be in terms of helping the patient *adjust to his illness or injury*. Much of the anxiety connected with being ill is due to the unknown. Furthermore, anxiety builds up when it is kept inside, and sharing one's feelings with other patients may well be a therapeutic action. Collectively, patients often find ways of handling anxiety that might not be arrived at individually, as in the case of "gallows humor" which Fox[25] describes in her book about a research ward. Patient society is probably most effective in helping individuals adjust when the setting is one of long-term illness, where the landmarks for recovery are not so clear and discouragement is likely to arise; but the influence of patient society must not be discounted, even in cases of acute and short-term illnesses.

From the dysfunctional point of view, the social structure of patients can be a force that runs counter to hospital values and routines, and perhaps even interferes with the therapeutic plans of hospital personnel. Physicians and nurses in tuberculosis hospitals sometimes become exasperated with breaks in the rest and diet routine which often occur through group action. Staff in mental hospitals are familiar with cycles of disruptive behavior that at first appear to be sporadic and uncoordinated, but on close analysis can be seen to rest on a set of shared expectations among patients and a definite social structure. In other situations, for example, in general hospitals, patients may flout hospital routine by not quieting down at the regular time, disobeying orders of nurses, drinking liquor, or eating food brought in from the outside in defiance of hospital regulations. At times the tensions arising from strains in patient social structure can have an adverse effect on the physiological processes of the patient.

In a companion article to the description of prestige factors on a metabolic ward, Schottstaedt and his associates[26] analyzed variations in certain metabolic indicators in relation to psychosocial events on the ward. They reported that major metabolic changes in terms of urinary excretion of water, sodium, potassium, calcium, nitrogen, and creatinine occurred repeatedly when patients were in stressful situations. When they examined those variations that were greater than two standard deviations from the patient's base level and compared them with events judged by the investigators to be stressful, some interesting findings emerged. When the general atmosphere of the ward was disturbed, 86 per cent of the presumed stressful events were accompanied by significant alterations in metabolic products, while during calm periods on the ward only 48 per cent of presumed stressful events were associated with significant metabolic changes. The data indicated quite clearly that patient social structure and disturbances in it play a role in intensifying or calming individual stress reactions and the physiological consequences thereof.

In passing, it is worth noting that disturbances among hospital personnel also were associated with altered metabolic balance. An anxiety situation among the nursing staff, of which the patients were supposedly unaware, was related to predominantly negative metabolic balance in all patients during the two-day period in which the anxiety situation persisted. Just as tension between parents cannot be successfully hidden from children, so it appears tension among hospital staff cannot be hidden from patients.

SUMMARY

In this chapter we have outlined some of the social structural variables that are generally to be found in hospitals and that influence and limit the behavior of people within the organization, both staff and patients. One of the main constraining variables, and a determinant of perception, is that of function. We noted a series of functions to which the hospital is committed, of which patient care is primary; and indicated how conflict among functions can lead to distorted perceptions by different people within the hospital structure. Hospital functions are carried out through a system of roles that are arranged in a power and authority structure. Since previous chapters had dealt with some of the main roles in the health team—physician, nurse, medical social worker—we concentrated here on the way in which the first two of these roles fitted into the power structure and brought in another role, that of hospital administrator. Differences between the hospital, as an example of a professional organization, and the traditional bureaucratic or business organization were noted. Particularly noted was the divided authority between the manager and expert, formal bureaucratic power of a limited nature versus informal, charismatic power that is the ultimate authority. Distorted perceptions arising from conflicts in the authority structure were also discussed. Finally, the patient was introduced into the discussion of social structure, with the patient regarded as a social role. Networks of relationships among patients and the effects of these things on both the total structure and the patient himself were considered. We now turn to the hospital as a unique subculture and look at the patient in terms of the psychological and cultural factors that are important in his efforts at adaptation to the patient role in the hospital.

NOTES TO CHAPTER 10

1. Interviews with respondents in Metropolis, in a study by Koos (Koos, Earl Lomon, "'Metropolis'—What City People Think of Their Medical Services," *American Journal of Public Health*, vol. 45, December, 1955, pp. 1551–1557), indicated an unfavorable reaction to hospital care. The majority of respondents were not able to identify specific events that lay behind their negative comments, but felt that their needs had not been met or would not be met in the hospital. Material of a different kind comes from an "exposé" in a popular magazine (Berg, Roland H., "A Report on Hospitals," *Look*, vol. 23, February 3, 1959, pp. 15–19). Presented as "a searing report on hospitals suppressed by doctors who found it 'too hot to handle,'" the article presents a picture of the patient's needs coming after the convenience of hospital personnel. Although negative comments are easy to evoke in conversations about hospitals, there is a generally favorable climate of opinion about medical care facilities. (See Freidson, Eliot, and Jacob J. Feldman, *The Public Looks at Hospitals*, Health Information Foundation, Research Series, no. 4, New York, 1958.) The evidence is clear, however, that a discussion of hospital care among the laity is filled with strong emotion, much of it positive and much of it negative. It is also entirely within reason to believe that the amount of positive emotional reaction could be increased in many cases by appropriate change of attitude or action on the part of hospital personnel.

2. For a discussion of functional analysis in sociology and of manifest and latent function, the reader is referred to Merton, Robert K., *Social Theory and Social Structure*, The Free Press, Glencoe, Ill., 1949. Merton differentiates between manifest and latent functions as follows: "*Manifest functions* are those objective consequences contributing to the adjustment or adaptation of the system which are intended and recognized by participants in the system; *latent functions*, correlatively, being those which are neither intended nor recognized." (p. 51.)

3. Wooden, Howard E., "The Hospital's Purpose Is the Patient, But—," *Modern Hospital*, vol. 92, January, 1959, pp. 90–96.

4. In such wards the emphasis is on control functions. Perception of mental patients in terms of chronicity is discussed more fully in von Mering, Otto, and Stanley H. King, *Remotivating the Mental Patient*, Russell Sage Foundation, New York, 1957. Chapter 2, Social Milieu and Patient Care is especially pertinent.

5. Merton, Robert, *op. cit.*

6. As yet hospitals have not followed the lead of many business establishments in adopting a "buy now, pay later" approach to potential patients. The use of time payments would make a hospital bill less threatening to a patient or his family, and relieve the hospital from requesting payment in advance, a procedure which many patients feel is onerous.

7. Association of University Programs in Hospital Administration (AUPHA), *A Study of Problems in the Hospital Field*, Program in Medical and Hospital Administration, Graduate School of Public Health, University of Pittsburgh, 1959. Mimeographed.

8. Fox, Renée C., *Experiment Perilous*. The Free Press, Glencoe, Ill., 1959.

9. Psychiatric aide is used here to cover the role that is often labeled orderly or attendant. Part of the problem of conflict in function stems from the low prestige afforded this position in hospital structure, low prestige which is intensified by poor

salaries and unwillingness to include the aide in treatment planning. Relabeling the role may be one step in the direction of better utilization of the person in greatest contact with the patient.

10. Rubington, Erwin, "The Psychiatric Aide." Unpublished doctoral dissertation, Yale University, 1955.

11. For a concise overview of the sociological analysis of hospital organizations see Reader, George G., and Mary E. W. Goss, "Medical Sociology with Particular Reference to the Study of Hospitals," *Transactions of the Fourth World Congress of Sociology*, vol. 2, International Sociological Association, London, 1959, pp. 139–152.

12. Etzioni, Amitai, "Authority Structure and Organizational Effectiveness," *Administrative Science Quarterly*, vol. 4, June, 1959, pp. 43–67.

13. Smith, Harvey, "The Sociological Study of Hospitals." Unpublished doctoral dissertation, University of Chicago, 1949. Dr. Smith brings data from military, Veterans Administration, and civilian general hospitals, showing that in each the table of organization represents one kind of authority, but that a different kind, not diagramed formally, is crucial to an understanding of the social system of the hospital. The other kind of authority is that of the professional, the physician, and it often results in a set of interpersonal relationships and obligations that tend to circumvent the formal authority system. The dissertation is available on microfilm from the University of Chicago.

14. Hall, Oswald, "The Informal Organization of the Medical Profession." *Canadian Journal of Economics and Political Science*, vol. 12, February, 1946, pp. 30–44.

15. Association of University Programs in Hospital Administration (AUPHA), *op. cit.*

16. Abdellah, Faye G., and Eugene Levine, "Work-Sampling Applied to the Study of Nursing Personnel," *Nursing Research*, vol. 3, June, 1954, pp. 11–16.

17. Gouldner, Alvin W., "Cosmopolitans and Locals: Toward an Analysis of Latent Social Roles—I," *Administrative Science Quarterly*, vol. 2, December, 1957, pp. 281–306. Robert Merton first discussed the terms "cosmopolitan" and "local" in his paper "Patterns of Influence: A Study of Interpersonal Influence and of Communications Behavior in a Local Community," which appeared in Lazarsfeld, Paul F., and Frank M. Stanton, editors, *Communications Research, 1948–1949*, Harper and Bros., New York, 1949, pp. 180–219. Merton drew on sociological sources in which the ideas had appeared in various forms but he made them into useful tools for sociological research. Gouldner has expanded the concepts and used them in an empirical study of a college.

18. Gouldner, Alvin W., *op. cit.*

19. In making decisions about day-to-day behavior, for example, buying books, clothing, or household utensils; or about longer range commitments, for example, choosing an occupation, or deciding where to live, people quite frequently take into account the opinions and values of certain groups of people, regarding which they have fairly strong positive or negative feelings. Sociologists call these groups reference groups, that is, groups to whose opinions or values people refer in making these decisions.

Reference groups may be fairly broad and general, for example, a social class, or the members of an occupation; or they may be more specific (one's family or street corner gang). They may be formally organized (a club or a university department), or they may be informal in nature (one's group of friends, one's neighbors).

20. Anonymous, "Hospital Ward: The Social Order," *Atlantic Monthly*, vol. 200, December, 1957, pp. 57–60.

21. Schottstaedt, William W., and others, "Prestige and Social Interaction on a Metabolic Ward," *Psychosomatic Medicine*, vol. 21, March–April 1959, pp. 131–141.

22. Caudill, William, and others, "Social Structure and Interaction Process on a Psychiatric Ward," *American Journal of Orthopsychiatry*, vol. 22, April, 1952, pp. 314–334.

23. Von Mering, Otto, and Stanley H. King, *op. cit.*

24. Schottstaedt, William W., and others, *op. cit.*

25. Fox, Renée C., *op. cit.*

26. Schottstaedt, William W., and others, "Sociologic, Psychologic and Metabolic Observations on Patients in the Community of a Metabolic Ward," *American Journal of Medicine*, vol. 25, August, 1958, pp. 248–257.

Chapter 11

Hospital Culture and Patient Expectations

TO THE UNINITIATED the world of the hospital is a strange, an exciting, and yet a forbidding place, full of sights, sounds, and smells that are not comparable to everyday experiences outside. Even for the patient who has been in a hospital before, there is a distinct break with familiar things as he steps or is carried through the door. Here is the world of sickness in which the patient must become immersed; here are different values, unusual routines; here is a host of strangers who will take liberties with the body that would be unthinkable elsewhere. Here is where emergency rules action, where pain is commonplace, where behavior ranges from heroism to disintegration, where some of the great dramas of life are acted out.

The hospital is unique as a way of life, a subculture of a sort within the total society. The round of life, the customs, the relationships between people, the particular problems of everyday living are sufficiently different from those of other social organizations to warrant consideration as a unique subculture. For a given time, the patient becomes a part of this subculture and must find some way of coming to terms with it, of adapting. To the extent that he is successful in this process, and hospital personnel support him in his efforts, the process of healing will be facilitated. Just as surely, when his efforts at adaptation do not meet with success, or he is not supported by hospital personnel, the healing process may be slowed up, even thwarted, or at the very least positive attitudes toward hospitals will be jeopardized.

This chapter deals with important variables that have to do with the process of adaptation and its ultimate success or failure. First, we will describe some of the strange and interesting features of the hospital round of life to which the patient must adjust, then discuss psychological and social factors that help us understand the patient's techniques of adaptation. Finally, we will turn to positive features in the hospital subculture and indicate how the concept of a therapeutic community can facilitate patient care, both directly and indirectly.

THE HOSPITAL AS A UNIQUE ROUND OF LIFE

Among the features of the hospital subculture that bear on the patient, one that he notices very quickly is *lack of privacy.* Upon admission the patient is divested of his clothes and is frequently given a kind of gown to wear that offers but little cover for most of his body. His anatomy is exposed repeatedly for examinations by the physician and, if the hospital has a teaching program, by residents, interns, medical students; for "shots" in the buttocks; for bed baths and backrubs; for enemas. Genital areas are shaved by strangers prior to certain kinds of surgery and childbirth. The process of elimination becomes a semipublic affair for the bedfast patient, bedpan and urinal mute testimony to a process that is usually conducted in privacy at home.[1] Intimate details of the patient's life are collected and written into a record, not only physiological data but material about his emotional and social life as well. He may be asked for information that has been revealed but to few if any of his friends and family; yet the material will be read by people he does not know, and his life as well as his body will be laid bare. All kinds of people invade his room, or his bedspace if he is on a ward, morning, noon, and night. Often they enter without knocking, sometimes without being introduced or stating their purpose for being there.[2] He is their object, to be manipulated at will, unable to throw up defenses to hold the invaders at bay, his castle walls of privacy breached for the duration.

A second feature that is important for all patients except those with extensive hospital experience comprises the *strange uniforms, equipment, and language*. Ways of dress are one of the main cues for ordering our perceptions of people with whom we deal; once having identified a person's role by his clothes we bring certain expectations into immediate operation. The patient finds that some of the uniforms and ways of dress in the hospital look familiar, but it is far from an easy task to differentiate them. Yet he realizes very quickly that sorting is important, for he observes that behavior toward people with varied uniforms differs markedly among hospital personnel. Some are shown deference and respect, others treated with equalitarian manners, or even shown a little disdain. Among the physicians there are those who wear short white coats with regular shirt and pants, short white coats with white skivvy shirts and white pants, long white coats; and then there are some who wear only regular business suits. Who is the medical student, the intern, the resident, the attending physician, the chief of staff? It is well to know but the hospital issues no guidebook. Other men besides physicians wear white, which complicates the picture. Some are orderlies, some laboratory technicians; and a different pattern of interaction is expected with each. Recognizing nurses should be easy, thinks the patient, just look for a cap; but there are so many different kinds of caps and uniforms that he does not always know whether the nurse is an R.N., a practical nurse, or an aide. Fortunately, the student nurses have distinctive uniforms. Again the picture becomes complicated by other women who wear uniforms, white coats, and assorted costumes—technicians of various sorts, aides from the Hospital Auxiliary or Grey Ladies, perhaps even a medical social worker. Only when all these are sorted out can the patient perceive with dispatch what is expected of him, and anticipate what may be said or done to him.

The patient has more than the problem of uniforms to contend with, for people in the hospital speak an unfamiliar language, quite incomprehensible to him. The patient who has been previously hospitalized knows most of the terms and enters conversations easily, while the newcomer realizes there is much to be learned. A few of the terms come easy, like OR (operating room), IV (intravenous), and stool "spec." It is more mystifying when the patient overhears one nurse ask another if she has done the TPRs (temperature, pulse, respiration), or when he misses his favorite nurse and someone volunteers the information that she is "on her minutes" (out for coffee). Of similar nature is the expression "tick tack toe," which emerges as a way of characterizing the schedule of ward activities. The patient may hear the word "stat" used frequently and observe that the directions to which it is attached are carried out quickly. Unfamiliar abbreviations are uttered, such as ECG (electrocardiogram), BMR (basal metabolism rate), GI (gastro-intestinal x-rays) series, WBC (white blood count), and even TLC. If he listens carefully, the patient may note that some of the physician's orders are accompanied by the expression PRN; and then learns this means that the physician's orders are to be carried out at the discretion of the nurse. He may even find that SOB has a legitimate medical meaning (shortness of breath). There are all kinds of strange words, expressions, and abbreviations, each day turning up something different, and until the patient gets some understanding of this language he misses a good many of the important cues for making sense out of happenings in his environment. Language is another of the major ways in which people in the hospital world structure their experiences, and until mastered in at least rudimentary form, it provides a barrier to the outsider, and if necessary, a way of keeping him at a distance.

The patient lives in the midst of strange equipment, far different from anything he knows at home. Some patients are in oxygen tents, complicated looking apparatuses equipped with bottles, gauges, steel cyclinders, and plastic tent; there are other patients with tubes inserted in their noses and the tubes are attached to large glass bottles, stomach pumps, the patient is told. A bottle may hang above a patient with a tube leading to a needle inserted in his arm. There are some patients with catheters; others are in various stages of traction, including elaborate arrangements of pulleys, weights, and a type of trapeze that enables the patient to raise himself.

Aside from these things, there are the medicine carts and the stretchers that are trundled by every day. If conscious when going into the operating or delivery room, the patient sees the fullest display of all, dominated by the great light over the table and the bottles, gauges, and tubes that are part of the anesthetist's equipment.

The "hospital-wise" patient comes to be familiar with the strange equipment, but few ever accept it fully. Never does the hospital quite lose the aspect of strangeness and difference from the normal world.

Sights, sounds, and smells constitute a third feature of the hospital world so familiar to those who work there but not necessarily to those who are patients. Sights comprise more than the strange equipment that we have just described, and more than the variety of uniforms, mainly white. They include people in bathrobes, pajamas, and nightgowns—the uniform that draws a sharp line between the patient and everybody else—or someone trying to walk down the hall on the arm of a nurse, taking tentative, halting steps, with a face marked by exertion and sometimes by pain. Sights also include people being wheeled by on stretchers. By and large the sights do not include rugs on the floor, frilly curtains, overstuffed furniture, and so much of the familiar surroundings of home. There is every indication that this is an institution, not a home.

Perhaps the sounds stand out most of all. Mechanical sounds are heard everywhere; the noise of elevators, of doors closing, of trays banging; the sound of wheels on stretchers and carts. In some hospitals the "intercom" is an ever-present voice that intrudes everywhere until the patient learns to ignore it. One never-to-be-forgotten sound is the rustle of uniforms, the kind of rustle that comes from starched cotton. One hears nurses and others not so much by footsteps but by the crackling of dresses and coats. Footsteps are important though, for the floors are either waxed or of tile, so that people's footsteps squeak or clatter, and there are many different kinds—fast, slow, jerky—so many that the patient rarely gets to the point of associating the sound of footsteps with certain people. Other sounds are also important, especially patient sounds. The person just back from surgery, still under sedation but moaning, perhaps talking incoherently; the woman having labor pains who screams her anguish to the world; the babel of different tongues and accents, made sharp by pain or fear or despair. Not to be ignored are the radios and television sets. One patient in a four-bed ward who tunes to rock-and-roll programs all day may be a source of annoyance to others, even though the volume be low, and some people do not think they can watch television without volume loud enough for the whole floor.

Although the smells soon become part of the environment and not so much a part of conscious sensation, they are nonetheless distinctive. Disinfectant is the dominant type, comprised of compounds used on floors and walls, antiseptic for wounds and alcohol for cleaning equipment. In close concert is ether, lingering long after the patient who has returned from the operating room has recovered consciousness. The odors are not the usual ones—of healthy perspiration, of perfume, of soap and shaving lotion and tobacco—but what human smells there are comprise the flat, even acrid odors of sickness.

Part of the feeling of comfortableness at home comes from the familiarity with routines of eating, sleeping, working, and relaxing. Families have their own customs concerning the time of day that meals are taken, the formality or informality of the occasion, the kinds of activities that go on concurrently. Routines for sleep are idiosyncratic, hours of retiring and arising varying considerably among next-door neighbors. Many other habits of everyday life, made comfortable by routine, vary accordingly. In contrast, the hospital world is characterized by *unvarying routines*, frequently of a nature somewhat foreign to the patient's habits. The two that are mentioned most frequently by patients are the early awakening in the morning and the hours for meals. Most readers are probably familiar with the 6:00 or 6:30 a.m. arousal of patients by the night shift in order that they can be washed and prepared for the attentions of the morning shift. Few hospitals have abandoned this routine, although some are in the process. Most back their continuation of the practice with claims for efficiency of operation, especially to the extent that it frees the day shift to prepare patients for "rounds," for special treatments, or for surgery. Patients often react by calling the practice "barbaric," especially if their own routines at home call for a much later rising. For many patients this is the most difficult change to make, especially where they feel that justification for continuation of the practice is weak.[3]

Meal hours are often different from those to which the patient is accustomed, especially the dinner hour, which in some hospitals may be as early as 4.30 p.m., and certainly earlier than most patients prefer. Furthermore, meals cannot be scheduled around natural cycles of hunger, as they can be at home, but come without regard to the state of the patient's interest in food.

Other routines particular to the hospital involve restriction of individual movement and of contact with people. When the patient is ambulatory, he is limited to the places he can go on foot or in his wheelchair; he feels rebuffed by the mysteries of closed doors and areas that are "off limits." Hospital personnel always appear to be suspicious of the movements of patients, even in Veterans Administration hospitals where patients have considerable freedom of movement. Again, movement routines at home are quite different.

Restriction of contact with people is of two kinds: on the one hand, the limitation of visitors in terms of numbers and the hours at which they can come; on the other hand, the formal type of relationship with the hospital staff. Informal and close relationships with people come most easily in family visits or contacts with other patients, both of which may be limited by factors of time and contiguity. The patient is not able to order his social relationships in his own way as he could at home. For many patients we could say that they are subject to control by others in social relationships, rather than being themselves the source of control.

In addition to the features of the hospital round of life which have just been described, there are *sets of expectations toward patients* on the part of hospital personnel, and these expectations are an important part of the subculture. The first general expectation is that of *dependence*, of compliance by the patient to hospital rules and regulations, to the daily routine, to the decisions that are made for him by physicians or nurses. The compliant patient is therefore likely to be perceived as the good patient by hospital staff, whereas the patient who tries to exert authority will be perceived negatively.

As an illustration of the "spread" of the expectation for dependence, it is routine practice for a patient to be conveyed to the door of the hospital in a wheelchair at the time of discharge and then, when released, walk off under his own power.

In line with dependence, the patient is expected *not to fulfill his normal role responsibilities*. This is one of the prerequisites of the sick role, which we discussed in Chapter 7, and a factor that receives strong support from hospital expectations. The patient is encouraged not to worry about cares of family or job and to concentrate on the process of getting well. It seems reasonable that one of the functions of the restriction on visitors is that of making family ties more tenuous, thus helping to relieve the patient of his family role responsibilities.[4] Hospital personnel often argue that visitors get in the way, having in mind a physical interference, but there is probably a feeling that they get in the way psychologically as well. Hospitals do not generally look with favor on the patient who takes up once again his business duties from his bedside as he is convalescing; they feel that if the patient is able to take on the well role, he should be out of the hospital. Even patients who are confined with injuries slow in healing and otherwise feeling fine are not viewed as able to carry a normal share of role responsibilities, even within that possible in a hospital environment.

A third expectation concerns the *de-emphasis on external power and prestige* which the patient carries in his life outside the hospital. The taking away of patients' clothes is a symbol of this loss, all patients being rendered as naked as the day they came into the world, and supposedly as innocent. Indeed, there is nothing quite so deflating to an individual's sense of prestige as his own nakedness in public. A positive function is also served by this action and expectation, that of emotional neutrality and fairness. In effect, the hospital tells the patient that all patients are equal and all will receive the best that the institution has to offer. Although this is never literally true, as many charity patients can attest, the gap between the ranks of men is greatly narrowed in the world of the hospital, both in terms of the expectations by hospital personnel and in the treatment given.

There are exceptions to all situations, in this case the VIP being the one to make impossible the de-emphasis on power and prestige. Especially difficult is the situation in which the VIP patient is an important member of the community from which the hospital draws its patients, or an important benefactor, past or potential, to the hospital. Under these circumstances the person cannot be treated as an ordinary patient, and there is likely to be grumbling by the staff over this shift in their regular set of expectations as well as "bowing and scraping" to him.

Suffering and pain are to be expected and should be borne with as much grace as possible under the circumstances, so goes the general expectation. Hospital personnel know that rarely do patients come without pain or malaise, and often the suffering is intense. Furthermore, the procedures involved in curing sickness in themselves often produce pain. The effect of surgery is one of the most common illustrations, and as many former patients know, this is not a pleasant experience. It is necessary, however, to the process of getting well and is part of the price that the patient has to pay. As a consequence of the expectation, hospital personnel have little patience with someone who complains greatly about minor discomfort, and great respect for a patient who is stoical in the face of severe suffering. Unfortunately, some patients, realizing the strength of the expectation, will suffer in silence when they might legitimately ask for medication.

Finally, *the patient should want to get well* and do all he can to aid the process. Again, this expectation grows out of the definition of the sick role and is an aspect of the role that is subject to rewards and punishments. The faintest hint of malingering can be picked up quickly by nurse or physician and is a sign that the patient is not living up to his obligations. If malingering can be clearly established, it acts to release the hospital from its obligations and brings about attempts to get rid of the patient as quickly as possible. Unfortunately, the expectation that the patient should want to get well may conflict with the correct perception of a patient who has difficulty striving in this direction because of deep-seated personality needs or conflicts. At the time he most needs understanding by hospital staff, he may be perceived as a malingerer and given short comfort by those whose job it is to help him.

For the patient in a mental hospital a different expectation comes into play, that of *deviance*. Although Parsons has referred to the sick role as a deviant role, that of the mental patient is regarded as deviant in a more definite and severe way. For the patient in many states of the union the deviance is underscored by law in terms of the loss of rights to vote, drive a car, transact business, and to fulfill other social functions. He is expected to be disturbed, although not necessarily in an assaultive or bizarre sense; hence, he is not able to apply the same efforts to get well as the patient with somatic disease. As we have seen earlier, the expectation for deviance can lead to distorted perception of the patient, as under the "Legend of Chronicity," but in enlightened hospitals it can give the patient relief from the pressures to conform to the world while he sets about the process of recovery.

Every subculture has certain values that are given high priority by most or all members of the group. In the case of the hospital, the most prominent of the values is the *importance attached to human life* and commitment to the process of prolonging and saving life. Death may be regarded as due to a limitation of modern scientific medicine if the patient has not yet reached the age when death can be expected as a natural course of events. Most physicians can well remember when they lost their first patient, and for many the event was accompanied by feelings of futility and depression. Pervading all of hospital activity is the idea of the worth of human life and a readiness to institute heroic procedures to try to save or prolong life. Expense, time, human effort can be used without stint in the process, and no one thinks for a minute that it should be otherwise. As scientific medicine has improved its diagnostic and therapeutic procedures, it has become remarkably successful in saving life, a fact that has helped to change the stereotype of the hospital as a place where people go to die.

At the same time, another value is the importance of *emotional neutrality*, or *detached concern*, a factor we have discussed a number of times in connection with the role expectations of the physician, nurse, and medical social worker. Those who care for a patient must not become intimately involved in his emotional life, in his suffering, his depression, his frustration, even though a proper appreciation and understanding of his feelings is important. Detached concern draws a fine line between understanding and emotional support, on the one hand, and intense emotional interaction and involvement on the other hand. As a result, there is likely to be more emphasis on bodies, or even parts of bodies, than people; more emphasis on the process of physical than of psychological treatment. In some instances an undue emphasis on emotional neutrality or detached concern can lead to an atmosphere as sterile emotionally as it is free from bacteria.

The value placed on emotional neutrality contributes in part to the set of formalized relationships that are characteristic of hospital life, not only between hospital staff and patients, but among hospital personnel themselves. The hierarchical nature of the treatment process, in terms of personnel, the necessity for prompt carrying out of orders, these are things that are facilitated by relationships that are more formal than informal, that rely on role expectations to a greater extent than expectations based on personality characteristics.[5] Between patients and staff the formality of relationships facilitates the slight emotional distance so necessary to protection against intense involvement. Once again, it is easy for relationships to become too formal, with the result that emotional warmth is squeezed out altogether.

Although both of these value orientations are characteristic of mental hospitals, one finds still another value there, that of *control*. An up-to-date mental hospital uses control only in terms of a therapeutic plan for the patient, yet many mental hospitals still make it a primary value in its own right. Studies of attendants and other nonprofessional personnel have shown that they tend to regard people with mental disorders as unpredictable and irrational, to follow pretty much the syndrome of belief about mental disease as outlined in Chapter 5. Resting on this set of assumptions is the necessity of control measures which serve to reduce unpredictability and at the same time keep the patient at a safe psychological distance. Even among the professional staff of physicians and nurses the value placed on control is high in many of our mental hospitals. There is no question that the importance of control as a value is being questioned on a manifest level, but on a latent level it still receives strong support.

PSYCHOLOGICAL FACTORS IN PATIENT ADAPTATION

Understanding the efforts of the patient to adapt to the world of the hospital requires information from two areas, that of psychological processes and that of cultural background. For purposes of exposition we have separated them here, devoting a section of the chapter to each, but the reader should keep in mind that they are intimately related and that the separation is only artificial.

Although the uniqueness of personality precludes any hard and fast generalizations about psychological patterns in adaptation, nevertheless there are aspects of the situation that are common to a great many patients. Problems of anxiety and hostility, conflicts about dependence and dominance occur with regularity as do the various techniques utilized to handle the disturbing feelings. Some of these factors were discussed in Chapter 7 relative to the relationship between physician and patient, but entering the hospital is usually more threatening to the individual and involves more psychologically relevant factors than does a visit to the physician's office. We shall, therefore, build on the material that was presented in Chapter 7.

Arising from many sources, the basic problem faced by the patient is *anxiety*. Primarily it is about death, mutilation, and suffering, with death the constant, though often repressed, thought. An illness that is sufficiently serious to require hospitalization is not to be treated lightly; complications may set in, more serious conditions may result, accidents may occur in the treatment procedure, especially in surgery. The patient may find it difficult to keep such ideas out of his mind. Even though he knows that the knowledge and skill of modern medicine is formidable, he also knows that there is much that it cannot do, and that people do die. Many patients suspect and fear cancer, a fear that can be aroused by an illness condition that is the least bit ambiguous. To them death is an ever-present threat. In this modern world life is not cheap; rather it is precious, with unbounded opportunities for enjoyment, and death is a threat of greater proportions than in many other periods of man's history.

Suffering may not constitute a threat quite so clear; nevertheless, the thought of it is a source of anxiety. The patient entering the hospital for a surgical operation knows that pain is an inevitable consequence, although it is difficult to imagine in advance its quality or intensity. Still he wonders how well he will be able to tolerate pain, and feels uneasy about it.

Mutilation, loss of function, disfigurement, some form of disability is often the consequence of hospitalization, be it from a disease like poliomyelitis, a disorder like cardiac infarction, or a surgical procedure like a radical mastectomy. Threat arising from disability is of two kinds: the limitation imposed on one's living routine with consequent changes in habits and activities, and social prejudice akin to that shown minority groups.[6] Of the two, that of social prejudice is more salient for most patients, especially if the potential disability is easily noticed, as in the case of a withered leg or facial scar. Even for the patient who has suffered a heart attack, a limitation in function may result that will disrupt his former patterns of social behavior to an extent that will change his status in subtle ways. Anxiety due to threatened disability will not be found in all patients because of the varying nature of their illnesses, but when it does occur the threat is of considerable proportions.

Another source of anxiety is the unknown. Most patients have little understanding of disease processes, about diagnostic and treatment procedures, and are not competent to make judgments in these areas. Furthermore, the world of the hospital may be strange to most patients, as we outlined earlier in the chapter, something that will have to be "figured out." The unknown is more threatening because the patient cannot act toward it in the same manner he might when well; during illness he is helpless or at least dependent, not able to control or manipulate his environment effectively. In all probability when he enters the hospital there is no one to greet him, to tell him explicitly what to do. People come at him unannounced and do not explain their missions. He cannot get information in his usual way because the hospital personnel are evasive in answering his questions. Thus, the threat of the unknown is heightened by the nature of the hospital subculture, and by the nature of his other fears, about his life or about suffering.

For many patients, children especially, there is a specific source of anxiety, that of intrusive procedures in the form of needles and enemas. In her analysis of doll play with pediatric patients, Erickson[7] found a great deal of anxiety about "shots," the enema tube, even the tongue depressor and otoscope. Other than the pain involved, which is slight compared to other kinds of suffering, there is probably a basic fear of the invasion of the body, represented in its extreme by surgery, but also found in the more common intrusive procedures. Aside from Erickson's study, research findings are meager, but there seems good empirical reason to hypothesize a basic intrusion anxiety to which all patients, but especially children, must make some adjustment.

Anxiety in the case of the mental patient arises out of the nature of his disease, but the act of hospitalization may have special connotations that are productive of anxiety, even for the patient who appears to be quite out of contact with reality. The discussion in Chapter 5 pointed to the prevalence of negative attitudes toward mental disease, and the stigma attached to the act of commitment to a mental hospital. Commitment for many is a sign that a person is crazy and never will be quite the same again. Even in his distorted view of the world the mental patient may feel that society is rejecting him, that indeed he is crazy.[8] Closely allied is a fear of impulses, heightened by the act of hospitalization, that the person may kill somebody or commit other drastic acts. The initial period of hospitalization is not easy for the patient with mental disease any more than it is for a patient with somatic disease, for in addition to anxiety about the unknown he is threatened by the meaning of the act of hospitalization.

Allied with the anxiety is an *emotional regression*, partly an ego defense against the anxiety, partly a reaction fostered by the enforced dependence which is the hospital's expectation toward the patient. The regression is evidenced in egocentricity, constriction of interests, emotional dependency, and hypochondriasis, an exaggerated concern with the self and the functions of the body and a seeking of emotional support from the environment. We noted in Chapter 7 that the tendency to perceive the physician as an authority figure is heightened under illness, and it is easy for the patient to project into his relationships with the physician a father-child situation. This is especially true when the patient is in the hospital in an enforced dependency situation. With emotional regression other figures in the hospital environment tend to be perceived in the light of family figures, in particular, the nurse as mother. In Chapter 8 we discussed the idea that the nurse is the *id mother* in distinction to the medical social worker, who fits more of an ego function, which means that the strong need for emotional support, for succor, by the patient is perceived as being fulfilled by the nurse. The autocratic, impersonal kind of nurse is therefore likely to be perceived in a much more negative light than perhaps she deserves or intends.

The patient is likely to perceive other hospital personnel, as well as the physician and nurse, in terms of a family relationship situation, especially with regular family ties made more tenuous and in the face of emotional regression. Emotionally speaking, at an unconscious level he seeks to be "part of the family," and is hypersensitive to rejection or to acceptance and psychological support. The various kinds of experience that occur while he is in the hospital may be perceived within this framework, from the attitude shown at the admitting desk, the approach of x-ray and laboratory technicians, to the kind of cup of coffee he receives on his breakfast tray. Hospitals that are run for the benefit of those who work there, hospitals in which the patient is regarded more as a body or a statistic than as a whole person, are at a great disadvantage in providing the emotional income which the patient seeks, even though they may show great efficiency and high standards according to physical criteria. Part of an interview which Koos quotes in his study of "Metropolis" shows the attitude of an expatient to such care:

> I don't say our hospitals don't turn you out alive—at least they most often don't kill you—but the way they treat you while you are in their hands is pitiful. . . . I was in ———— Hospital for four weeks last spring. They didn't do anything to hurt me, but they certainly didn't do anything to help me psychologically to get well. . . . I can't put my finger on it, exactly. I think what I am trying to say is nobody gave a darn about me as a person. I was just somebody filling a bed.[9]

In contrast, the administrator of a new hospital in a suburb of an eastern city showed a class of student hospital administrators a drawer full of notes from patients, written on all kinds of paper in all kinds of styles, all full of praise for the service rendered and the "homelike" quality of the hospital. The spirit pervaded the hospital; physicians, nurses, orderlies, volunteers, and patients could not help feeling its effects.

Earlier in the chapter we pointed out the ingroup feeling on the part of hospital personnel and the separation they feel between themselves and patients, a "we and they" kind of situation. As we have seen, this arises partly out of the necessity for emotional neutrality or objectivity and the formalization of relationships which are part of the social structure. A psychological line between staff and patients based on these factors does not necessarily mean that emotional warmth and acceptance of the patient should be avoided; objectivity is not synonymous with rejection and coldness. Rather, physicians and nurses may have had inadequate training in ways of establishing warm relationships with patients, may not have the knowledge of principles of human interaction that forms the basis of acceptance and support. Also, when the hospital's purpose becomes diverted from the main emphasis on the needs of the patient, the psychological line necessary between staff and patient can lead to emotional sterility. When, however, interest in the patient as a person remains primary, and adequate knowledge of human behavior is present, then objectivity can free the emotional resources of staff for a full measure of giving to all patients, accepting regression and helping them back to health emotionally and physically.

Special Problems of Adaptation

The combination of expectations concerning patient behavior, anxieties of various kinds, and emotional regression may lead to difficulties in adaptation to the hospital when certain strong personality needs are threatened. By looking at some of the more common problems of adaptation, psychologically speaking, we can see more clearly the interplay of hospital pressures and personality variables.

Loss of power and prestige, except in the case of the VIP patient, has been described as part of the introduction into the hospital subculture from the patient's point of view. Appendicitis is still appendicitis, whether it occurs in the abdomen of a rich man or a poor man, a laborer or the executive vice president of a corporation. For patients who have enjoyed a full measure of power and prestige outside the hospital, there may be difficulty in relinquishing these things, especially if the prestige feeds strong needs within the personality. Loss of power and prestige can therefore be frustrating and can lead to feelings of hostility toward those who are perceived as having taken them away. The hostility can be expressed through irritability, constant demands for services, small and large, and vociferous complaints about food, noise, temperature of the room, or the inattentiveness of personnel. Hostility is usually directed against people other than the physician, most frequently against nurses and auxiliary personnel of all kinds. Unfortunately, a vicious circle goes into operation, hostility by the patient leading to less attention, less psychological support, then to increased frustration and more hostility. Those in the hospital breathe a sigh of relief when such patients leave, but few understand the basis for the reaction, perceiving these individuals only as bad patients, the bane of hospital life.

Closely allied is the problem created by the person who has a basic conflict about dependence, who feels threatened when he has to be dependent on other people. His conflict is increased by hospital expectations, and perhaps by the nature of his illness, leading in many cases to an exaggeration of independence strivings. The end result may be difficulty in utilizing the treatment plan prepared for him, securing the proper amount of bed rest after a heart attack, following a rigid diet, refraining from tobacco, or at the very least, difficulty in adhering to hospital routine. Unfortunately, our culture is one that places great emphasis on independence, especially among males and especially in the middle and upper-middle classes. When cultural pressure fuses with neurotic need, the enforced dependency of hospitalization makes for difficulty of adaptation.

Strong dependency wishes, rather than fear of them, provide the basis for a different problem, that of overadaptation. Patients who evidence this syndrome wish to be taken care of rather than to assert their independence, and hospital personnel have difficulty when the stage of convalescence is reached. One can view this period of illness much as one views the adolescent period of development, a time when there is vacillation between childhood dependence and adult independence. Like some adolescents, there are patients who are reluctant to cut the ties that bind them to the institutional setting, preferring the emotional gratifications there to the requirements of emotional life as a well person. Hospital personnel are familiar with the patient whose symptoms return as time for discharge comes around, usually very real symptoms not consciously produced by the patient. If not symptoms, there may be much crying, or open evidence of anxiety. Sometimes there is a realistic basis for the patient's feelings, if discharge means return to a disagreeable or enervating job, to burdensome responsibilities of a large family, or to a threatening and unpleasant set of interpersonal relationships. However, the medical social worker may find it an easier task to help the patient change the environmental situation than to deal with strong intrapsychic needs of long standing.

Another variation of the dependence theme occurs when strong aggressive and dominance drives are fused with the enforced dependence on the hospital. Manipulation of the situation by the patient to dominate and control those around him often results. Here we have the picture of the sickroom despot whose rule is exercised not by overt tyranny but by appeals to his helpless state, by constant reference to his suffering, by pitiful-sounding requests for aid. He thinks nothing of asking much in the way of time and effort by family or hospital staff in order to satisfy whims. If long continued, as is usually the case, this pattern of behavior interferes with hospital routine and arouses hostility on the part of dietitians, nurses, orderlies, other patients, and house staff. Not able to display open aggression toward the patient, hospital staff displace it onto each other, keep it pent up, or in some cases withdraw from the patient or indirectly take it out on him.

In the patterns of behavior just cited we see the effect of two important kinds of variables. On the one hand, there are *the effects of the hospital situation*, expectations toward the patient, routinized procedures, all pressures of the subculture of the hospital. On the other hand, there are the effects of the illness and of the *intrapsychic factors in the patient relative to his illness*, anxiety and defenses against it, emotional regression, and strong personality needs of various kinds. The two sets of variables play into each other, meaning that the patient's behavior cannot be understood apart from either, but also meaning that a change in one of the sets of variables will have direct effect on the other. Hospital personnel are therefore not helpless in dealing meaningfully with patients who have difficulties in adaptation and can aid them psychologically as well as physically.

The Phenomenon of Loss

Earlier in the chapter, under the discussion of sources of anxiety, we talked about mutilation, loss of function, disfigurement, or some other form of disability as a problem that some patients have to face. At that time we did not discuss the special problems of adaptation faced by the patient with a disability, reserving till this point a consideration of the phenomenon of loss. Death of a friend or loved one is not the only situation that produces grief and the necessity of working through the sorrow in some constructive manner. The loss of part of the body, of an important function, the changing of important body characteristics also cause despair and lead to the necessity of adequate "grief work" for a return to health, psychological as well as physical. Psychologists, clergymen, and physicians are well aware of the effects of unexpressed sorrow, of which some of the more extreme effects have been documented by Lindemann[10] in his study of the families of victims of the Coconut Grove Fire of 1941 in Boston. In Lindemann's cases an inability to express anguish fully, to carry out the "grief work," was associated later on with various kinds of psychosomatic disorders, some of them serious. Lindemann felt that the process of grief work gave the individual an opportunity to face his problem and deal with it realistically.

The hospital patient who incurs a loss in the form of disability or disfigurement faces the same problem of grief work, of expressing suffering openly, of going through a depressive phase, of facing his problem and working through his feelings regarding it. Until he has faced the loss in this manner he will have difficulty in adjusting to his altered status, of coping adequately with the world.

Some data on heart attacks, as yet unpublished, illustrate the loss phenomenon and the necessity of grief work for optimum recovery.[11] Twenty-five patients with coronary infarction were seen shortly after admission to the hospital and visited regularly until discharge, and in some cases after discharge. In a certain proportion of the patients there was an initial period of disorganization and depression, a kind of emotional shock. Other patients avoided the reaction by minimizing the illness, almost refusing to believe they were ill, or depersonalizing the situation and behaving as though it were not happening to them. The data indicated that the patients who avoided the initial shock and depression were predisposed to excessive disability and other maladaptive reactions to the illness, such as noncooperation.

Later in the illness the problem became one of handling drives, especially aggression, and finding new outlets for them. Patients who were successful in directing aggression away from the self and toward problems were able to protect self-esteem and mobilize energies for learning new patterns of behavior that would enable them to live successfully with their disability.

Much research needs yet to be done in the area of the loss phenomenon, detailing the effects of depression and shock versus avoidance of depression, and the relationship of grief work to the ability of the patient to handle other emotional problems connected with his disease. However, the area is interesting, especially when we consider some of the expectations of hospital staff toward patient behavior. The cheerful patient is considered a good patient; hospital personnel do not like depressed patients, those who cry, who bemoan their fate, who see no future for themselves. Rather than accept these feelings, hospital staff usually try to get the patient to "look on the bright side of things," put his mind on more cheerful subjects, and forget his problems. In the case of long-continued depression, the morbid variety, the perception of the patient as not a good patient can be understood. In the case of a reactive depression, the initial shock to a loss of function, inability to help the patient express grief openly may be damaging therapeutically. The question is still very much of an open nature but one for serious thought by those who work in hospitals.

CULTURAL BACKGROUND AND PATIENT ADAPTATION

Personality variables are overlaid with reaction patterns that find their source in relevant social groupings to which the patient belongs—religious, social class, regional, and ethnic groups. Throughout the book we have noted the effect of these groups in terms of beliefs and attitudes, values, and customs; and in Chapter 7 we indicated rather specifically how they influenced the physician-patient relationship. Here we consider how they may facilitate or hinder the patient's adaptation to the hospital.

Ethnic Background and Response to Pain

Hospital personnel hold stereotypes about certain ethnic and racial groups in terms of the way they will react to pain. Thus, they expect patients with a south European or Latin-American background to be more sensitive to pain and more voluble in expression of their feelings about it. Negroes come under the same stereotype, with the specific feature of overreaction to the sight of needles. On the other hand, patients of Oriental or north European extraction are expected to be more stoical and less sensitive to pain.

Emotional reactivity to pain does seem to vary among different ethnic groups, as indicated in the interesting study by Zborowski.[12] Patients were classified as having an Irish, an Italian, a Jewish, or an Old American background, and were observed in a variety of pain-inducing situations. Italian and Jewish patients were characterized as being very emotional in their response, with a tendency to overexaggerate the experience. However, the underlying attitude toward pain in the two groups was different. Italian patients seemed to be more concerned with the pain experience itself, the actual pain sensation, while Jewish patients were anxious about the symptomatic meaning of the pain and its significance for their future health.

Reactions of Italian and Jewish patients to the general treatment situation were also indicative of underlying differences. The initial reaction of the Jewish patient tended to be one of considerable complaining and emotional expression, which subsided as soon as the patient was assured that adequate care was forthcoming. Zborowski suggests that this sequence indicates that the emotional reactivity to pain may serve to create a setting where the pathological causes of pain will best be taken care of, especially when one considers the future-oriented health concerns of the Jewish patient. The illustration by Spiegel in Chapter 7 of the reactions of an eastern European Jew in his relationship with a physician adds support to the idea that the patient is concerned with creating a favorable environment for treatment.

Zborowski found that Italian patients were less concerned with setting up a favorable treatment situation, taking it for granted that adequate care would be given.

Pain reactions of Old American patients showed little emphasis on complaining, and could be characterized more as a reporting on pain, taking at times almost the detached role of an unemotional observer. Strong pain frequently caused a withdrawal from people, as though one might lose control.

Like the Jewish patient, the Old American patient had a future-oriented anxiety toward pain in line with a pronounced health consciousness. While in the hospital there was evidence of wishing to cooperate with those expected to take care of him, a situation where emotionality was seen as a hindering factor to the adequate carrying out of the therapeutic process.

The expression of emotions in response to threatening situations such as pain depends a great deal on one's cultural heritage, a factor which each patient brings with him to the hospital. However, hospital culture tends to exemplify a stereotyped expectation about emotional reaction in the "good" patient which is similar to that described by Zborowski in his Old American patients. Observed behavior which runs counter to the stereotype may not be perceived with the sympathy that the patient expects but rather may provoke distrust on the part of hospital personnel. Under these circumstances the therapeutic endeavor between hospital and patient cannot reach its maximum potential.

Modesty and the Lack of Privacy

When the relationship between physician and patient was discussed in Chapter 7 we noted that ethnic background and modesty can cause disturbances. In the illustration cited, a woman of Puerto Rican background was most uneasy about submitting to a pelvic examination by the physician and this uneasiness was traced to sexual attitudes and customs in Puerto Rican culture. Modesty conflicts with the lack of privacy in the hospital and with the expectation on the part of hospital personnel that patients' bodies are emotionally neutral. Thus, the same kind of difficulty that appeared in the obstetrician's clinic can be multiplied in certain hospital settings, especially those that have a teaching program for medical students, residents, and interns. Not only are the physicians in training strange males, they are also young and sexually attractive, potential threats to the self-esteem of a woman who has not been trained to regard certain areas of her body in an objective way. Examination by a number of strange young men or participation in teaching rounds can be an unsettling experience for a woman patient of an ethnic background that places strong emphasis on sexual modesty.

Attitudes of modesty vary a great deal among patients and are not restricted to sex or to patients from a particular ethnic background. Often men are uneasy about exposing their bodies to the attention of nurses, especially to the young student nurses. Some will suffer in silence rather than undergo an enema, or will be hostile and uncooperative regarding the bed bath. As to cultural groups, there are many that emphasize the privacy of the genitalia and have taboos about sexual function that conflict with the emotional neutrality of the hospital round of life. Nor is this limited to areas where "ethnic pockets" are to be found. Most hospitals serve some patients who have a reserve about their bodies, who unconsciously perceive exposure and manipulation of body parts as sexual activity and who feel quite upset by the lack of privacy in the hospital.

Conflict between modesty and hospital practice may have some long-range effects on patient care. In some cases it can be influential in causing delay in coming to the hospital, delay that is costly in terms of therapeutic advantage. Once in the hospital, extreme modesty can disturb the relationship between hospital personnel and patient to the extent that the patient may not get the best medical care or may refuse procedures that are necessary to his treatment. Acceptance of attitude and alteration of routine to the point where the patient can be psychologically comfortable contribute much more to effective care of the patient than does exasperation with him or pressure without understanding. Patients can change in attitude with insight and help by the hospital staff.

Emotional Significance of Food

Some of the deepest emotional experiences of our lives are concerned directly or indirectly with food. Hallowed by tradition, enriched with the joy and security of family bonds, sanctified in religious sacrament, food is more than just nourishment for the body. Celebrations and joyous events often have a meal as the central part of the observance; the "breaking of bread" is symbolic of hospitality and acceptance; the observance of dietary laws reinforces the value system of a religion. In everyday life mealtime may be one of the few occasions when the whole family are together, a time perhaps when they can mull over the day's happenings and gain some perspective for the future. In some cases it may be, of course, the time for quarreling and bitterness, for hostility rather than warmth and security. The weight of evidence points, however, to mealtime as one of fond remembrances for most people and food has nostalgic value that bespeaks emotional as well as physical nourishment. Motivation research has been quick to realize this fact, or indeed the fact was known long before by businessmen with good common sense, and food products are often said to be "like the kind that mother used to make." The young bride knows that one of her fiercest competitors may be "Mom's apple pie," but she also knows that "one of the best ways to a man's heart is through his stomach." Food subconsciously tells us much about people, whether they like us or not, if they can be trusted, if we belong together, perhaps even what we can expect from them in the future.[13]

Food preferences and customs vary among social classes and among ethnic groups, even in the same community, as shown by the studies of Cussler and de Give, and by Bennett, Smith, and Passin. Among factors to be considered in food customs are the manner in which certain foods are prepared, foods that are particularly liked or disliked, foods that are taboo or thought to be harmful in some way, and foods that are used for festive occasions, or foods that are especially helpful to the sick. To be sure, there are many variations possible within these areas, but by ignoring food sensitivities the hospital may be conveying unwittingly to the patient important emotional messages.

Some illustrations are in order. The first concerns a common American beverage, coffee, a staple commodity in the diet kitchen of every hospital. A good cup of coffee in our culture denotes friendliness, sociability, warmth, camaraderie, exemplified in the coffee break at work, the neighborhood kaffeeklatches, or the casual "let's stop in for a cup of coffee." A few years ago one of the major coffee companies ran a series of advertisements in national magazines in which they portrayed scenes of Americana, scenes that represented warmth and security like a farm kitchen. In each case someone in the picture was holding a coffee cup and inviting a figure outside to come in for coffee. The advertisement reinforced a custom and an emotional meaning that is prevalent throughout these United States.

An Italian patient refused the diet offered him following major surgery and proved resistant to all efforts of nurses and kitchen staff to persuade him otherwise. A medical social worker who had patience and a keen sense of cultural factors talked to him about food and found that the gruel which had been prescribed for him was the kind of food they fed to pigs at his farm. He could hardly trust the hospital to take care of him if they served him the same food that he would give to the pigs.

The Mexican-American patient who is used to a diet of highly seasoned food may find the bland hospital diet repulsive and without substance, fit for babies but not for grown men. He may feel that there is no strength in it and wonder how the hospital expects him to get well on such food.

To all these things must be added the fact that food prepared at home is usually hot and seasoned to the tastes of the family. Hospital food is often cold and the seasoning is left to the salt and pepper shakers on patients' trays. Also, when a person is sick at home the family often try to cater to his food preferences, making dishes he is especially fond of, or preparing food that they think will "go down easily" or "bring back his strength." Thus, food prepared for the sick person at home has emotional overtones that may be lacking in the hospital situation.

When food is cold, coffee bitter, meals unappetizing and unseasoned, special diets offensive, or when the food customs and preferences of the patient are violated, the ability of the patient to adapt to the hospital round of life is jeopardized, for he feels unwanted or even rejected. On the other hand, a dietary situation that fits both the patient's physiological needs and his emotional and cultural expectations can be one of the strongest bonds that the hospital is capable to forge with him.

Pattern of Family Relationships

The type of relationship between family members often has a direct relationship to the problem of adaptation to illness and to the hospital world. Sickness disrupts normal role relationships and frequently necessitates a shift in responsibility which a family member may not be able to make, or the shift may have consequences which are threatening to the patient. For example, in the pattern where the husband is the supreme authority, leaving little or no room for his wife to make decisions, the wife, when her husband is hospitalized, may not know what to do about even the simplest financial matters or problems in maintaining the house, especially if there are no other male members of the family to assist her. Should this occur, she cannot offer him full emotional support and he is likely to be concerned about her helpless state. The case cited in Chapter 9 of the medical social worker and the Mexican-American wife is pertinent here, the worker finding it necessary to shift from his accustomed permissive role and to assume an authoritarian approach to the patient's wife. In that situation both the patient and his wife were relieved.

Stress to the patient may be forthcoming in the same situation but for quite different reasons, when the apparently helpless spouse is able to cope with the situation in an efficient manner. If the dominance and control which the husband has assumed as part of his family role rests on personality needs for power, the thought of a competent wife filling his shoes can be most disturbing. Under stress from outside conditions of this sort the patient is hampered in marshaling his full resources for recovery.

Another aspect of family relationships concerns the closeness of family ties and the extent to which various members are involved in making decisions and in supporting the patient. For example, in her study of "Sal si Puedes" Clark[14] found that in the Mexican-American community decisions about surgery or other major medical procedures had to be discussed with the whole family and usually with the *compadres* as well, those outside the family who held a kind of honorary family status. Decisions, therefore, could not be hurried; they required group support. Other ethnic groups emphasize the same tradition, especially where the ties between members of the family are close and where the extended family in one form or another is still evident. The slowness of the decision-making can be exasperating to hospital personnel, especially as expectations of the dominant middle-class American culture are for quick individual decisions. It is this cultural tradition that fuses with the social expectation of quick decisions in hospital work and causes lack of patience with other methods.

The decision-making process is only one aspect of generalized group support, which is reflected in the interest of all the family in hospital happenings and in visiting the patient. Sickness may be a time when the family are expected to rally to the patient's side, whether he is at home or in the hospital. Unfortunately, the influx of relatives may disrupt hospital routine too much and the persistent questions of each member of the group can consume valuable nursing time in an already crowded day. Before hospital personnel dismiss these actions out of hand, it must be remembered that therein is strong psychological support for the patient, especially if the hospital is a new world for him and if he comes from a background where the knowledge of scientific medicine is limited.

Religious Background

Coping with the problem of illness and adaptation to the hospital can be both facilitated and hampered by the religious belief system of the patient and his family. In extreme cases, we have situations such as those in which religious beliefs prevent the use of certain medical procedures like blood transfusions. At times the difficulties are more subtle, when, for example, disease is perceived as punishment for sin and therefore justly deserved. We noted in the discussion of mental disease in Chapter 5 that some people believe diseases of the mind are caused by sin and usually the sin occurs in the sexual sphere. The believed association between masturbation and insanity is a case in point. Personnel in mental hospitals, therefore, face greater difficulties with patients and families on this score than their colleagues in general or chronic disease hospitals, but even in these latter institutions the association between sin and disease is sometimes found. In some religious groups the sin-punishment-disease theme may be supported by religious leaders, making it difficult for physicians and nurses to proceed on the basis of scientific medicine; and there are cases on record where patients have left the hospital against medical advice. We see here the conflict between the principles of scientific medicine and those of primitive medicine, which were discussed in Chapter 4, between natural and supernatural causes of disease. Only when hospital personnel can shift the situation from one of conflict to one of coexistence or cooperation can the perceptual distortions be changed sufficiently to permit the patient to cope fully with the disease situation. Here the medical social worker may be in the best position to effect some perceptual changes.

Another deleterious aspect of religious belief can be that of fate where man is regarded as a passive and helpless being caught up in the powers of the universe. When drought strikes, storms ravage the land, death and illness come, these events are seen as God's will and man is not to question the Almighty but accept his actions. In times of peril, when man is truly helpless to do anything, this kind of religious belief can contribute to peace of mind and, indeed, in certain illness situations where death is inevitable, it can be a source of strength. Belief in fate does conflict, however, with the action-oriented, optimistic outlook of scientific medicine where one "does something" when illness occurs.[15] The resignation and acceptance of fate evidenced by some cultural groups is difficult for most hospital personnel to understand and again the perceptual distortions may lead to inadequate coping with an illness situation.

Religious beliefs may also be an important facilitating agent in the adjustment of the patient to his disease and to the world of the hospital. The behavior of those who truly live out the principles of their faith can greatly enrich the lives of those around them, be they patients, physicians, or nurses. When a patient has faith of this order, his adjustment to the hospital situation may well be an inspiration to other patients, giving them a kind of auxiliary strength.

The effect of religious belief on the adjustment of the patient to his own illness can be regarded in two ways: the extent to which it enables him to handle a difficult or threatening situation, and the extent to which it may facilitate the healing process. As to the former, beliefs about death and the destiny of man have a direct relationship to incurable disease and the potentiality of death. In scientific medicine death is a final event; in many religious systems it is far from final, and the resources of the religious system can be brought to bear to help the patient meet the inescapable facts of his situation. The wise physician knows well that support from the chaplain or family clergyman may make his handling of the case much easier and be beneficial to the patient.

In terms of facilitating the healing process we have little direct experimental evidence, but there is the demonstrated association between emotional states and physiological reactions and the testimony of many practicing physicians that the patient's attitude toward the illness is important in recovery, at least in certain situations. Religious beliefs are seldom held in insulation but are part of group processes; hence, there is immediate group support for the individual. Regardless of one's feeling about the efficacy of prayer in a religious sense, there is little doubt about the symbolic indication of group support that it presents. Group support thus rendered toward the process of recovery helps the patient's own attitude or belief that he will recover, that there are forces available to facilitate the healing process. Here religion is not seen as a healing process apart from scientific medicine but as a cooperating agent, and the explanation for recovery still resides in the area of natural causes.

Sensitization to Prejudice

In the course of the patient's reaction to illness there is a constriction of interests and an egocentricity, factors discussed earlier. Thus, there is a natural tendency to personalize things, fragments of conversation, glances, and other kinds of behavior such as being ignored. A patient may think that a conversation between physician and nurse applies to him, when in reality it may have relevance to something quite different. He may interpret the attention of personnel to another patient as rejection of himself, when the reason lies in a special procedure his physician has ordered, or some kind of emergency. When the tendency to personalize fuses with a sensitivity to minority group status, perceptual distortions may be increased drastically. Members of minority groups who have suffered many rebuffs or other expressions of hostility may perceive this intent in the actions of others when such prejudice is not meant at all. Hospitalization in a situation where minority group status is a factor, as a Jewish patient in a Christian hospital, or a Negro patient in a hospital that treats white patients predominantly, can increase sensitivity and hinder adaptive measures. Also not to be forgotten is the fact that members of the staff may have prejudices about minority groups and may express them, consciously or unconsciously. The patient may react by complaining, perhaps by an exacerbation of symptoms, or by a passivity and withdrawal that negates the best efforts of staff. The interaction feedback to hospital personnel leads to perceptual distortions on their part which can generalize to others of the patient's cultural group and preclude the openness and frankness in interpersonal relations which is necessary to good treatment and patient adaptation. Once again, awareness by physicians, nurses, and others of the effect of sensitization to prejudice can lead to efforts on their part to face the issue with the patient and thus reduce the distortion.

FACTORS CONDUCIVE TO PATIENT ADAPTATION

In the opening paragraph of the preceding chapter the statement was made that very few people in our society now regard the hospital as a place where one goes to die; rather it is viewed as a place where illness may be treated in the most competent manner possible. The hospital as a positive social institution has become thoroughly accepted and is as important a part of our culture as mass transportation, television, and public schools. There must be factors in the situation that favor the adaptation of the patient and on which hospital personnel can depend for help in working with patients. Consideration of these factors is our next step.

Trust in physicians and nurses provides a great reservoir of feeling on which both the patient and hospital personnel can draw in meeting the problems of illness and its treatment. Both roles have a high positive value in our society, with the picture of the nurse as the angel of mercy and the physician as the firm but kindly worker of miracles. People in both roles do not always measure up to expectations and there is the problem of ambivalence, especially toward the physician, but these negative pressures do not seriously disrupt the favorable feelings. Competent help is the expectation toward physicians and nurses, and the air of assurance they give in their work lends a feeling of security. They seem to know what they are doing.

With a feeling of trust the patient can concentrate his energy on the process of getting well, counting on hospital personnel to do their part, to take care of him in the best manner possible. On the other hand, those who care for the patient can make decisions for him with more ease, knowing they will not be seriously questioned. Also, they can be more positive in their emotional support of him, for positive outgo of emotions is a reciprocating situation.

A second factor is the *generally favorable attitude toward hospitals* which characterizes people in the United States. Data on this point come from the study of health attitudes by the National Opinion Research Center in conjunction with the Health Information Foundation, which was discussed earlier in Chapter 4, and are based on questions asked respondents and their physicians about hospitals.[16] Sixty-six per cent of the sample rated their local hospitals as good or excellent, a figure that jumped to 78 per cent when the local doctors made the rating. The factors that came in for criticism, both by doctors and other respondents, were physical plant, location, number of beds, and the like. In terms of positive features, patients and other respondents reported equipment, service, and personnel. Furthermore, all respondents who had been patients in hospitals at some time were asked if they could recall anything in particular that they liked, and then anything they disliked. Results showed that favorable memories were more often reported than unfavorable ones. The crucial factors in determining this response were the apparent courtesy and efficiency of the hospital staff, particularly the nurses. The quality of the food added to a favorable evaluation, although in some cases it apparently worked the other way.

When those who had complaints about hospitals were asked if their complaints would make them feel worse or better about going to the hospital again, 40 per cent replied that they would feel no different and 52 per cent said that they would feel better. The annoyances of previous sessions in the hospital were not sufficient to make most patients resist going again.

Freidson and Feldman, in reporting on these results, conclude that the bulk of the American public now holds positive attitudes toward hospitals, that there is almost no evidence of the old fears about hospitals, and that critical opinions about hospitals appear to be mild.

Two conclusions may be drawn from these data for our purposes. First, most patients come to the hospital with a positive attitude, a factor which can be utilized by hospital personnel in medical care. Like the trust in physicians and nurses, positive attitudes toward hospitals can give psychological support to both patients and staff.

The second conclusion is more sobering. A significant minority of the respondents in the NORC-HIF study were critical of hospitals, focusing their objections on the attitude and manner of personnel, bad food, insufficient service, negligence, and the annoyance of certain routines, especially being awakened at odd hours. To this must be added the fact that nearly half of the physicians in the sample reported some personal dissatisfaction with local hospitals. It would seem that there is much yet to be done before the quality of hospital care reaches a point where patients and their families regard it in an entirely favorable light.

There is *positive reinforcement, in that most patients who go to hospitals do get well.* The great majority of people have had family members or friends who were patients in hospitals and who were helped to recover. In many cases the experience may have been very vivid and phrased in strong terms such as: "I don't know what I would have done without Hospital X. I was in pretty bad shape and they pulled me through." Accounts of dramatic operations or valiant efforts by hospital personnel against disease appear regularly in the public press, adding to those of personal experiences. Most patients go to the hospital expecting to get well, even though they may have anxieties about their health, and expecting that the hospital will do much to help them.

For some patients who have been deprived of many things in life there is added reinforcement in terms of the care and attention they receive. The food may be quite superior to their accustomed fare, the physical surroundings more pleasant than quarters at home, and the experience of having someone wait on them, cater to their whims, may be most unusual. For these patients the positive reinforcement of getting well is compounded by the favorable surroundings and services.

Some patients make a decision about entering the hospital, others go there when they are unconscious or helpless. The majority fall into the first category and the fact that *they have made a decision* is an important feature. It is a common experience that anxiety is reduced when decision on a course of action has been taken. In the case of the hospital it means that the patient has faced the fact that something needs to be done and that he must turn to technically competent help. Having made this decision, he realizes there will be discomfort involved, a certain amount of pain and suffering, disruption of normal routines. He knows that there are a number of things that he will have to put up with, but in most cases he also realizes that hospitalization is a temporary situation. Even in the event of long-term hospitalization, faced by the patient with chronic disease, the decision to undergo the treatment involves the realization that he must accept a change in his way of living.

The patient has probably received *group backing* for his decision, especially if he is a member of an ethnic group that stresses family ties and has a form of the extended family organization. The factor of group support is important because it extends into the hospital and also affects the patient who was not in a position to make a decision about hospitalization. This is a time when there is a mobilization of the emotionally significant people of the patient's life, an event that may not often happen to him. Their attention and solicitation, their cards, flowers, and visits can go a long way to make up for the suffering and disruption of normal life that hospitalization entails.

Group support is of sufficient importance that when it does not occur, or cannot be mobilized because of unusual circumstances, the patient and hospital may face a serious handicap in fostering adaptation.

There are *a number of factors within hospital social structure and culture* that can offer support to the mutual endeavor between patient and hospital of therapy and adaptation to illness. We have mentioned some of them previously, but re-emphasis is in order. First is the *value given to the prolonging of life.* Few people believe that patients are used as experimental subjects or that they go untreated to the point of death. In fact, the example of heroic efforts to prolong life in moribund patients, beyond the point where the result seems justified in practical terms, is common knowledge to most people. Although they may criticize the medical profession for prolonging life when it no longer seems necessary, this very action is a powerful indicator of attention given to life.[17] In times of peril there is comfort in this thought.

Expert knowledge and equipment, the fruits of scientific research and industrial technology, are available in the hospital, adequate tools for carrying out the aims of medical care. Not only does the hospital place high value on saving life, it also has the facilities to put the value into action. The NORC-HIF study indicated that factors finding general favor among the respondents centered around the physical equipment of the hospitals and the competence of staff. They saw hospitals as having the skills necessary for a good technical job even though they might criticize hospitals on the emotional climate, the food, or the crowded conditions. We mentioned above that physicians, nurses, and others in the hospital world have an air of competence and assurance in their work, indicating to the patient that they know how to use the tools at hand. Good equipment and technical knowledge are important deterrents to anxiety.

Hospital society constitutes a *firmly established social group*, with delegation of authority, differentiation of skills, and commitment to tasks. Although a legitimate criticism can often be made of rigidity of structure and inability to adapt to new and better routines, the old structure is not useless. Having worked for so long, the patient can be sure that it will continue to work for him even though he may find it inconvenient or uncomfortable. The workableness of the social system means that the patient can put himself in the hands of hospital personnel, knowing that the system can give him adequate care. He can undergo the necessary dependence for recovery from illness. Again there is a deterrent to anxiety.

A corollary in the firmness of the social system is the *protection it provides the patient from outside tensions and interferences*. We have mentioned that the hospital acts to make family ties somewhat more tenuous, and it also protects the patient insofar as it can from making decisions or becoming involved in the affairs of the outside world. The restriction of visitors can have a most beneficial effect at certain stages of an illness, as most former patients will attest. Protection from the outside is also evidenced in the remark often heard from expectant mothers, that it will be good to go to the hospital and get a rest.

Finally, we must return to the first function of the hospital which we discussed in the previous chapter, that of patient care. Few hospitals are perfect and some miss the mark by a considerable extent, but it is fair to say that by and large *hospitals are committed to good patient care* and strive to utilize their facilities and service to that end.

To this must be added the *growing concern for the emotional life of the patient* and for an understanding of factors that influence his emotional life. Recent advances in medicine, in the diagnosis and treatment of disease, are freeing the energies of hospital personnel for other aspects of their lives than merely the physical. Patient care can more easily be seen as comprehensive, encompassing both physical and emotional aspects, both hospital and home aspects of treatment and convalescence.

All these factors give support to the patient in his efforts to adapt to his illness and to the world of the hospital. That they can be strengthened is clear, a consideration we must deal with in the final section.

THE HOSPITAL AS A THERAPEUTIC COMMUNITY

In recent years the literature about mental hospitals has begun to stress the concept of a therapeutic community, a term and an idea presented originally by Maxwell Jones in England.[18] The assumptions within the concept are that all aspects of hospital life can and should be used to the benefit of the patient, that a therapeutic plan must take into consideration every part of the social system with which the patient comes in contact. All activities of personnel can have some therapeutic significance. Although still an idea and not an actuality in most mental hospitals, the concept of a therapeutic community has provided a goal toward which efforts could be directed, a yardstick against which to measure progress, and a rallying point for change in the often discouraging picture of mental patients.

The concept has not been applied in particular to other kinds of hospitals—general, pediatric, or those for long-term care—although concern about the "whole patient" and about "patient centrism"[19] is evident among people who give serious thought to hospital administration and medical care. The idea of a therapeutic community does have relevance, however, for all kinds of hospitals and within such a framework the material which has been presented in this book becomes more meaningful. If the hospital as a social institution is to fulfill completely its major function of patient care, a conceptual approach like that of the therapeutic community and its practical application will undoubtedly be necessary.

Two areas are of concern in thinking about patient care and the hospital world when one views the situation in terms of the idea of a therapeutic community. One involves the patient directly, the other involves the social system of the hospital. The needs of neither the patient nor the personnel can be neglected. That they are closely interrelated should be evident, at least the attempt of this chapter and the preceding has been to bring out the interaction. Based on what we know about human behavior, and drawing on much of the material that has been presented in this book, we can outline a number of major points that apply to each area.

Optimum attention to the needs of the patient requires some assumptions, at least two in number. First, there is a close relationship between emotional states or reactions and physiological reactivity. Both affect each other, and adverse stresses of all kinds—physical, biological, social—are reflected in altered emotional state and physiological balance. The recovery of the patient from his illness is related, therefore, to what happens to him in a social sense, both in relation to hospital personnel and to his family and other social groups outside the hospital. Phrased in another way, the patient is a biological and social entity in which one part cannot be treated to the exclusion of other parts without losing something important in therapeutic advantage in the treatment plan. The body or parts of it cannot be excluded from the personality of the individual or from his world of important people, his network of social beings.

The second assumption is that the behavior of patients is understandable, and is the result of factors in body chemistry, personality variables, and pressures from cultural background. The point of view emphasized in this book is that physiological, emotional, and social factors influence the way people perceive situations of which they are a part, and that they act according to their perceptions. So regarded, patient behavior can be understood objectively by the observer if he does not distort it by value judgments, and a plan of dealing with the patient can be formulated that starts from his set of perceptions. Patient needs can be met fully only when people in the health professions assess those needs without distorting them.

Relative to the second assumption, gaps are present in behavioral science research about patient behavior and its determinants, gaps that can be filled both by descriptive studies of specific situations, or of different ethnic groups, or of particular kinds of hospital-patient interaction. A definitive analysis of patient behavior awaits that research. At the same time there is need for an educational effort with hospital personnel, using the available theoretical frameworks and relevant empirical data about behavior and its determinants. Education of those concerned is a keystone of any change in procedures or attitudes relative to patient care.

Shifting consideration to the social system of the hospital and the needs of personnel, the first principle is that *all aspects of the hospital world affect the patient and his family*. Skills in personal interaction are important, as well as technical competence in such areas as radiology, bookkeeping, nursing, and administration. Those who plan for medical care need to be aware of the impact of what they say and do as well as how they do it. An efficient admissions clerk who handles the front desk with dispatch and who obtains the necessary information quickly may at the same time be cold and sarcastic. A laboratory technician may be skilled at doing a venipuncture and drawing blood, yet give the patient the feeling that he is just another body waiting to be stuck. The telephone operator, the resident physician, the nursing student—all have technical contributions toward patient care that are essential, but the way these are carried out makes a lasting impression on the patient and may even slow up his recovery. No longer is there a distinction between personnel directly involved with patients, in diagnosis, treatment or bedside care, and those who have no direct contact with patients. The actions of all in the final analysis affect the patient.

The second principle is that *strains in the social system lead to tension* which must be discharged in some way. The rigid status hierarchy of the hospital often makes it difficult for the tension to be discharged directly at those who cause it; hence, it is diverted and disguised. Most hospitals limit the expression of interpersonal feelings, but they manifest themselves in irritability, job dissatisfaction, even poor patient care. Furthermore, it is easy for individuals to become so involved in tension problems that they get carried away from the central concern of the hospital, care of the patient. Energy expended in interpersonal difficulties means there is less available for the main job at hand.

Strains in the system are partly the result of poor understanding about the system, taking some action personally when it is more role directed, misperceiving or not seeing the strains under which other people operate, expecting more in the way of rewards or authority than the system is set to allow. Knowledge of organizational behavior, especially as it is applied to the hospital, may help many groups within the social system see their own behavior and that of others in a new light, and may even lead to a readiness for change. More than this, however, there must be an awareness of the emotional need of staff members in the hospital and a desire to use administrative procedures or psychological intervention to meet this need.

Flexibility, not rigid tradition, is the third factor that affects the social system of the hospital as part of the concept of a therapeutic community. In Chapter 10 we discussed the latent function of keeping the system going, a function that can be observed in many social organizations but especially in those with a rigid structure. The jealous guarding of prerogatives of authority or systems of rewards may block new ways of thinking about patient care or wreck a plan of action as soon as it is conceived. A system of inflexible tradition is much like the bed of Procrustes, the legendary highwayman of Attica who either stretched or cut off the legs of his victims to make them fit his own bed. The patient may fit but be mishandled in the process.

The changes now going on in concepts of patient care and the delivery of services call for a flexibility of approach by all concerned that may not always be pleasant to hospital personnel. However, the concept of a therapeutic community can only come into being as issues are squarely faced.

Although little has been said in this book concerning *the physical qualities of the hospital*, they have a part to play in optimum care. Arrangement of facilities for their most efficient use by staff is important, a truth that can be demonstrated by a good time-motion study. The irritations caused by misplaced equipment as well as by overtired personnel can become part of a vicious circle. There are also esthetic aspects to the physical world of the hospital that tell a great deal about its character. Much of the construction in form and material must be functional, but within limits there is a great deal that can be done through color, decoration, and the arrangement of furniture and facilities to reduce the impression of institution and heighten the feeling of home or club. Warmth can come in part from physical surroundings as well as the people that inhabit them.

Finally, *the hospital as a social organization cannot be separated from the rest of society.* To serve as a therapeutic community its concerns must extend into the social and economic aspects of community life that affect the patient's adjustment to his illness and to hospital life. The ability of people to pay for the services which the hospital renders, to utilize its instructions and facilities for convalescence grows from the interest that the hospital itself takes in these matters. Relationships between the hospital and the community are reciprocal and are strengthened only to the extent that activity and interest are initiated by both sides.

SUMMARY

Characteristics of the hospital world to which the patient must make some kind of adaptation constituted the first section of this chapter. The hospital world was described as a unique round of life, a subculture, with distinctive features. We noted the lack of privacy for the patient; the strange uniforms, equipment, and language; the sights, sounds, and smells; and the unvarying routine—all of which may constitute quite a variation from the patient's accustomed way of living. Hospital personnel also have certain expectations of the patient. Among these are dependence, or compliance with rules, routines, and decisions, nonfulfillment of normal role responsibilities, de-emphasis of external power and prestige, expectation of suffering and pain, and a desire to get well. At the same time hospital personnel exemplify the importance which they attach to the value of human life and emphasize emotional neutrality as well as support in caring for patients. These are some of the main features of the world into which the patient comes. Most patients are anxious and tend to show an emotional regression in which it is easy to project early feelings about the family onto hospital staff. In addition, there are special problems of adaptation revolving around the loss of power and prestige, or of conflicts about dependence. Here the intrapsychic variables in the patient interact with the subcultural pressures of the hospital world and patient behavior cannot be understood without regard for both sets of factors.

Important background variables must also be considered in patient adaptation, as in the effect of ethnic group membership on response to pain. We noted other reactions that are affected by ethnic background, including modesty and lack of privacy, the emotional significance of food, and patterns of family relationships. Religious practice was also discussed in terms of ways it may hamper or may greatly facilitate successful coping with the illness.

Finally, we noted some general factors that are conducive to patient adaptation. Among these were trust in medical personnel, generally favorable attitudes toward hospitals, and group backing at the time of hospitalization. The hospital world also provides many protections for the patient during his illness. A goal toward which hospital care can move was described in terms of the concept of the therapeutic community, and stress was laid on the fact that all aspects of the hospital world can be brought to bear on the therapeutic endeavor between hospital staff and patient.

NOTES TO CHAPTER 11

1. The reader will find an amusing and incisive account of body ritual procedures in a familiar tribe known as the Nacerima by reading Miner, Horace, "Body Ritual Among the Nacerima," *American Anthropologist*, vol. 58, June, 1956, pp. 503–507.

2. The trials and tribulations of a patient whose background was that of another culture bear eloquent testimony to the problems of privacy in the hospital. See Tao-Kim-Hai, André M., "Orientals Are Stoic," *The New Yorker*, vol. 33, September 28, 1957, pp. 105–123.

3. There are many accounts by former patients of their hospital experience and the reader can find as common threads through them all the major points of this chapter, and many things not mentioned here. For one humorous and insightful report the reader is referred to Brown, John Mason, *Insides Out*, McGraw-Hill Book Co., New York, 1942.

4. In convalescence from severe poliomyelitis the hospital tries to loosen the affective ties with home and family and immerse the patient in the subculture of illness.

This is done by restricting visitation by parents and by having hospital personnel assume many parental functions. In the case of polio the adjustment to a long illness and to a possible disability can be facilitated by the weakening of normal role behavior and the substitution of that of sickness. For a full explanation of this process the reader is referred to Davis, Fred, "Definitions of Time and Recovery in Paralytic Polio Convalescence," *American Journal of Sociology*, vol. 61, May, 1956, pp. 582–587.

5. Formalized relationships between physicians and nurses can vary from one set of circumstances to another, as between medical and surgical wards. Coser describes the "joking behavior" between interns and nurses on a surgical ward in a situation where the interns have very little formal authority in their role and the lack of such behavior on a medical ward where the medical relationship between nurse and intern is more distant. The apparently informal interaction on the surgical ward might well be a protective device for releasing tension arising out of threats to the self-esteem of interns, although this is my interpretation and not that made by Dr. Coser. See Coser, Rose L., "Authority and Decision Making in a Hospital: A Comparative Analysis," *American Sociological Review*, vol. 23, February, 1958, pp. 56–63.

6. The literature on psychological aspects of disability is extensive, but for a comprehensive account, and one that analyzes the problem of social prejudice, see Wright, Beatrice A., *Physical Disability*: A Psychological Approach, Harper and Bros., New York, 1960.

7. Erickson, Florence, *Play Interviews for Four-Year-Old Hospitalized Children*. Society for Research in Child Development, Purdue University, Lafayette, Ind., vol. 23, no. 3, 1958.

8. A classic account of the feeling of rejection, written by a man who was once a mental patient, is to be found in Beers, Clifford W., *A Mind That Found Itself*, Doubleday, Doran and Co., Garden City, New York, 1931.

9. Koos, Earl Lomon, "'Metropolis'—What City People Think of Their Medical Services," *American Journal of Public Health*, vol. 45, December, 1955, p. 1553.

10. Lindemann, Erich, "Symptomatology and Management of Acute Grief," *American Journal of Psychiatry*, vol. 101, September, 1944, pp. 141–148.

11. Caron, Herbert S., "Psychological Factors in Disability: Coronary Infarction." Unpublished Summary Report, Heart Disease Control Program, U. S. Public Health Service. Also "The Crisis Factor in Illness and Disability," paper read at the Cleveland Symposium on Rehabilitation, November 4–6, 1959.

12. Zborowski, Mark, "Cultural Components in Response to Pain," *Journal of Social Issues*, vol. 8, no. 4, 1952, pp. 16–30.

13. A number of studies of the emotional and cultural implications of food habits have been made; among them are the following: Lewin, Kurt, "Group Decision and Social Change" in Swanson, Guy E., Theodore M. Newcomb, and Eugene L. Hartley, editors, *Readings in Social Psychology*, Henry Holt and Co., New York, 1952, pp. 459–473; Babcock, Charlotte G., "Food and Its Emotional Significance," *Journal of the American Dietetic Association*, vol. 24, May, 1948, pp. 390–393; Mead, Margaret, "Dietary Patterns and Food Habits," *Journal of the American Dietetic Association*, vol. 19, January, 1943, pp. 1–5; *Manual for the Study of Food Habits*, Report of the Committee on Food Habits, Bulletin of the National Research Council, January, 1945, National Academy of Sciences, Washington; Cussler, Margaret, and Mary L. de Give, '*Twixt the Cup and the Lip*, Twayne Publishers, New York, 1952; Bennett, John W., Harvey L. Smith, and Herbert Passin, "Food and Culture in Southern Illinois: A Preliminary Report," *American Sociological Review*, vol. 7, October, 1942, pp. 645–660; and Cassel, John, "Social and Cultural Implications of Food and Food Habits," *American Journal of Public Health*, vol. 47, June, 1957, pp. 732–740.

14. Clark, Margaret, *Health in the Mexican-American Culture*: A Community Study. University of California Press, Berkeley, Calif., 1959.

15. Lyle Saunders provides a clear discussion of the belief in fate among the Spanish-speaking groups of the Southwest and its effect on an illness situation. See his *Cultural Difference and Medical Care*, Russell Sage Foundation, New York, 1954, pp. 128–133.

16. Freidson, Eliot, and Jacob J. Feldman, *The Public Looks at Hospitals*. Health Information Foundation, Research Series, no. 4, New York, 1958.

17. See Fletcher, Joseph, "The Patient's Right to Die," *Harper's Magazine*, vol. 221, October, 1960, pp. 139–143.

18. Jones, Maxwell, *The Therapeutic Community:* A New Treatment Method in Psychiatry. Basic Books, New York, 1953.

19. The term "patient centrism" has been used by Howard E. Wooden in his article "The Hospital's Purpose Is the Patient, But—," *Modern Hospital*, vol. 92, January, 1959, pp. 90–96. This article also includes a series of concepts which are important to a patient-centered program in medical care and which I have drawn upon in presenting Part Four of this book.

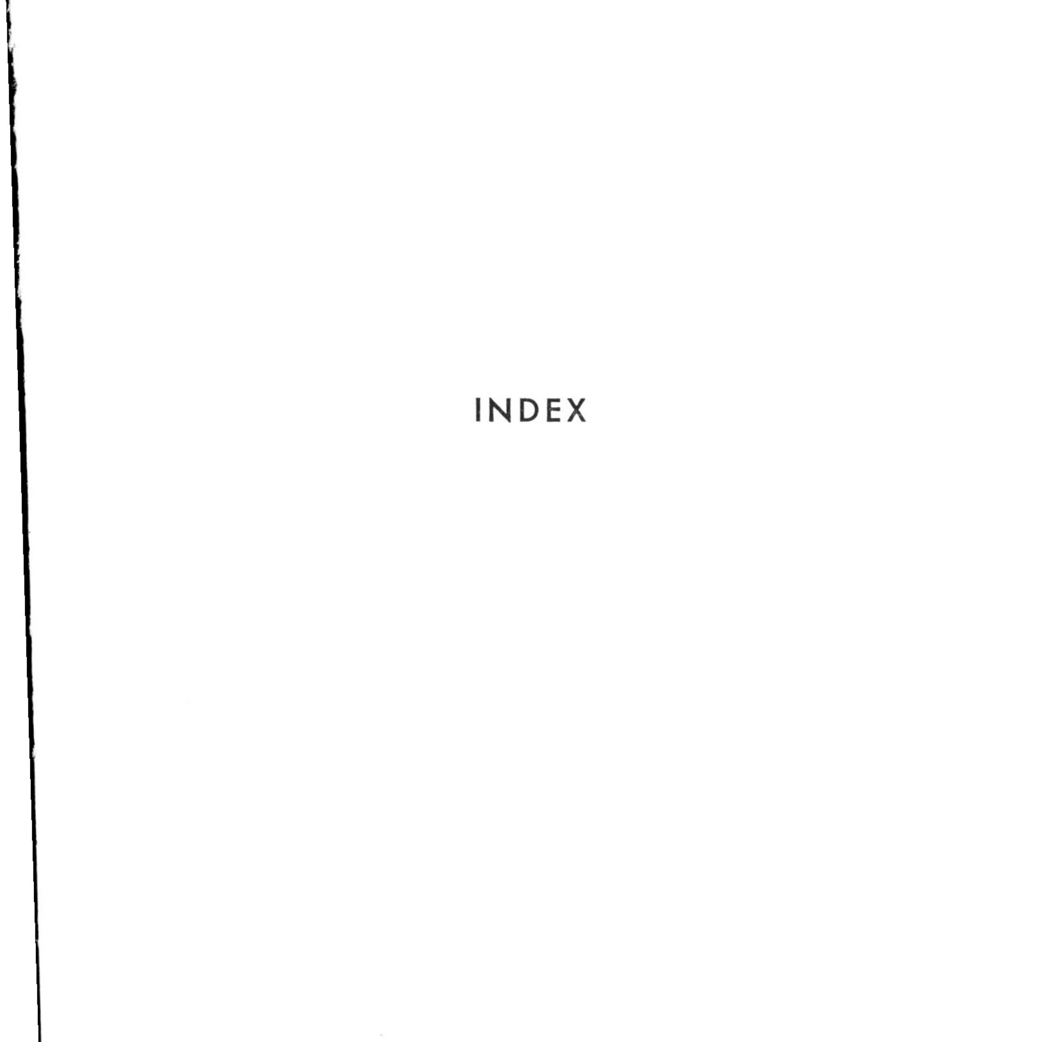

INDEX

Index

THE [illegible]